THE
INTERNATIONAL SERIES
OF
MONOGRAPHS ON PHYSICS

GENERAL EDITORS

N. F. MOTT   E. C. BULLARD

THE INTERNATIONAL SERIES OF MONOGRAPHS ON PHYSICS

GENERAL EDITORS

N. F. MOTT
Cavendish Professor of Physics
in the University of
Cambridge

E. C. BULLARD
Director of the National
Physical Laboratory
Teddington

Already Published

RECENT ADVANCES
IN OPTICS

BY

E. H. LINFOOT

JOHN COUCH ADAMS ASTRONOMER IN THE
UNIVERSITY OF CAMBRIDGE

OXFORD
AT THE CLARENDON PRESS
1955

Oxford University Press, Amen House, London E.C.4

GLASGOW NEW YORK TORONTO MELBOURNE WELLINGTON
BOMBAY CALCUTTA MADRAS KARACHI CAPE TOWN IBADAN

Geoffrey Cumberlege, Publisher to the University

———

PRINTED IN GREAT BRITAIN

PREFACE

THE main purpose of this book is to give an account of some of the
more interesting developments in instrumental optics during the last
twenty years. A complete survey would have taken up more than the
available space, and the book therefore deals with selected topics.
Many of these reflect the author's special interests; in particular the
discussion of image assessment and error balancing at the beginning of
Chapter I is based on previously unpublished work by him and by
P. A. Wayman. It is hoped, however, that the choice is wide enough to
convey a good general idea of the renaissance in instrumental optics
which has taken place since F. Zernike's pioneer work on the phase-
contrast microscope and on the analysis of partial coherence. The
remainder of Chapter I deals with what is commonly called the diffraction theory of aberrations and with the imaging of coherent and partially
coherent object-surfaces.

It has not seemed appropriate to refer specifically to the techniques
of practical optics, but the importance of new types of optical system
of very high theoretical performance is closely bound up with the
existence of a high level of practical figuring technique. This in turn
depends on the availability and adequate understanding of test pro-
cedures, among which the Foucault knife-edge test still occupies a
prominent place. An account of the diffraction theory of this test is
given in Chapter II.

Among the newer types of optical system introduced in recent years,
the Schmidt camera stands out as one of the most successful, especially
in astronomy, where Schmidt telescopes of large aperture and small
fast Schmidt spectrograph cameras have set up an entirely new standard
of photographic performance. A systematic account of the fifth-order
optics of the Schmidt camera and of the field-flattened Schmidt camera
is given in Chapter III.

In Chapter IV, C. R. Burch's method of plate-diagram analysis is
developed and applied to discuss the Seidel properties of Schmidt–
Cassegrain systems, of the Schmidt camera with aspherized mirror,
and of coma-free two-mirror systems.

My grateful thanks are due to Dr. R. Kingslake, Professor F. Zernike,
Professor A. Maréchal, and Dr. C. R. Burch for their kindness in
supplying original photographs and drawings reproduced in Chapters I
and IV. Thanks are also due to the Societies concerned for permission

to reproduce long extracts from papers published in the Proceedings of the Royal Society, the Proceedings of the Physical Society, and the Monthly Notices of the Royal Astronomical Society, and to the Clarendon Press for their unfailing care and courtesy.

E. H. L.

THE OBSERVATORIES
UNIVERSITY OF CAMBRIDGE
October 1954

CONTENTS

LIST OF PLATES

I

THE OPTICAL IMAGE

1. Geometrical theory

1.1. *Introduction*

IN spite of its mathematical elegance, general ikonal theory does not provide a very satisfactory starting-point for a discussion of the images formed by optical instruments. In its general form, the theory does not show any natural tendency to centre round the special preoccupations of instrumental optics; when it is made to do this by appropriate mathematical restatement, the analysis loses most of its elegance and still does not give much insight into the actual working of optical systems. A more physical approach is therefore adopted in the present section, and ikonal theory only makes brief appearances as a convenient analytical tool.

In instrumental optics, we usually have to deal with what is effectively a single infinity of pencils of rays issuing from the separate points of a symmetrical object surface, passing through a centred optical system, and emerging as bundles of rays each of which is approximately concurrent. The points of approximate concurrence (in some agreed sense) form a thin shell or image-layer in the image-space and the receiving surface or 'image surface' may be supposed to be anywhere in this layer, though of course some positions will be preferable to others.

The first problem is evidently the determination of the image-layer corresponding to a prescribed object surface for a given optical system, and the choice within this layer of the best receiving surface according to a prescribed method of assessing image quality.

It is easy to show that the Petzval surface lies in the image-layer and that, as Conrady first pointed out, it forms a convenient and natural field reference surface. But a comparison of the relative merits of the different receiving surfaces within this layer requires the setting up of analytical formulae which describe the behaviour in the image-layer of the rays issuing from an arbitrary point of the object surface. Exact formulae are almost useless for this purpose, even in the investigation of two-component systems like the Schmidt camera, because of their formidable complexity. With more elaborate systems such as a Taylor triplet lens the situation would be much worse. A general analytical discussion of these systems, if it is to be made at all, should from the nature of the problem be based on an appropriate use of approximations.

It is obvious that mere inequalities giving upper limits to the size of the geometrical images do not give enough information; they will not even prescribe the best choice of the receiving surface within the image-layer, still less indicate optimum values for the design-constants of the system.

We need approximate formulae, valid in the image-layer, consisting of a leading term plus an error-term. Such formulae may allow the best receiving surface to be determined, with an error which is too small to affect seriously the performance of the system, and the structure of the image in this surface to be analysed.

For the present, we suppose the light monochromatic; the effects of chromatism will be considered later.

1.2. *Notation*

Fig. 1 represents an axially symmetric system **S** which images the points of a spherical or flat object surface on to a receiving surface in the image-layer, both object surface and receiving surface being symmetrical about the optic axis of **S**. We suppose that **S** works over a field of angular diameter $O(\mu)$ radians, where $O(\mu)$ means 'not exceeding a moderate multiple of μ' and μ is the numerical aperture of **S**, suitably normalized. Then all the rays which pass through **S** make angles $O(\mu)$ with the optic axis.

Slightly different choices of μ-normalization are preferable in different applications. In a Schmidt camera, μ may be conveniently defined as H/R, where H is the semi-aperture and R the radius of curvature of the spherical mirror; this makes μ nearly equal to half the numerical aperture, whence $\mu^2 \simeq \frac{1}{64}$ in an f/2 Schmidt and our approximate formulae are accurate to a few per cent. In an f/1 Schmidt, $\mu^2 \simeq \frac{1}{16}$ and the accuracy of these formulae is correspondingly reduced. In a refracting system, a definition of μ which puts its value near to the numerical aperture improves the verisimilitude of the picture given by the error-term assessments. In a general discussion, it seems better to leave the μ-normalization arbitrary to the extent of a factor comparable with unity, and this will be done here.

By Gauss imaging of its aperture stop, the entry and exit pupils of **S** are obtained. We set up Cartesian coordinates (x, y, z) in the image-space of **S**, taking the origin O' at the centre of the exit pupil and the axis $O'z$ along the optic axis (see Fig. 1). The exit pupil then fills a circle $x^2 + y^2 \leqslant H'^2$ in the plane $xO'z$, where $H' = O(f\mu)$ and f is the focal length.

In this plane, and in the space near it, we introduce scale-normalized lateral coordinates u, v by means of the equations

$$x = H'u, \qquad y = H'v. \tag{1.1}$$

The scale-normalized polar coordinates r, ϕ in the space surrounding the exit pupil are connected with u, v by the equations

$$u = r \cos \phi, \qquad v = r \sin \phi, \qquad r = +\sqrt{(u^2 + v^2)}. \qquad (1.2)$$

The exit pupil occupies the region $u^2 + v^2 \leqslant 1$ of the plane $xO'y$.

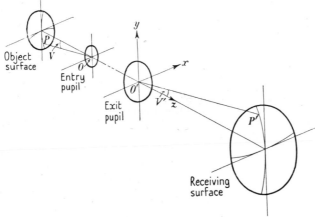

F_IG. 1.

From the off-axis object point P a pencil of rays passes through the system $\mathbf{S}$ to form an image-patch on the receiving surface. We call the ray through O' the *principal ray* of the emerging pencil and its intersection P' with the receiving surface the *principal point* of the image. Because of the axial symmetry of $\mathbf{S}$, there is no loss of generality in supposing the off-axis displacement of P' to be in the positive y-direction.

By the *angular off-axis distance of the image* we mean the angle $V' = P'O'z$. As P runs over the object field, V' ranges over a certain interval $(0, V_0')$. We define $\Theta = V'/V_0'$, so that the field is defined by the inequalities $0 \leqslant \Theta \leqslant 1$.

Because of the aberrations of the system, the rays of the emerging pencil trace out in the plane $xO'y$ a region which does not exactly coincide with the exit pupil; their boundaries may differ by $O(f\mu^3)$.

Some or all of the optical surfaces of $\mathbf{S}$ may be figured; we suppose that no figuring depths exceed $O(f\mu^4)$. This condition is satisfied by all 'useful' figurings in systems for which angular aperture and angular field radius are both $O(\mu)$.

We restrict the discussion to 'useful' receiving surfaces, namely those sufficiently close to the best focal surface not to increase the size of the geometrical image-spreads by more than a factor $O(1)$. This means that we consider only receiving surfaces lying within the *image layer* of § 1.1.

Such receiving surfaces can be specified by means of a displacement function $f\mu^2\epsilon(\Theta)$† which, for each value of the normalized off-axis distance Θ, measures to a sufficient approximation the focus shift of the receiving surface relative to a selected *field-reference surface*.

As field-reference surface we choose the Petzval surface of $\mathbf{S}$ imaging from the given object surface, namely the spherical surface, of curvature $1/\rho_P$ given by the equation

$$\frac{1}{\rho_P} - \frac{1}{\rho_0} = \sum_i \left[\frac{n_i-1}{n_i}\left(\frac{1}{r_2^{(i)}} - \frac{1}{r_1^{(i)}}\right) \quad \text{or} \quad \frac{-2}{r_i} \right], \qquad (1.3)$$

which cuts the optic axis orthogonally at the paraxial focus. The quantities r on the right of (1.3) stand for the paraxial radii of curvature of the optical surfaces (including figurings); these radii, like ρ_P, are taken positively when the surface is concave towards the incident light;‡ $1/\rho_0$ is the curvature of the object surface.

When the Seidel aberrations dominate the image, or, in particular, when $\mathbf{S}$ is an aplanat,§ the order of magnitude of the image-spreads at best focus is $f\mu^3$ and the thickness of the image-layer is $O(f\mu^2)$. In this case we could use the Gauss plane as field-reference surface, with some gain in simplicity in those cases where a flat field is aimed at in the design. But when $\mathbf{S}$ is an anastigmat, with image-spreads of order $f\mu^5$ at best focus, the image-layer lies everywhere within a distance $O(f\mu^4)$ of the Petzval surface, and the Gauss plane could only be used as field-reference surface in systems for which the Petzval curvature $1/\rho_P = O(\mu^2/f)$. We call such systems *flat-fielded anastigmats*.

When the Petzval surface and not the Gauss plane is chosen as field-reference surface, the approximation technique which is used for the aplanats and for general centred systems can be adapted without

† Or $f\mu^4\epsilon(\Theta)$ in an anastigmat; it is more convenient to have $\epsilon(\Theta) = O(1)$ in both cases.

‡ We do not define the Petzval surface by applying (1.3) to the optical surfaces divested of their figurings, because it is desirable (e.g. in discussing the Schmidt camera and plate-mirror systems generally) to permit the presence of an r^2-term, of coefficient not exceeding $O(f\mu^4)$, in the function which defines the figuring depths. The position of the Petzval surface would not then be determined uniquely by the system and the object surface. Conrady's definition of the Petzval surface by means of 'thin radial pencils' has the practical inconvenience that the surface so defined is not strictly spherical.

§ By an aplanat we mean a system in which the first two Seidel errors (spherical aberration and coma) are reduced to very small values and the biggest remaining aberration is the off-axis astigmatism used to flatten the field; the image-spreads are $O(f\mu^3)$. By an anastigmat we mean a system in which the image-spreads are $O(f\mu^5)$ in the selected receiving surface. This approximates to the present commercial use of the terms.

essential change to the anastigmats. In the aplanats the displacement function $f\mu^2\epsilon(\Theta) = O(f\mu^2)$; in the anastigmats the displacement function $f\mu^4\epsilon(\Theta) = O(f\mu^4)$.

1.3. *The aberration function*

With each pencil of rays is associated an orthogonal family of surfaces called the *geometrical wave surfaces* or *wave-fronts*. If the rays of a pencil all pass through a single point, the wave-fronts are evidently spheres. This is the case of an aberration-free geometrical image. In the more usual case where the rays are not strictly concurrent, but pass within a distance $O(f\mu^3)$ of each other, the wave-fronts are no longer strictly spherical, but are distorted by amounts $O(f\mu^4)$ from the spherical form. Near a focus, the wave-fronts may now develop singularities; to avoid this complication we exclude from the discussion wave-fronts whose distance from a focus is small compared with f.

Each wave-front W is cut in a unique point Q by the ray through the point (u, v) in the exit pupil; we call (u, v) the *coordinate numbers* of the ray, and of the point Q on W. In its passage through the system, the ray also defines coordinate numbers (u, v) on the optical surfaces and in the entry pupil. In the entry pupil u, v agree, to within $O(\mu^2)$, with the values of the corresponding scale-normalized Cartesian coordinates there.

The *principal point* of W is the point of coordinate numbers $(0, 0)$ on W; when W is in the image-space, this is the intersection with W of the principal ray $O'P'$.

The *reference sphere of W* is defined in the image-space as the sphere, centred on P', which passes through the principal point of W. It can be defined in the intermediate image-spaces of the system as the sphere centred on the intersection of the ray $(0, 0)$ with the corresponding intermediate Petzval surface and passing through the principal point of W.

In a general centred system, W lies everywhere within a distance $O(f\mu^4)$ of its reference sphere; in the (final) image-space of an anastigmat, within a distance $O(f\mu^6)$.†

The *aberration function* $\phi(u, v; \Theta)$ is defined for each u, v as the distance, measured along the optical ray of coordinate numbers (u, v), by which W lags behind its reference sphere. Evidently $\phi(0, 0; \Theta) = 0$. As the wave surface progresses, $\phi(u, v; \Theta)$ remains unchanged to within $O(f\mu^6)$ in a general centred system; in the image-space of an anastigmat it remains unchanged to within $O(f\mu^{10})$.

---

† The truth of this statement depends on the fact that the receiving surface lies in the image-layer.

In an aplanat or in a general centred system we can write

$$\phi(u, v; \Theta) = f\mu^4 \Phi(u, v; \Theta);$$

in an anastigmat we can write

$$\phi(u, v; \Theta) = f\mu^6 \Phi(u, v; \Theta),$$

the function Φ being $O(1)$ in both cases.

We call ϕ a 'smooth' function when the order of magnitude of $\partial\phi/\partial u$ and $\partial\phi/\partial v$ is the same as that of ϕ itself. If the optical surfaces of **S** are spherical, then ϕ will be smooth. ϕ will still be smooth if the surfaces of **S** carry figurings of the type represented by an equation of the form

$$\zeta = f\mu^4 \left[c_2 \frac{x^2+y^2}{h^2} + c_4 \left(\frac{x^2+y^2}{h^2}\right)^2 \right] + f\mu^6 c_6 \left(\frac{x^2+y^2}{h^2}\right)^3 + f\mu^8 \chi\left(\frac{x^2+y^2}{h^2}\right), \quad (1.4)$$

where the coefficients c_2, c_4, c_6 are $O(1)$, h denotes the semi-diameter of the axial pencil at the surface under consideration, χ is $O(1)$ and a smooth function of its argument $(x^2+y^2)/h^2$, and ζ denotes the figuring depth, measured parallel to the z direction, at the surface-point of Cartesian coordinates x, y. When only the Seidel errors of the system are under discussion, the value of c_6 is irrelevant and (1.4) may be used in the simplified form

$$\zeta = f\mu^4 \left[c_2 \frac{x^2+y^2}{h^2} + c_4 \left(\frac{x^2+y^2}{h^2}\right)^2 \right] + O(f\mu^6). \quad (1.5)$$

Useful surface deformations of more general type than (1.5) are possible, for example those of the form

$$\zeta = f\mu^4 \left[c_2 \frac{x^2+y^2}{h^2} + c_4 \left(\frac{x^2+y^2}{h^2}\right)^2 + c_6' \left(\frac{x^2+y^2}{h^2}\right)^3 \right] + O(f\mu^6),$$

where the error-term is a smooth function of $(x^2+y^2)/h^2$. Their effect is to introduce third-order aberrations of a different type from those occurring 'naturally' (that is to say, in centred systems with spherical surfaces); the latter are of the third order and the third degree.† When the object of introducing figurings is the better control of the classical aberration coefficients, it is appropriate to use figurings of the special form (1.4). We call these *normal figurings*.

The quantities x/h, y/h are evidently scale-normalized Cartesian coordinates on the figured surface, which agree to within $O(\mu^2)$ with the coordinate numbers u, v imprinted on this surface by the pencil from the axial object point. If the object point moves off axis in the negative

---

† That is to say, of the form $f\mu^3 P(u, v; \Theta) + O(f\mu^5)$, where $P = O(1)$ is a polynomial of maximum total degree 3 in u, v, Θ and the error-term is a smooth function of u, v. Compare p. 16, below.

y-direction, the new coordinate numbers u, v on the surface are connected with $x/h, y/h$ by equations

$$u = \frac{x}{h} + O(\mu^2), \qquad v = \frac{y}{h} + l\Theta + O(\mu^2),$$

in which the value of the constant l is given to the necessary accuracy by Gauss theory.

In a general centred system with normal figurings, imaging on the Petzval surface, the monochromatic aberration function

$$\phi(u, v; \Theta) = f\mu^4 \Phi_0^*(u, v; \Theta) + O(f\mu^6), \tag{1.6}$$

where

$$\Phi_0^*(u, v; \Theta) = \frac{H}{f\mu}\left[\tfrac{1}{4}a_1(u^2+v^2)^2 + a_2 \Theta v(u^2+v^2) + \tfrac{1}{2}a_3 \Theta^2(3u^2+v^2)\right] \tag{1.7}$$

and the coefficients a_1, a_2, a_3 are $O(1)$.† H stands for the semi-diameter of the entry pupil,‡ so that the factor $H/f\mu$ is comparable with unity.§

We call $f\mu^4\Phi_0^*(u, v; \Theta)$ the *Seidel aberration function* or the *fourth-order aberration function* of the system working on the Petzval surface. The corresponding aberration-deviations ξ_0, η_0 are given by the equation

$$(\xi_0, \eta_0) = \frac{f\mu}{H} f\mu^3\left(\frac{\partial}{\partial u}, \frac{\partial}{\partial v}\right)\Phi_0^* + O(f\mu^5) \tag{1.8}$$

or

$$\xi_0 = \xi_0^* + O(f\mu^5), \qquad \eta_0 = \eta_0^* + O(f\mu^5),$$

where

$$\left.\begin{aligned}\xi_0^* &= f\mu^3[a_1 u(u^2+v^2) + 2a_2 \Theta uv + 3a_3 \Theta^2 u]\\ \eta_0^* &= f\mu^3[a_1 v(u^2+v^2) + a_2 \Theta(u^2+3v^2) + a_3 \Theta^2 v]\end{aligned}\right\}. \tag{1.9}$$

If, introducing scale-normalized polar coordinates (r, ϕ) in the exit pupil, we write

$$u = r\cos\phi, \qquad v = r\sin\phi, \tag{1.10}$$

equations (1.9) can be given the more compact form

$$\xi_0^* + i\eta_0^* = f\mu^3[a_1 r^3 e^{i\phi} + ia_2 r^2 \Theta(2 - e^{2i\phi}) + a_3 r\Theta^2(2e^{i\phi} - e^{-i\phi})]. \tag{1.11}$$

When the receiving surface is displaced forward from the Petzval surface by an amount $f\mu^2\epsilon(\Theta) + O(f\mu^4)$, the main term $\Phi^*(u, v; \Theta)$ is replaced by

$$\Phi^*(u, v; \Theta) = \Phi_0^*(u, v; \Theta) + \tfrac{1}{2}(u^2+v^2)\left(\frac{H}{f\mu}\right)^2 \epsilon(\Theta) \tag{1.12}$$

---

† See for example A. E. Conrady, *M.N.* **80** (1919), 320–8. The presence of the error-term in (1.6) allows a certain freedom of choice in the values assigned to a_1, a_2, a_3; they may be changed by amounts $O(\mu^2)$ without invalidating the representation.

‡ Not the exit pupil.

§ H/f is equal to the numerical aperture of the emerging pencil.

and approximate aberration displacements ξ_0^*, η_0^* by ξ^*, η^*, where

$$\xi^* + i\eta^* = f\mu^3\left[a_1 r^3 e^{i\phi} + ia_2 r^2\Theta(2 - e^{2i\phi}) + a_3 r\Theta^2(2e^{i\phi} - e^{-i\phi}) + \frac{H}{f\mu}\epsilon(\Theta)re^{i\phi}\right],$$

(1.13)

the approximation error being $O(f\mu^5)$.

The equations

$$\xi = \xi^* + O(f\mu^5), \qquad \eta = \eta^* + O(f\mu^5) \tag{1.14}$$

give an evaluation in the desired form (viz. a leading term of manageable complexity plus an error-term) of the monochromatic aberrations in any axially symmetric receiving surface lying in the image-layer. Inside the square bracket of (1.13) the term $a_1 r^3 e^{i\phi}$ represents the primary spherical aberration, $ia_2 r^2\Theta(2 - e^{2i\phi})$ the Seidel coma, $[2a_3\Theta^2 + (H/f\mu)\epsilon(\Theta)]e^{i\phi}$ the focus shift relative to the reference surface, and $-a_3 r\Theta^2 e^{-i\phi}$ the off-axis astigmatism, the deviations being measured from the principal point of the image-patch. It makes no difference to the form of (1.13) and (1.14) if ξ, η be measured perpendicular to the normal drawn from the receiving surface at some point P'' of the image-patch (the η-direction being taken, as before, in the meridional plane through P''). For this alters the values of ξ, η only by $O(f\mu^5)$.

(1.13), (1.14) allow the determination, to a sufficient accuracy, of the best field surface corresponding to a given definition of image quality. A procedure which is both analytically convenient and physically acceptable in many practical applications is to define the effective radius of a single monochromatic image-patch as the square root of the expression

$$\rho^2 = \frac{1}{\pi}\iint\limits_{u^2 + v^2 \leqslant 1} (\xi^2 + \eta^2)\,dudv \tag{1.15}$$

and the effective monochromatic image radius over the working field $V' \leqslant V_0'$ on a given receiving surface as the square root of

$$E = \frac{2}{\pi}\int_0^1 \Theta\,d\Theta \iint\limits_{u^2 + v^2 \leqslant 1} (\xi^2 + \eta^2)\,dudv. \tag{1.16}$$

This amounts to defining the effective radius of each image-patch as the radius of gyration of its ray-density distribution about its principal point† and the effective monochromatic image radius over the working field as the root mean square average of these effective radii over the field area $\Theta \leqslant 1$.

† The alternative (and in some ways more natural) definition by means of the radius of gyration about the centre of gravity of the image-patch will be considered later.

1.4. *Best field surface*

When ξ, η are replaced by ξ^*, η^* in (1.15) and (1.16), the resulting changes in value of ρ and $E^{\frac{1}{2}}$ are $O(f\mu^5)$, and so are negligible in the present approximation. Therefore we may define the best field surface as that for which $\epsilon(\Theta)$ minimizes the quantity

$$E^* = \frac{2}{\pi} \int\limits_0^1 \Theta \, d\Theta \iint\limits_{u^2+v^2 \leqslant 1} (\xi^{*2}+\eta^{*2}) \, du dv. \tag{1.17}$$

We proceed to determine this surface, and to evaluate the effective image radius there, in terms of the coefficients a_1, a_2, and a_3.

By (1.13), (1.11),

$$\xi^* = \xi_0^* + f\mu^3 \frac{H}{f\mu} \epsilon(\Theta)u, \qquad \eta^* = \eta_0^* + f\mu^3 \frac{H}{f\mu} \epsilon(\Theta)v,$$

where

$$\left. \begin{array}{l} \xi_0^* = f\mu^3(a_1 ur^2 + 2a_2 \Theta uv + 3a_3 \Theta^2 u) \\ \eta_0^* = f\mu^3(a_1 vr^2 + a_2 \Theta(u^2+3v^2) + a_3 \Theta^2 v) \end{array} \right\}, \tag{1.18}$$

and therefore

$$\xi_0^2 + \eta_0^2 = f^2\mu^6[a_1^2 r^6 + 6a_1 a_2 \Theta vr^4 + 2a_1 a_3 \Theta^2 r^2(3u^2+v^2) +$$

$$+ a_2^2 \Theta^2(u^4+10u^2v^2+9v^4) + a_2 a_3 \Theta^3(14u^2v+6v^3) + a_3^2 \Theta^4(9u^2+v^2)];$$

$$\rho_0^{*2} = \frac{1}{\pi} \iint (\xi_0^2 + \eta_0^2) \, du dv$$

$$= f^2\mu^6[\tfrac{1}{4}a_1^2 + \tfrac{4}{3}a_1 a_3 \Theta^2 + \tfrac{5}{3}a_2^2 \Theta^2 + \tfrac{5}{2}a_3^2 \Theta^4]. \tag{1.19}$$

Thus the quantity

$$E_0^* = \frac{2}{\pi} \int\limits_0^1 \Theta \, d\Theta \iint (\xi_0^{*2}+\eta_0^{*2}) \, du dv$$

$$= f^2\mu^6[\tfrac{1}{4}a_1^2 + \tfrac{2}{3}a_1 a_3 + \tfrac{5}{6}a_2^2 + \tfrac{5}{6}a_3^2]. \tag{1.20}$$

(The square root of E_0^* is the effective image radius over the region $\Theta \leqslant 1$ on the Petzval surface.)

By (1.13)

$$\xi^{*2}+\eta^{*2} = (\xi_0^{*2}+\eta_0^{*2}) + 2f\mu^3 \frac{H}{f\mu} \epsilon(\Theta)(u\xi_0^* + v\eta_0^*) + f^2\mu^6 \left[\frac{H}{f\mu} \epsilon(\Theta)\right]^2 r^2;$$

thus

$$E^* = E_0^* + f\mu^3 \frac{H}{f\mu} \int\limits_0^1 2\epsilon(\Theta)\mathscr{L}(\Theta)\Theta \, d\Theta + f^2\mu^6 \left(\frac{H}{f\mu}\right)^2 \int\limits_0^1 \epsilon^2(\Theta)\Theta \, d\Theta, \tag{1.21}$$

where

$$\mathscr{L}(\Theta) = \frac{2}{\pi} \iint (u\xi_0^* + v\eta_0^*)\, du\, dv = f\mu^3[\tfrac{2}{3}a_1 + 2a_3\,\Theta^2]. \qquad (1.22)$$

An infinitesimal variation $\delta\epsilon(\Theta)$ in the function $\epsilon(\Theta)$ changes E^* by an amount

$$f\mu^3\frac{H}{f\mu}\int_0^1 \delta\epsilon(\Theta)\mathscr{L}(\Theta)2\Theta\, d\Theta + f^2\mu^6\left(\frac{H}{f\mu}\right)^2\int_0^1 2\epsilon(\Theta)\delta\epsilon(\Theta)\Theta\, d\Theta$$

$$= f\mu^3\frac{H}{f\mu}\int_0^1 \delta\epsilon(\Theta)\left[\mathscr{L}(\Theta)+f\mu^3\frac{H}{f\mu}\,\epsilon(\Theta)\right]2\Theta\, d\Theta. \quad (1.23)$$

When the choice of $\epsilon(\Theta)$ minimizes E^*, this expression vanishes for every choice of $\delta\epsilon(\Theta)$. Therefore, in the best field surface,

$$\frac{H}{f\mu}\,\epsilon(\Theta) = -\frac{1}{f\mu^3}\,\mathscr{L}(\Theta) = -[\tfrac{2}{3}a_1 + 2a_3\,\Theta^2], \qquad (1.24)$$

and the value of E^* there is

$$E_1^* = E_0^* - \int_0^1 [\mathscr{L}(\Theta)]^2\Theta\, d\Theta$$

$$= f^2\mu^6[(\tfrac{1}{4}a_1^2 + \tfrac{2}{3}a_1\,a_3 + \tfrac{5}{6}a_2^2 + \tfrac{5}{6}a_3^2) - (\tfrac{2}{9}a_1^2 + \tfrac{2}{3}a_1\,a_3 + \tfrac{2}{3}a_3^2)]$$

$$= \tfrac{1}{36}f^2\mu^6(a_1^2 + 30a_2^2 + 6a_3^2). \qquad (1.25)$$

(1.24) shows that the best field surface is spherical (to within $O(f\mu^4)$) and lies at a distance

$$f\mu^2\epsilon(\Theta) = -\frac{f\mu}{H}f\mu^2[\tfrac{2}{3}a_1 + 2a_2\,\Theta^2] \qquad (1.26)$$

in front of the Petzval surface.

If the deviations are measured from a reference point other than P', namely one which itself possesses deviations α, β relative to P', the quantities ξ^*, η^* are replaced by $\xi^*-\alpha$, $\eta^*-\beta$ respectively, and the expression

$$\rho^{*2} = \frac{1}{\pi}\iint (\xi^{*2}+\eta^{*2})\, du\, dv \qquad (1.27)$$

by

$$\rho^{*2} - \frac{2\alpha}{\pi}\iint \xi^*\, du\, dv - \frac{2\beta}{\pi}\iint \eta^*\, du\, dv + (\alpha^2+\beta^2).$$

This is least when

$$\alpha + i\beta = \frac{1}{\pi} \int\int (\xi^* + i\eta^*)\, du\, dv$$

$$= \frac{1}{\pi} \int\int f\mu^3 \Big[a_1 r^3 e^{i\phi} + i a_2 r^2 \Theta(2 - e^{2i\phi}) + a_3 r\Theta^2(2e^{i\phi} - e^{-i\phi}) +$$

$$+ \frac{H}{f\mu}\epsilon(\Theta)re^{i\phi}\Big] r\, dr\, d\phi$$

$$= 2f\mu^3 \int_0^1 2i a_2 r^2\Theta\, r\, dr$$

$$= if\mu^3 a_2\, \Theta \tag{1.28}$$

and its value is then

$$\rho^{*2} - (\alpha^2 + \beta^2) = \rho^{*2} - f^2\mu^6 a_2^2\, \Theta^2.$$

That is, the centre of gravity of the image-patch has coordinates $f\mu^3(0, a_2\,\Theta) + O(f\mu^5)$ relative to its principal point and the r.m.s. effective radius of the image-patch about its centre of gravity is the square root of

$$\rho^{*2} - f^2\mu^6 a_2^2\, \Theta^2. \tag{1.29}$$

The quantity E^* is therefore reduced by the amount

$$2\int_0^1 \Theta\, d\Theta\, f^2\mu^6 a_2^2\, \Theta^2 = \tfrac{1}{2} f^2\mu^6 a_2^2,$$

which is independent of the choice of $\epsilon(\Theta)$. It follows that the best field surface has the same position on the new definition of effective image radius as on the old, and that the minimized value of E^* is now

$$E_2^* = E_1^* - \tfrac{1}{2} f^2\mu^6 a_2^2 = \tfrac{1}{36} f^2\mu^6[a_1^2 + 12a_2^2 + 6a_3^2]. \tag{1.30}$$

(1.25) and (1.30) give some idea of the relative harmfulness of spherical aberration, coma, and astigmatism in a monochromat. The coefficients a_1, a_2, a_3 are of course not free variables, but are determined by the free parameters of the system (spacings, radii of curvature and figurings of the optical surfaces), and the design of the monochromat may be said to be optimized for given f and μ when the free parameters are chosen to minimize $(a_1^2 + 30a_2^2 + 6a_3^2)$ or $(a_1^2 + 12a_2^2 + 6a_3^2)$, according to the definition of effective image radius adopted.

It appears that, on either definition of effective image radius, spherical aberration is relatively harmless and that coma is the aberration which has the worst effect on image quality. Besides increasing the effective radii of the image patches about their centre of gravity, coma destroys their symmetry and thereby increases the uncertainty of position measurements in the image-field. The use of the first definition provides a simple means of penalizing this property.

1.5. *Chromatism*

The effect of a variation of refractive indices by an amount $O(\mu^2)$ as the wavelength λ varies in the effective spectral range is to introduce variations of size $O(f\mu^2)$ in the focal position of the image and in the focal length (plate scale), and variations $O(\mu^2)$ in the coefficients of the third-order monochromatic aberrations on a given receiving surface.

Thus the chromatism may be expressed, to the Seidel order of accuracy, by adding to $\xi + i\eta$ the expression

$$f\mu^3[A_1 re^{i\phi} + iA_2\,\Theta] + O(f\mu^5), \tag{1.31}$$

where the coefficients A_1, A_2 are smooth functions of λ which are $O(1)$ over the effective wavelength range and vanish at the wavelength λ_0 in which the monochromatic aberrations were calculated. The displacements, measured from the principal point of the λ_0-image-patch, are then ξ_λ, η_λ, where

$$\xi_\lambda = \xi_\lambda^* + O(f\mu^5), \qquad \eta_\lambda = \eta_\lambda^* + O(f\mu^5) \tag{1.32}$$

and

$$\xi_\lambda^* + i\eta_\lambda^* = \xi_0^* + i\eta_0^* + f\mu^3\left[\left(\frac{H}{f\mu}\,\epsilon(\Theta) + A_1\right)re^{i\phi} + iA_2\,\Theta\right]$$

$$= \xi_0^* + i\eta_0^* + f\mu^3[A_1' re^{i\phi} + iA_2\,\Theta]; \tag{1.33}$$

the symbol A_1' stands for $A_1 + (H/f\mu)\epsilon(\Theta)$. Then

$$\rho_\lambda^{*2} = \frac{1}{\pi}\iint (\xi_\lambda^{*2} + \eta_\lambda^{*2})\,dudv$$

$$= \rho_0^{*2} + f\mu^3 A_1'\,\mathcal{L}(\Theta) + f^2\mu^6[\tfrac{1}{2}A_1'^2 + (2a_2 A_2 + A_2^2)\Theta^2],$$

and

$$E_\lambda^* = \int_0^1 \rho_\lambda^{*2}\,2\Theta\,d\Theta = E_0^* + f\mu^3\int_0^1 A_1'\,\mathcal{L}(\Theta)\,2\Theta\,d\Theta +$$

$$+ f^2\mu^6\left[\int_0^1 \tfrac{1}{2}A'^2\,2\Theta\,d\Theta + a_2 A_2 + \tfrac{1}{2}A_2^2\right].$$

Here

$$\int_0^1 \tfrac{1}{2}A_1'^2\,2\Theta\,d\Theta = \tfrac{1}{2}A_1^2 + \frac{H}{f\mu}\int_0^1 \epsilon(\Theta)2\Theta\,d\Theta + \frac{1}{2}\left(\frac{H}{f\mu}\right)^2\int_0^1 \epsilon^2(\Theta)\,d\Theta.$$

Therefore the weighted λ-mean of E_λ^*,

$$\overline{E_\lambda^*} = E_0^* + f^2\mu^6[\tfrac{1}{2}\overline{A_1^2} + \tfrac{1}{2}\overline{A_2^2} + a_2\overline{A_2} + (\tfrac{2}{3}a_1 + a_3)\overline{A_1}] +$$

$$+ f\mu^3 \frac{H}{f\mu} \int_0^1 \epsilon(\Theta)[\mathscr{L}(\Theta) + f\mu^3\overline{A_1}]2\Theta \, d\Theta +$$

$$+ f^2\mu^6 \frac{1}{2}\left(\frac{H}{f\mu}\right)^2 \int_0^1 \epsilon^2(\Theta) \, 2\Theta \, d\Theta, \quad (1.34)$$

where $\overline{A_1}$, $\overline{A_1^2}$,.... denote the weighted λ-means of A_1, A_1^2,.... When the weighting corresponds to the effective spectral density distribution of the light, $\overline{E_\lambda^*}$ is the mean square effective radius of the polychromatic images over the given angular field. Arguing as before, we see that $\overline{E_\lambda^*}$ is ϵ-minimized when

$$f\mu^3 \frac{H}{f\mu} \epsilon(\Theta) = -\mathscr{L}(\Theta) - f\mu^3\overline{A_1} = -f\mu^3[(\tfrac{2}{3}a_1 + \overline{A_1}) + 2a_3\Theta^2] \quad (1.35)$$

and that the ϵ-minimized value E_3^* which $\overline{E_\lambda^*}$ assumes in the corresponding best field surface is given by the equation

$$E_3^* = E_0^* + f^2\mu^6[\tfrac{1}{2}\overline{A_1^2} + \tfrac{1}{2}\overline{A_2^2} + a_2\overline{A_2} + \overline{A_1}(\tfrac{2}{3}a_1 + a_3)] -$$

$$- \tfrac{1}{2} \int_0^1 [\mathscr{L}(\Theta) + f\mu^3\overline{A_1}]^2 2\Theta \, d\Theta;$$

$$\frac{1}{f^2\mu^6} E_3^* = \tfrac{1}{36}(a_1^2 + 12a_2^2 + 6a_3^2) + \tfrac{1}{2}[\overline{A_1^2} - (\overline{A_1})^2] + \tfrac{1}{2}[\overline{A_2^2} - (\overline{A_2})^2] +$$

$$+ \tfrac{1}{2}(a_2 + \overline{A_2})^2. \quad (1.36)$$

The expressions $\overline{A_1^2} - (\overline{A_1})^2 = \overline{(A_1 - \overline{A_1})^2}$ and $\overline{A_2^2} - (\overline{A_2})^2 = \overline{(A_2 - \overline{A_2})^2}$ are the mean square deviations d_1^2 and d_2^2 of the coefficients A_1, A_2 from their mean values $\overline{A_1}$, $\overline{A_2}$ and we can write (1.36) in the form

$$E_3^* = f^2\mu^6[\tfrac{1}{36}(a_1^2 + 12a_2^2 + 6a_3^2) + \tfrac{1}{2}d_1^2 + \tfrac{1}{2}d_2^2 + \tfrac{1}{2}(a_2 + \overline{A_2})^2]. \quad (1.37)$$

The values of $\overline{A_1}$, $\overline{A_2}$, d_1, d_2 depend on the spectral distribution of the light passing through the system, since a change in this distribution alters the weighting which is appropriate in the mean values.

If the deviations, instead of being measured relative to P', the principal point of the λ_0-image-patch, are measured relative to an origin which itself has deviations α, β from P', then ρ_λ^{*2} is replaced by

$$\rho_\lambda^{*2} - \frac{2\alpha}{\pi} \iint \xi_\lambda^* \, du dv - \frac{2\beta}{\pi} \iint \eta_\lambda^* \, du dv + (\alpha^2 + \beta^2)$$

$$= \rho_\lambda^{*2} - 2\beta f\mu^3\Theta(a_2 + \overline{A_2}) + (\alpha^2 + \beta^2), \quad (1.38)$$

by (1.33), and the weighted mean $\overline{\rho_\lambda^{*2}}$ by

$$\overline{\rho_\lambda^{*2}} - 2\beta f\mu^3\Theta(a_2 + \overline{A_2}) + (\alpha^2 + \beta^2). \tag{1.39}$$

This is least when $\alpha = 0$, $\beta = f\mu^3\Theta(a_2 + \overline{A_2})$, and its value is then

$$\overline{\rho_\lambda^{*2}} - f^2\mu^6\Theta^2(a_2 + \overline{A_2})^2. \tag{1.40}$$

(1.40) gives the value of the mean square effective radius of each poly-chromatic image-patch about its centre of gravity. The corresponding value of the mean square effective radius over the working field is

$$\int_0^1 [\overline{\rho_\lambda^{*2}} - f^2\mu^6\Theta^2(a_2 + \overline{A_2})^2]2\Theta \, d\Theta = \overline{E_\lambda^*} - \tfrac{1}{2}f^2\mu^6(a_2 + \overline{A_2})^2. \tag{1.41}$$

We have to minimize (1.41) by choice of $\epsilon(\Theta)$. Since only the term $\overline{E_\lambda^*}$ involves $\epsilon(\Theta)$, it follows that the minimizing choice of $\epsilon(\Theta)$ is still given by (1.35) and the best field surface is the same as before, namely spherical (to within an accuracy $O(f\mu^4)$) with curvature $4a_3 f\mu/HV_0'^2$ less than the Petzval curvature $1/\rho_P$ and with its axial point $(f\mu/H)f\mu^2(\tfrac{2}{3}a_1 + \overline{A_1})$ behind that of the Petzval surface. On this surface the mean square effective image radius over the working field is

$$E_4^* = E_3^* - \tfrac{1}{2}f^2\mu^6(a_2 + \overline{A_2})^2$$
$$= f^2\mu^6[\tfrac{1}{36}(a_1^2 + 12a_2^2 + 6a_3^2) + \tfrac{1}{2}d_1^2 + \tfrac{1}{2}d_2^2]. \tag{1.42}$$

1.6. *Aberration functions of anastigmats*

As already noted in § 1.3, the distortion function in the image space of an anastigmat working in monochromatic light can be written in the form $f\mu^6\Phi(u, v; \Theta)$, where Φ is a smooth function of u, v, and Θ which is $O(1)$ for $u^2 + v^2 \leqslant 1$, $0 \leqslant \Theta \leqslant 1$ and which remains constant to within $O(\mu^4)$ as the wave advances, provided its distance from focus remains comparable with f.

It follows in particular that any approximate representation of the aberration function by an equation

$$f\mu^6\Phi(u, v; \Theta) = f\mu^6\Phi^*(u, v; \Theta) + O(f\mu^8), \tag{1.43}$$

where Φ^* is a smooth polynomial in u, v, and Θ of maximum total degree 6, remains valid without change of analytical form as the wave-front advances.

In the final image-space of an anastigmat, with receiving surface in the image-layer of thickness $O(f\mu^6)$, the aberration function can be given the form (1.43) and the aberration displacements ξ, η in the receiving surface are given by the equation

$$(\xi, \eta) = \frac{f\mu}{H}f\mu^5\left(\frac{\partial}{\partial u}, \frac{\partial}{\partial v}\right)\Phi^* + O(f\mu^7), \tag{1.44}$$

which is analogous to (1.8). In the intermediate image-spaces of the system, the aberration function takes the form

$$f\mu^4\Phi(u, v; \Theta) = f\mu^4\Phi^*_{(4)}(u, v; \Theta)+f\mu^6\Phi^*_{(6)}(u, v; \Theta)+O(f\mu^8), \quad (1.45)$$

in which $\Phi^*_{(4)}$, $\Phi^*_{(6)}$ are polynomials in u, v, Θ of maximum total degrees 4, 6 respectively, and are $O(1)$ over the wave-fronts. As the wave-fronts move forward, the first term in (1.45) may change by $O(f\mu^6)$, and consequently (1.45) does not remain invariant in form; its second term as well as its error-term undergoes a transformation. Transformation formulae which make it possible to follow wave-fronts through anastigmats, and so to evaluate their sixth-order aberration functions in the form (1.43), have been given by P. A. Wayman in an important thesis (Cambridge 1952) and applied by him to the aberration theory of the Schmidt camera and of Schmidt–Cassegrain systems. The present discussion makes extensive use of ideas contained in Wayman's thesis.

In the representations of a given aberration function by expressions of the form (1.43) or (1.45), there is a certain amount of freedom of choice in the values assigned to the coefficients in the polynomials Φ^*, $\Phi^*_{(4)}$, $\Phi^*_{(6)}$. For in (1.43) a change $O(\mu^2)$ in the coefficients of Φ^* causes a change of only $O(f\mu^8)$ in the value of the leading term $f\mu^6\Phi^*(u, v; \Theta)$, and this change can be absorbed in the error-term. In (1.45), changes $O(\mu^2)$ in the coefficients assigned to $\Phi^*_{(4)}$ are permissible provided their effect is offset by corresponding changes $O(1)$ in the coefficients of $\Phi^*_{(6)}$, while changes $O(\mu^2)$ in the coefficients of $\Phi^*_{(6)}$ produce effects which can be absorbed in the error-term.

When a *normal anastigmat* (i.e. one whose surface deformations are restricted to normal figurings) images monochromatic light on to the Petzval surface or, more generally, on to any spherical surface S lying in the image-layer,† the aberration function in the image-space takes the form

$$f\mu^6\Phi_0(u, v; \Theta) = f\mu^6\Phi^*_0(u, v; \Theta)+O(f\mu^8), \quad (1.46)$$

where

$$\frac{f\mu}{H}\Phi^*_0(u, v; \Theta) = \tfrac{1}{2}a''r^2-m''\Theta v+$$
$$+\tfrac{1}{4}b'r^4-f'\Theta vr^2+c'\Theta^2v^2+\tfrac{1}{2}d'\Theta^2r^2-e'\Theta^3v-$$
$$-S_2\,\Theta^4r^2-S_3\,\Theta^5v-S_4\,\Theta^2r^4-S_5\,\Theta^3vr^2-$$
$$-S_6\,\Theta^4v^2-S_7\,r^6-S_8\,\Theta vr^4-S_9\,\Theta^2v^2r^2-$$
$$-S_{10}\,\Theta^3v^3.‡ \qquad\qquad (1.47)$$

† A flat surface S is regarded as a special case of a spherical surface.
‡ This notation is essentially Schwarzschild's.

When the receiving surface lies in the image-layer at a distance $f\mu^4\epsilon(\Theta)$ in front of the reference surface S, the monochromatic aberration function can be written

$$f\mu^6\Phi(u,v;\Theta) = f\mu^6\left[\Phi_0(u,v;\Theta) + \frac{H}{f\mu}\epsilon(\Theta).\tfrac{1}{2}r^2\right] + O(f\mu^8)$$

$$= f\mu^6\left[\Phi_0^*(u,v;\Theta) + \frac{H}{f\mu}\epsilon(\Theta).\tfrac{1}{2}r^2\right] + O(f\mu^8) \quad (1.48)$$

and the aberration displacements ξ, η relative to the principal point of the image-patch are given by the equations

$$(\xi,\eta) = \frac{f\mu}{H}f\mu^5\left(\frac{\partial}{\partial u},\frac{\partial}{\partial v}\right)\Phi(u,v;\Theta) + O(f\mu^7) = (\xi^*,\eta^*) + O(f\mu^7), \quad (1.49)$$

where
$$(\xi^*,\eta^*) = f\mu^5\left[\frac{f\mu}{H}\left(\frac{\partial}{\partial u},\frac{\partial}{\partial v}\right)\Phi_0^*(u,v;\Theta) + (u,v)\epsilon(\Theta)\right]. \quad (1.50)$$

In (1.47), the coefficients a'', m'' measure fractional variations of order $O(\mu^4)$ in the focal position and magnification ('Gaussian' parameters of the system); b', f', c', d', e' measure traces of retained Seidel aberration, less by a factor $O(\mu^2)$ than the amounts to be expected in an uncorrected system; S_2, S_3,..., S_{10} measure the aberrations called fifth-order by Schwarzschild and other writers.

In the more detailed nomenclature used here, the aberration terms $f\mu^6(H/f\mu)a''r^2$ and $-f\mu^6(H/f\mu)m''\Theta v$ are of the sixth order and the second degree, the retained traces

$$f\mu^6\frac{H}{f\mu}[\tfrac{1}{4}b'r^4 - f'\Theta vr^2 + c'\Theta^2v^2 + \tfrac{1}{2}d'\Theta^2r^2 - e'\Theta^3v] \quad (1.51)$$

of Seidel aberration are of the sixth order and the fourth degree, while the remaining aberration terms contributed by $f\mu^6\Phi_0^*$ are of the sixth order and the sixth degree. The sixth-order term $f\mu^6(H/f\mu)\epsilon(\Theta).\tfrac{1}{2}r^2$ in (1.48) does not possess a degree so long as $\epsilon(\Theta)$ remains arbitrary. But if $\epsilon(\Theta)$ has the form $\alpha+\beta\Theta^2+\gamma\Theta^4+O(\mu^2)$, where α, β, γ are $O(1)$, then the effect of the change of receiving surface is merely to alter the values of the coefficients a'', d', S_2 in (1.47).

(1.47) can be written in the form

$$(f\mu/H)\Phi_0^*(u,v;\Theta) = \sum_{n=1}^{16} a_n\sigma_n = \sum_{klm} c_{klm}\Theta^k v^l r^{2m}, \quad (1.52)$$

where the non-negative integers k, l, m satisfy the conditions

$$l \leqslant k; \quad k-l \text{ even}; \quad k+l+2m = 2, 4 \text{ or } 6; \quad l+2m > 0 \quad (1.53)$$

and the coefficients a_n and c_{klm} are all $O(1)$. Table I gives the connexion†

† In the first column, those values of n for which l is odd are in italic.

TABLE I

n	k	l	m	$c_{klm}=a_n$	$\sigma_n = \Theta^k v^l y^{2m}$	Aberration term $\xi^* + i\eta^*$	Name of aberration
1	0	0	1	$\frac{1}{2}a''$	r^2 ⎱ Gauss	$a''(u+iv)$	focus shift
2	1	1	0	$-m''$	Θv ⎰ (2nd degree)	$-m''v\Theta$	plate-scale difference
3	0	0	2	$\frac{1}{4}b'$	r^4	$b'r^2(u+iv)$	primary spherical aberration
4	1	1	1	$-f'$	Θvr^2 ⎫	$-f'[2uv+i(r^2+2v^2)]$	primary coma
5	2	2	0	c'	$\Theta^2 v^2$ ⎬ Seidel	$2ic'\Theta^2 v$	primary astigmatism
6	2	0	1	$\frac{1}{2}d'$	$\Theta^2 r^2$ (4th degree)	$d'\Theta^2(u+iv)$	field-curvature difference
7	3	1	0	$-e'$	$\Theta^3 v$ ⎭	$-ie'\Theta^3$	Seidel distortion
8	0	0	3	$-S_7$	r^6	$-6S_7\, r^4(u+iv)$	secondary spherical aberration
9	1	1	2	$-S_8$	Θvr^4	$-S_8\Theta[4uvr^2+i(r^4+v^2r^2)]$	secondary coma
10	2	0	2	$-S_4$	$\Theta^2 r^4$	$-4S_4\,\Theta^2 r^2(u+iv)$	lateral spherical aberration
11	2	2	1	$-S_9$	$\Theta^2 v^2 r^2$	$-2S_9\Theta[uv^2+ivr^2+iv^3]$	wings (Flügelfehler)
12	3	3	0	$-S_{10}$	$\Theta^3 v^3$	$-3iS_{10}\Theta^3 v^2$	arrows (Pfeilfehler)
13	3	1	1	$-S_5$	$\Theta^3 vr^2$	$-S_5\Theta^3[2uv+ir^2+2iv^2]$	lateral coma
14	4	0	1	$-S_2$	$\Theta^4 r^2$	$-2S_2\Theta^4(u+iv)$	secondary (or lateral) field curvature
15	4	2	0	$-S_6$	$\Theta^4 v^2$	$-2iS_6\Theta^4 v$	lateral astigmatism
16	5	1	0	$-S_3$	$\Theta^5 v$	$-iS_3\Theta^5$	secondary (or lateral) distortion

Rows 8–16 bracketed: Schwarzschild (6th degree)

between the notations (1.47) and (1.52) and Fig. 2 indicates the form of the aberration-figure corresponding to each term taken separately. The entries Θ^2, Θ^4, Θ^6 which appear in Fig. 2 do not represent aberrations in the geometrical theory, but acquire a meaning in the diffraction theory of the imaging of coherent or partially coherent objects; they can be included in (1.52) by dropping the condition $l+2m > 0$.

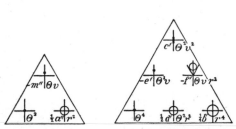
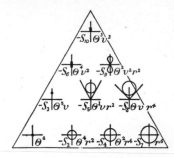

Second-degree (Gauss)   Fourth-degree (Seidel)   Sixth-degree (Schwarzschild)
aberration terms.   aberration terms.   aberration terms.

FIG. 2. Aberration terms $\Theta^k v^l r^{2m}$.

In systems containing refracting surfaces, the values of the coefficients in (1.47) depend on the wavelength λ. We suppose that the variation in refractive index ratio over the effective spectral range is $O(\mu^2)$ at each surface. At a reflecting surface it will of course be zero.

In a general centred system with normal figurings, the coefficients of the 'Gauss' (or second-degree) terms in the aberration function vary by $O(f\mu^4)$, those of the 'Seidel' (or fourth-degree) terms by $O(f\mu^6)$ and those of the 'Schwarzschild' (or sixth-degree) terms by $O(f\mu^8)$. Then the monochromatic aberration function at a selected wavelength λ_0 in the effective spectrum has the form

$$f\mu^4\Phi_{\lambda_0}(u, v; \Theta)$$

$$= f\mu^4\frac{H}{f\mu}[\tfrac{1}{4}Br^4 - F\Theta vr^2 + C\Theta^2v^2 + \tfrac{1}{2}D\Theta^2r^2 - E\Theta^3v] + O(f\mu^6), \quad (1.54)$$

the polychromatic aberration function (referred to the spherical surface S as reference surface) has the form

$$f\mu^4\Phi_\lambda(u, v; \Theta) = f\mu^4\Phi_{\lambda_0}(u, v; \Theta) + f\mu^4\frac{H}{f\mu}[\tfrac{1}{2}a'_\lambda r^2 - m'_\lambda\Theta v] + O(f\mu^6) \quad (1.55)$$

and the Schwarzschild aberrations do not enter into the leading terms of this approximation. This is the case treated in §§ 1.3–1.5. If the system happens to be anastigmatic in λ_0-light, so that

$$f\mu^4\Phi_{\lambda_0}(u, v; \Theta) = O(f\mu^6),$$

equation (1.55) reduces to

$$f\mu^4\Phi_\lambda(u, v; \Theta) = f\mu^4\frac{H}{f\mu}[\tfrac{1}{2}a'_\lambda r^2 - m'_\lambda \Theta v] + O(f\mu^6) \qquad (1.56)$$

and the colour-errors dominate the image. However, the thickness of the image-layer is still $O(f\mu^2)$, the Schwarzschild aberrations are still irrelevant to the practical problem of optimizing performance, and the analysis of §§ 1.3–1.5 is still appropriate.

A more elaborate analysis is only called for in systems where not only are the monochromatic Seidel aberrations reduced to mere traces, of order μ^2 times the normal size, but also the Gauss terms in the poly-chromatic aberration function have been reduced to $O(f\mu^6)$ over the effective spectrum. It is convenient here to use the term *anastigmat* to denote a system of this kind.† Anastigmats are then characterized by polychromatic image-spreads as low as $O(f\mu^5)$ over the whole of their working field, and the leading term of their aberration functions takes the form (1.47) or (1.52). The Schmidt camera, the field-flattened Schmidt camera and the Schmidt–Cassegrain cameras are anastigmats in this sense.

1.7. *Image assessment and error-balancing in anastigmats*

1.71. *Introduction.* Suppose now that equation (1.52) gives the aberration function of an anastigmat imaging on the spherical surface S and that in light of wavelength λ the aberration displacements, referred to the principal point of the λ_0-image-patch, are

$$(\xi, \eta) = f\mu^5\frac{f\mu}{H}\left(\frac{\partial}{\partial u}, \frac{\partial}{\partial v}\right)\Phi^* + O(f\mu^7) = (\xi^*, \eta^*) + O(f\mu^7). \quad (1.57)$$

Then

$$\xi^{*2} + \eta^{*2} = f^2\mu^{10}\left[\left(\frac{\partial}{\partial u}\sum_{klm}c_{klm}\Theta^k v^l r^{2m}\right)^2 + \left(\frac{\partial}{\partial v}\sum_{klm}c_{klm}\Theta^k v^l r^{2m}\right)^2\right]$$

$$= f^2\mu^{10}\sum c_{klm}c_{k'l'm'}\Theta^{k+k'}[ll'r^2 + 2(l'm + lm' + 2mm')v^2]\times$$

$$\times v^{l+l'-2}r^{2(m+m'-1)}, \quad (1.58)$$

---

† This definition of anastigmatism, which presupposes an angular field radius comparable with μ, appears rather forced when applied to ordinary camera lenses or other wide-field systems. But it seems helpful to use it for the classification of astronomical objectives.

where k, l, m and k', l', m' are both subject to (1.53). And the quantity

$$E^* = \frac{1}{\pi} \int_0^1 2\Theta \, d\Theta \iint_{u^2+v^2 \leqslant 1} (\xi^{*2}+\eta^{*2}) \, du \, dv$$

$$= f^2 \mu^{10} \sum c_{klm} c_{k'l'm'} \int_0^1 2\Theta^{k+k'+1} \, d\Theta \times$$

$$\times \frac{1}{\pi} \iint [ll'r^2 + 2(l'm+lm'+2mm')v^2] v^{l+l'-2} r^{2(m+m'-1)} \, du \, dv$$

$$= f^2 \mu^{10} \sum c_{klm} c_{k'l'm'} \frac{2}{(k+k'+2)(l+l'+2m+2m')} \times$$

$$\times [ll' I_{l+l'-2} + 2(l'm+lm'+2mm') I_{l+l'}], \dagger \qquad (1.59)$$

where
$$I_p = \frac{1}{\pi} \int_0^{2\pi} \sin p\theta \, d\theta = 2 \cdot \frac{1.3.5...(p-1)}{2.4.6...p} \quad (p \text{ even})$$
$$= 0 \quad (p \text{ odd}). \qquad (1.60)$$

We can write this
$$\frac{1}{f^2 \mu^{10}} E^* = \sum_{n,n'=1}^{16} \cdot a_n a_{n'} t_{nn'} \qquad (1.61)$$

where Table I gives the triad (k, l, m) corresponding to each value of n and

$$t_{nn'} = \frac{2}{(k+k'+2)(l+l'+2m+2m')} [ll' I_{l+l'-2} + 2(l'm+lm'+2mm') I_{l+l'}]. \qquad (1.62)$$

The values of $t_{nn'}$ are shown in Table II.‡ As before,

$$\rho^{*2} = \frac{1}{\pi} \iint (\xi^{*2}+\eta^{*2}) \, du \, dv$$

measures, with sufficient accuracy, the radius of gyration of the image-patch about the corresponding point $(\xi, \eta) = (0, 0)$ of the receiving surface and E^* measures the mean value of ρ^{*2} over the whole field.

To each value of n corresponds a value of l in accordance with Table I, and similarly for n', l'. We call those terms $a_n \sigma_n$ of (1.52) for which l is even 'even' terms, because $v^l r^{2m}$ is then an even function of (u, v); the others we call 'odd' terms. From Table II, or from (1.58), it is seen that cross products between odd and even terms contribute nothing to E^* and that we can therefore write

$$E^* = E'^* + E''^*, \qquad (1.63)$$

† The term in $I_{l+l'-2}$ drops out if l or $l' = 0$.
‡ Table II here corresponds to Table IV in Wayman's thesis.

where

$$
\left.
\begin{aligned}
E'^* &= f^2\mu^{10} \sum_{l,l'\,\text{odd}} a_n a_{n'} t_{nn'} = f^2\mu^{10} \sum_{r,s} t_{rs} a_r a_s \\
&\quad\quad\quad\quad (r, s = 2, 4, 7, 9, 12, 13, 16) \\
E''^* &= f^2\mu^{10} \sum_{l,l'\,\text{even}} a_n a_{n'} t_{nn'} = f^2\mu^{10} \sum_{r,s} t_{rs} a_r a_s \\
&\quad\quad\quad\quad (r, s = 1, 3, 5, 6, 8, 10, 11, 14, 15)
\end{aligned}
\right\}. \quad (1.64)
$$

TABLE II

Non-zero Values of $t_{nn'}$ in (1.61)

The other $t_{nn'}$ in (1.61) are zero.

$n \backslash n'$	2	4	7	9	12	13	16
2	$\frac{1}{2}$	$\frac{1}{2}$	$\frac{1}{3}$	$\frac{1}{2}$	$\frac{1}{4}$	$\frac{1}{3}$	$\frac{1}{4}$
4	$\frac{1}{2}$	$\frac{5}{6}$	$\frac{1}{3}$	1	$\frac{5}{12}$	$\frac{5}{9}$	$\frac{1}{4}$
7	$\frac{1}{3}$	$\frac{1}{3}$	$\frac{1}{4}$	$\frac{1}{3}$	$\frac{3}{16}$	$\frac{1}{4}$	$\frac{1}{5}$
9	$\frac{1}{2}$	1	$\frac{1}{3}$	$\frac{13}{10}$	$\frac{1}{2}$	$\frac{2}{3}$	$\frac{1}{4}$
12	$\frac{1}{4}$	$\frac{5}{12}$	$\frac{3}{16}$	$\frac{1}{2}$	$\frac{9}{32}$	$\frac{5}{16}$	$\frac{3}{20}$
13	$\frac{1}{3}$	$\frac{5}{9}$	$\frac{1}{4}$	$\frac{2}{3}$	$\frac{5}{16}$	$\frac{5}{12}$	$\frac{1}{5}$
16	$\frac{1}{4}$	$\frac{1}{4}$	$\frac{1}{5}$	$\frac{1}{4}$	$\frac{3}{20}$	$\frac{1}{5}$	$\frac{1}{6}$

$n \backslash n'$	1	3	5	6	8	10	11	14	15
1	2	$\frac{8}{3}$	$\frac{1}{2}$	1	3	$\frac{4}{3}$	$\frac{2}{3}$	$\frac{2}{3}$	$\frac{1}{3}$
3	$\frac{8}{3}$	4	$\frac{2}{3}$	$\frac{4}{3}$	$\frac{24}{5}$	2	1	$\frac{8}{9}$	$\frac{4}{9}$
5	$\frac{1}{2}$	$\frac{2}{3}$	$\frac{1}{3}$	$\frac{1}{3}$	$\frac{3}{4}$	$\frac{4}{9}$	$\frac{7}{18}$	$\frac{1}{4}$	$\frac{1}{4}$
6	1	$\frac{4}{3}$	$\frac{1}{3}$	$\frac{2}{3}$	$\frac{3}{2}$	$\frac{8}{9}$	$\frac{4}{9}$	$\frac{1}{2}$	$\frac{1}{4}$
8	3	$\frac{24}{5}$	$\frac{4}{3}$	$\frac{3}{2}$	6	$\frac{12}{5}$	$\frac{6}{5}$	1	$\frac{1}{2}$
10	$\frac{4}{3}$	2	$\frac{4}{9}$	$\frac{8}{9}$	$\frac{12}{5}$	$\frac{4}{3}$	$\frac{2}{3}$	$\frac{2}{3}$	$\frac{1}{3}$
11	$\frac{2}{3}$	1	$\frac{7}{18}$	$\frac{4}{9}$	$\frac{6}{5}$	$\frac{2}{3}$	$\frac{13}{24}$	$\frac{1}{3}$	$\frac{7}{24}$
14	$\frac{2}{3}$	$\frac{8}{9}$	$\frac{1}{4}$	$\frac{1}{4}$	1	$\frac{2}{3}$	$\frac{1}{3}$	$\frac{2}{5}$	$\frac{1}{5}$
15	$\frac{1}{3}$	$\frac{4}{9}$	$\frac{1}{4}$	$\frac{1}{4}$	$\frac{1}{2}$	$\frac{1}{3}$	$\frac{7}{24}$	$\frac{1}{5}$	$\frac{1}{5}$

Coefficient notation

Gauss		Seidel					Schwarzschild								
a_1	a_2	a_3	a_4	a_5	a_6	a_7	a_8	a_9	a_{10}	a_{11}	a_{12}	a_{13}	a_{14}	a_{15}	a_{16}
$\frac{1}{2}a''$	$-m''$	$\frac{1}{4}b'$	$-f'$	c'	$\frac{1}{2}d'$	$-e'$	$-S_7$	$-S_8$	$-S_4$	$-S_9$	$-S_{10}$	$-S_5$	$-S_2$	$-S_6$	$-S_3$

In E'^* appear the distortion and plate-scale error coefficients m'', e', S_3, the three coma coefficients f', S_5, S_6, and the 'arrows' (Pfeilfehler) coefficient S_{10}.

In E''^* appear the field-surface adjustment coefficients a'', d', S_2, the three spherical aberration coefficients b', S_7, S_4, the primary astigmatism coefficients c', S_6, and the 'wings' (Flügelfehler) coefficient S_9.

As the wavelength varies in the effective spectral range, the coefficients $a_1, a_2, \ldots a_7$ (that is, $-m''$, $\frac{1}{2}a''$, $\frac{1}{4}b'$, $-f'$, c', $\frac{1}{2}d'$, $-e'$) vary by $O(1)$; the Schwarzschild coefficients remain constant to the order of accuracy involved.

To discuss the performance of the system in monochromatic light of wavelength λ, we must first adjust the (ξ, η)-origin for each image-patch to the centre of gravity of the patch. This can be done by minimizing

$E*$ with respect to m'', e', S_3 (i.e. with respect to a_2, a_7, a_{16}) treated as free variables. For a change $\Delta m''$, $\Delta e'$, ΔS_3 in m'', e', S_3, without any change in the design parameters of the system, is equivalent to a shift

$$-f\mu^5(\Delta m''.\Theta + \Delta e'.\Theta^3 + \Delta S_3.\Theta^5) \tag{1.65}$$

of the (ξ, η)-origin away from the optic axis.

Since $E''*$ is independent of a_2, a_7, a_{16} by (1.64), it is sufficient to minimize $E'*$. The minimizing values of a_2, a_7, a_{16} satisfy the equations

$$\frac{\partial E'*}{\partial a_2} = 0, \qquad \frac{\partial E'*}{\partial a_7} = 0, \qquad \frac{\partial E'*}{\partial a_{16}} = 0 \tag{1.66}$$

or, by Table II,

$$\left. \begin{aligned} \tfrac{1}{2}a_2 + \tfrac{1}{2}a_4 + \tfrac{1}{3}a_7 + \tfrac{1}{2}a_9 + \tfrac{1}{4}a_{12} + \tfrac{1}{3}a_{13} + \tfrac{1}{4}a_{16} &= 0 \\ \tfrac{1}{3}a_2 + \tfrac{1}{3}a_4 + \tfrac{1}{4}a_7 + \tfrac{1}{3}a_9 + \tfrac{3}{16}a_{12} + \tfrac{1}{4}a_{13} + \tfrac{1}{5}a_{16} &= 0 \\ \tfrac{1}{4}a_2 + \tfrac{1}{4}a_4 + \tfrac{1}{5}a_7 + \tfrac{1}{4}a_9 + \tfrac{3}{20}a_{12} + \tfrac{1}{5}a_{13} + \tfrac{1}{6}a_{16} &= 0 \end{aligned} \right\}. \tag{1.67}$$

On writing

$$X = a_2 + a_4 + a_9, \qquad Y = a_7 + \tfrac{3}{4}a_{12} + a_{13}, \qquad Z = a_{16}, \tag{1.68}$$

equations (1.67) take the form

$$\left. \begin{aligned} \tfrac{1}{2}X + \tfrac{1}{3}Y + \tfrac{1}{4}Z &= 0 \\ \tfrac{1}{3}X + \tfrac{1}{4}Y + \tfrac{1}{5}Z &= 0 \\ \tfrac{1}{4}X + \tfrac{1}{5}Y + \tfrac{1}{6}Z &= 0 \end{aligned} \right\}. \tag{1.69}$$

Since

$$\begin{vmatrix} \tfrac{1}{2} & \tfrac{1}{3} & \tfrac{1}{4} \\ \tfrac{1}{3} & \tfrac{1}{4} & \tfrac{1}{5} \\ \tfrac{1}{4} & \tfrac{1}{5} & \tfrac{1}{6} \end{vmatrix} = \tfrac{1}{43200} \neq 0, \tag{1.70}$$

the only solution of (1.69) is $X = Y = Z = 0$; that is,

$$\left. \begin{aligned} a_2 &= -a_4 - a_9 \\ a_7 &= -\tfrac{3}{4}a_{12} - a_{13} \\ a_{16} &= 0 \end{aligned} \right\}. \tag{1.71}$$

(1.71) gives the values which a_2, a_7, a_{16} must have in order that the (ξ, η)-origins shall be at the centroids of the respective image-patches.

Now if, writing the terms of $E'*/f^2\mu^{10}$ in a square array†

$$\sum_{rs} t_{rs} a_r a_s \quad (r, s = 2, 4, 7, 9, 12, 13, 16)$$

and giving a_2, a_7, a_{16} the values (1.71), we subtract the rows

$$\sum_s t_{rs} a_r a_s \quad (r = 2, 7, 16)$$

---

† We could simply substitute the values (1.71) for a_2, a_7, a_{16} into $E'*$ and rearrange the terms; the procedure used saves a little labour.

with zero sum, and also the columns

$$\sum_r t_{rs} a_r a_s \quad (s = 2, 7, 16)$$

with zero sum, we are left with the new expression

$$\sum_{rs} t_{rs} a_r a_s - \sum_{pq} t_{pq} a_p a_q \quad (p, q = 2, 7, 16; r, s = 4, 9, 12, 13)$$

$$= \sum_{rs} t_{rs} a_r a_s - t_{22}(a_4 + a_9)^2 - t_{77}(\tfrac{3}{4}a_{12} + a_{13})^2 -$$

$$- (t_{27} + t_{72})(a_4 + a_9)(\tfrac{3}{4}a_{12} + a_{13}) \quad (r, s = 4, 9, 12, 13)$$

for the value of

$$\frac{1}{f^2\mu^{10}} E_1'^* = \frac{1}{f^2\mu^{10}} \min_{a_2, a_7, a_{16}} \sum'^* = \sum_{rs} t_{rs}^{(1)} a_r a_s \quad (r, s = 4, 9, 12, 13). \quad (1.72)$$

The values of the coefficients $t_{rs}^{(1)}$ are given in Table III a. The (a_2, a_7, a_{16})-minimized value of E^*, namely

$$E_0^* = E_1'^* + E''^*, \quad (1.73)$$

is the *mean square effective image radius over the given field* in the surface S; the suffix 1 in $E_1'^*$ indicates that the r.m.s. effective radius of each image-patch is measured relative to its own centroid.

TABLE III a

Values of $t_{rs}^{(1)}$ in E'^*

r \ s	4	9	12	13
4	$\frac{1}{3}$	$\frac{1}{2}$	$\frac{1}{6}$	$\frac{2}{9}$
9	$\frac{1}{2}$	$\frac{4}{5}$	$\frac{1}{4}$	$\frac{1}{3}$
12	$\frac{1}{6}$	$\frac{1}{4}$	$\frac{9}{64}$	$\frac{1}{8}$
13	$\frac{2}{9}$	$\frac{1}{3}$	$\frac{1}{8}$	$\frac{1}{6}$

1.72. *Best field surface.* To obtain the best field surface, we have to minimize the E_0^* of (1.73) with respect to the focus-shift coefficients a'', d', S_2 (i.e. with respect to a_1, a_6, a_{14}) treated as free variables. For a change $\Delta a''$, $\Delta d'$, ΔS_2 in a'', d', S_2, without any change in the design parameters of the system, is the analytical expression of the effects of a forward displacement

$$f\mu^4 \frac{f\mu}{H} (\Delta a'' + \Theta^2 \Delta d' - 2\Theta^4 \Delta S_2) \quad (1.74)$$

of the receiving surface from the reference surface S.

Since $E_1'^*$ is independent of a_1, a_6, a_{14} by Table III a, it is sufficient to minimize E''^*. The minimizing values of a_1, a_6, a_{14} are given by the equations

$$\frac{\partial E''^*}{\partial a_1} = 0, \qquad \frac{\partial E''^*}{\partial a_6} = 0, \qquad \frac{\partial E''^*}{\partial a_{14}} = 0, \tag{1.75}$$

or

$$\left.\begin{aligned}
2a_1 + \tfrac{8}{3}a_3 + \tfrac{1}{2}a_5 + a_6 + 3a_8 + \tfrac{4}{3}a_{10} + \tfrac{2}{3}a_{11} + \tfrac{2}{3}a_{14} + \tfrac{1}{3}a_{15} &= 0 \\
a_1 + \tfrac{4}{3}a_3 + \tfrac{1}{3}a_5 + \tfrac{2}{3}a_6 + \tfrac{3}{2}a_8 + \tfrac{8}{9}a_{10} + \tfrac{4}{9}a_{11} + \tfrac{1}{2}a_{14} + \tfrac{1}{4}a_{15} &= 0 \\
\tfrac{2}{3}a_1 + \tfrac{8}{9}a_3 + \tfrac{1}{4}a_5 + \tfrac{1}{2}a_6 + a_8 + \tfrac{2}{3}a_{10} + \tfrac{1}{3}a_{11} + \tfrac{2}{5}a_{14} + \tfrac{1}{5}a_{15} &= 0
\end{aligned}\right\}. \tag{1.76}$$

Set

$$X' = 2a_1 + \tfrac{8}{3}a_3 + 3a_8, \qquad Y' = a_5 + 2a_6 + \tfrac{8}{3}a_{10} + \tfrac{4}{3}a_{11},$$
$$Z' = 2a_{14} + a_{15}; \tag{1.77}$$

then the equations to be satisfied are

$$\left.\begin{aligned}
X' + \tfrac{1}{2}Y' + \tfrac{1}{3}Z' &= 0 \\
\tfrac{1}{2}X' + \tfrac{1}{3}Y' + \tfrac{1}{4}Z' &= 0 \\
\tfrac{1}{3}X' + \tfrac{1}{4}Y' + \tfrac{1}{5}Z' &= 0
\end{aligned}\right\}, \tag{1.78}$$

and since

$$\begin{vmatrix} 1 & \tfrac{1}{2} & \tfrac{1}{3} \\ \tfrac{1}{2} & \tfrac{1}{3} & \tfrac{1}{4} \\ \tfrac{1}{3} & \tfrac{1}{4} & \tfrac{1}{5} \end{vmatrix} = \tfrac{1}{2160} \neq 0,$$

the only solution is $X' = Y' = Z' = 0$, that is

$$\left.\begin{aligned}
a_1 &= -\tfrac{4}{3}a_3 - \tfrac{3}{2}a_8 \\
a_6 &= -\tfrac{1}{2}a_5 - \tfrac{4}{3}a_{10} - \tfrac{2}{3}a_{11} \\
a_{14} &= -\tfrac{1}{2}a_{15}
\end{aligned}\right\}. \tag{1.79}$$

(1.79) gives the values which a_1, a_6, a_{14} must have in the best field surface. Let $a_1^{(S)}$, $a_6^{(S)}$, $a_{14}^{(S)}$ be the value which they have on the reference surface S, and write

$$\Delta a_r = a_r - a_r^{(S)} \quad (r = 1, 6, 14).$$

Then the best field surface is displaced forward from the reference surface S by $f\mu^4\epsilon(\Theta)$, where

$$\epsilon(\Theta) = \frac{f\mu}{H}(2\Delta a_1 + 2\Theta^2 \Delta a_6 + 2\Theta^4 \Delta a_{14})$$

$$= -\frac{2f\mu}{H}\left[(a_1^{(S)} + \tfrac{4}{3}a_3 + \tfrac{3}{2}a_8) + \Theta^2(a_6^{(S)} + \tfrac{1}{2}a_5 + \tfrac{4}{3}a_{10} + \tfrac{2}{3}a_{11}) + \right.$$
$$\left. + \Theta^4(a_{14}^{(S)} + \tfrac{1}{2}a_{15})\right]. \tag{1.80}$$

It is interesting to see, from the form of (1.80), that the axial focus shift of the best field surface relative to the surface S depends only on the values of a'', b' and S_7 in the latter, the field-curvature change depends only on the values of c', d', S_4 and S_9 in the reference surface S, and the secondary field curvature of the best field surface only on the values of S_2 and S_6 in the surface S.

In particular, the form of the term in Θ^4 shows that an aspheric receiving surface is of advantage if and only if the lateral field curvature coefficient S_2 on the reference surface S and the lateral astigmatism coefficient S_6 there satisfy the condition $S_2 + \frac{1}{2}S_6 \neq 0$.

By using (1.79), the value E_1^* of the mean square image radius over the best field surface is found to be $E_1'^* + E_1''^*$, where

$$\frac{1}{f^2 \mu^{10}} E_1''^* = \sum_{rs} t_{rs}^{(1)} a_r a_s \quad (r, s = 3, 5, 8, 10, 11, 15) \tag{1.81}$$

and the values of $t_{rs}^{(2)}$ are given in Table IIIb.

TABLE IIIb

Values of $t_{rs}^{(1)}$ in $E_1''^*$

r \ s	3	5	8	10	11	15
3	$\frac{4}{9}$	0	$\frac{4}{5}$	$\frac{2}{9}$	$\frac{1}{9}$	0
5	0	$\frac{1}{6}$	0	0	$\frac{1}{6}$	$\frac{1}{8}$
8	$\frac{4}{5}$	0	$\frac{3}{2}$	$\frac{2}{5}$	$\frac{1}{5}$	0
10	$\frac{2}{9}$	0	$\frac{2}{5}$	$\frac{4}{27}$	$\frac{2}{27}$	0
11	$\frac{1}{9}$	$\frac{1}{6}$	$\frac{1}{5}$	$\frac{2}{27}$	$\frac{53}{216}$	$\frac{1}{8}$
15	0	$\frac{1}{8}$	0	0	$\frac{1}{8}$	$\frac{1}{10}$

1.73. *Best spherical field surface.* To obtain the best spherical field surface, we have to minimize E''^* over a_1, a_6 instead of over a_1, a_6, a_{14}. For now $\epsilon(\Theta)$ is restricted to the form $\alpha + \beta\Theta^2 + O(\mu^2)$ and the coefficient a_{14} no longer varies perceptibly when the receiving surface is varied within the image-layer.

The equations to be satisfied are consequently

$$X' + \tfrac{1}{2}Y' + \tfrac{1}{3}Z' = 0,$$

$$\tfrac{1}{2}X' + \tfrac{1}{3}Y' + \tfrac{1}{4}Z' = 0,$$

and their solution in X', Y' is

$$X' = \tfrac{1}{6}Z' = \tfrac{1}{3}a_{14} + \tfrac{1}{6}a_{15},$$

$$Y' = -Z' = -2a_{14} - a_{15}, \tag{1.82}$$

which gives

$$a_1 = -\tfrac{4}{3}a_3 - \tfrac{3}{2}a_8 + \tfrac{1}{6}a_{14} + \tfrac{1}{12}a_{15}$$
$$a_6 = -\tfrac{1}{2}a_5 - \tfrac{4}{3}a_{10} - \tfrac{2}{3}a_{11} - a_{14} - \tfrac{1}{2}a_{15}$$
$$\left.\right\}. \qquad (1.83)$$

These equations specify the best spherical field surface, which is obtained on taking

$$\epsilon(\Theta) = -\frac{2f\mu}{H}\left[(a_1^{(S)} + \tfrac{4}{3}a_3 + \tfrac{3}{2}a_8 - \tfrac{1}{6}(a_{14} + \tfrac{1}{2}a_{15})) + \right.$$
$$\left. + \Theta^2(a_6^{(S)} + \tfrac{1}{2}a_5 + \tfrac{4}{3}a_{10} + \tfrac{2}{3}a_{11} + (a_{14} + \tfrac{1}{2}a_{15}))\right]; \quad (1.84)$$

as before, $a_1^{(S)}$, $a_6^{(S)}$ denote the values of a_1, a_6 on the reference surface S.

The value E_2^* of the mean square image radius over the best spherical field surface is given by the equations

$$E_2^* = E_1^{\prime *} + E_2^{\prime\prime *} = f^2\mu^{10}\left[\sum_{4,\,9,\,12,\,13} t_{rs}^{(1)}\, a_r\, a_s + \sum_{3,\,5,\,8,\,10,\,11,\,14,\,15} t_{rs}^{(2)}\, a_r\, a_s\right],$$
$$(1.85)$$

where the values of $t_{rs}^{(1)}$, $t_{rs}^{(2)}$ are given in Tables III a, IV respectively.

TABLE IV

Values of $t_{rs}^{(2)}$ in $E_2^{\prime\prime *}$

r \ s	3	5	8	10	11	14	15
3	$\tfrac{4}{9}$	0	$\tfrac{4}{5}$	$\tfrac{2}{9}$	$\tfrac{1}{9}$	0	0
5	0	$\tfrac{1}{6}$	0	0	$\tfrac{1}{6}$	0	$\tfrac{1}{8}$
8	$\tfrac{4}{5}$	0	$\tfrac{3}{2}$	$\tfrac{2}{5}$	$\tfrac{1}{5}$	0	0
10	$\tfrac{2}{9}$	0	$\tfrac{2}{5}$	$\tfrac{4}{27}$	$\tfrac{2}{27}$	0	0
11	$\tfrac{1}{9}$	$\tfrac{1}{6}$	$\tfrac{1}{5}$	$\tfrac{2}{27}$	$\tfrac{53}{216}$	0	$\tfrac{1}{8}$
14	0	0	0	0	0	$\tfrac{1}{90}$	$\tfrac{1}{180}$
15	0	$\tfrac{1}{8}$	0	0	$\tfrac{1}{8}$	$\tfrac{1}{180}$	$\tfrac{37}{360}$

1.74. *Aberration balancing in monochromats.* (1.85) can be used to obtain an answer to the question: What amounts of residual Gauss and Seidel aberration will give the smallest r.m.s. image radius over the best spherical field surface of a monochromat with specified Schwarzschild aberration coefficients?

Stated in analytical terms, the problem is to minimize the E_2^* of (1.85) by proper choice of the remaining fourth-degree coefficients a_3, a_4, a_5 (i.e. $\tfrac{1}{2}b'$, $-f'$, c') treated as free variables. (Changes in a_1, a_2, a_6, a_7 do not alter E_2^*; they merely change the position and curvature of the best spherical field surface and the distance of the (ξ, η)-origin from the centroid of each image-patch.)

By (1.85), this is equivalent to minimizing $E_1'^*$ with respect to a_4 and $E_2''^*$ with respect to a_3, a_5. Using the same method as before, we find that the minimizing values of a_3, a_4, a_5 are given by the equations

$$\left. \begin{aligned} a_3 &= -\tfrac{9}{5}a_8 - \tfrac{1}{2}a_{10} - \tfrac{1}{4}a_{11} \\ a_4 &= -\tfrac{3}{2}a_9 - \tfrac{1}{2}a_{12} - \tfrac{2}{3}a_{13} \\ a_5 &= -a_{11} - \tfrac{3}{4}a_{15} \end{aligned} \right\} \tag{1.86}$$

and that the minimized value of E^* is

$$E_3^* = f^2\mu^{10} \sum_{rs} t_{rs}^{(3)} a_r a_s \quad (r,\, s = 8,\, 9,\, 10,\, 11,\, 12,\, 13,\, 14,\, 15), \tag{1.87}$$

where the coefficients $t_{rs}^{(3)}$ are given in Table V. That is to say,

$$E_3^* = f^2\mu^{10}\big[\tfrac{3}{50}S_7^2 + \tfrac{1}{20}S_8^2 + (\tfrac{1}{27}S_4^2 + \tfrac{1}{27}S_4 S_9 + \tfrac{11}{216}S_9^2) +$$
$$+ (\tfrac{11}{192}S_{10}^2 + \tfrac{1}{36}S_{10} S_5 + \tfrac{1}{54}S_5^2) + (\tfrac{1}{90}S_2^2 + \tfrac{1}{90}S_2 S_6 + \tfrac{13}{1440}S_6^2)\big] \tag{1.88}$$

on the best spherical field surface, which is itself obtained on taking

$$\epsilon(\Theta) = -\frac{2f\mu}{H}\big[(a_1^{(S)} - \tfrac{9}{10}a_8 - \tfrac{2}{3}a_{10} - \tfrac{1}{3}a_{11} - \tfrac{1}{6}a_{14} - \tfrac{1}{12}a_{15}) +$$
$$+ \Theta^2(a_6^{(S)} + \tfrac{4}{3}a_{10} + \tfrac{1}{6}a_{11} + a_{14} + \tfrac{1}{8}a_{15})\big]. \tag{1.89}$$

TABLE V

Values of $t_{rs}^{(3)}$ in E_3^*

$t_{88}^{(3)} = \tfrac{3}{50}$

$t_{99}^{(3)} = \tfrac{1}{20}$

$r \backslash s$	10	11
10	$\tfrac{1}{27}$	$\tfrac{1}{54}$
11	$\tfrac{1}{54}$	$\tfrac{11}{216}$

$r \backslash s$	12	13
12	$\tfrac{11}{192}$	$\tfrac{1}{72}$
13	$\tfrac{1}{72}$	$\tfrac{1}{54}$

$r \backslash s$	14	15
14	$\tfrac{1}{90}$	$\tfrac{1}{180}$
15	$\tfrac{1}{180}$	$\tfrac{13}{1440}$

The remaining $t_{rs}^{(3)}$ in E_3^* are zero.

For the error-balanced monochromatic images on the best spherical field surface, with (ξ, η)-origins taken at the centroids of the image-patches, we have from (1.71), (1.83) and (1.86)

$$\left. \begin{aligned} a_1 &= -\tfrac{4}{3}a_3 - \tfrac{3}{2}a_8 + \tfrac{1}{6}a_{14} + \tfrac{1}{12}a_{15} = \tfrac{9}{10}a_8 + \tfrac{2}{3}a_{10} + \tfrac{1}{3}a_{11} + \tfrac{1}{6}a_{14} + \tfrac{1}{12}a_{15} \\ a_2 &= -a_4 - a_9 = \tfrac{1}{2}a_9 + \tfrac{1}{2}a_{12} + \tfrac{2}{3}a_{13} \\ a_3 &= -\tfrac{9}{5}a_8 - \tfrac{1}{2}a_{10} - \tfrac{1}{4}a_{11} \\ a_4 &= -\tfrac{3}{2}a_9 - \tfrac{1}{2}a_{12} - \tfrac{2}{3}a_{13} \\ a_5 &= -a_{11} - \tfrac{3}{4}a_{15} \\ a_6 &= -\tfrac{1}{2}a_5 - \tfrac{4}{3}a_{10} - \tfrac{2}{3}a_{11} - a_{14} - \tfrac{1}{2}a_{15} = -\tfrac{4}{3}a_{10} - \tfrac{1}{6}a_{11} - a_{14} - \tfrac{1}{8}a_{15} \\ a_7 &= -\tfrac{3}{4}a_{12} - a_{13} \end{aligned} \right\} \tag{1.90}$$

and the Schwarzschild coefficient $a_{16} = 0$. In the more usual notation $(A = \mu^4 a''$, $M = \mu^4 m''$, $B = \mu^2 b'$, $F = \mu^2 f'$, $C = \mu^2 c'$, $D = \mu^2 d'$, $E = \mu^2 e'$, $a_8 = -S_7$, $a_9 = -S_8$, $a_{10} = -S_4$, $a_{11} = -S_9$, $a_{12} = -S_{10}$, $a_{13} = -S_5$, $a_{14} = -S_2$, $a_{15} = -S_6$, $a_{16} = -S_3)$ for the aberration function

$$f\mu^6\Phi(u, v; \Theta) = f\mu^2[\tfrac{1}{2}Ar^2 + Mv\Theta] +$$

$$+ f\mu^4[\tfrac{1}{4}Br^4 - F\Theta vr^2 + C\Theta^2 v^2 + \tfrac{1}{2}D\Theta^2 r^2 - E\Theta^3 v] -$$

$$- f\mu^6[S_2\,\Theta^4 r^2 + S_3\,\Theta^5 v + S_4\,\Theta^2 r^4 + S_5\,\Theta^3 vr^2 + S_6\,\Theta^4 v^2 +$$

$$+ S_7\,r^6 + S_8\,\Theta vr^4 + S_9\,\Theta^2 v^2 r^2 + S_{10}\,\Theta^3 v^3] + O(f\mu^8), \quad (1.91)$$

this result becomes

$$\left.\begin{aligned}
A &= -\mu^4[\tfrac{1}{6}S_2 + \tfrac{2}{3}S_4 + \tfrac{1}{12}S_6 + \tfrac{9}{10}S_7 + \tfrac{1}{3}S_9] \\
M &= -\mu^4[\tfrac{2}{3}S_5 + \tfrac{1}{2}S_8 + \tfrac{1}{2}S_{10}] \\
B &= \mu^2[\tfrac{1}{2}S_4 + \tfrac{4}{5}S_7 + \tfrac{1}{4}S_9] \\
F &= \mu^2[\tfrac{2}{3}S_5 + \tfrac{3}{2}S_8 + \tfrac{1}{2}S_{10}] \\
C &= \mu^2[S_9 + \tfrac{3}{4}S_6] \\
D &= \mu^2[S_2 + \tfrac{4}{3}S_4 + \tfrac{1}{8}S_6 + \tfrac{1}{6}S_9] \\
E &= \mu^2[S_5 + \tfrac{3}{4}S_{10}] \\
S_3 &= 0
\end{aligned}\right\} \qquad (1.92)$$

and the field surface is that obtained by setting

$$\epsilon(\Theta) = \frac{f\mu}{H}\frac{\Delta A + \Theta^2 \Delta M}{\mu^2}, \qquad (1.93)$$

where ΔA, ΔM are the amounts by which the optimum values (1.92) of A, M exceed their values on the reference surface S.

1.75. *Aberration balancing in presence of chromatism.* In a colour-corrected anastigmat containing refracting surfaces and imaging on the spherical reference surface S the aberration coefficients $\tfrac{1}{2}a''$, $-m''$, $\tfrac{1}{4}b'$, $-f'$, c', $\tfrac{1}{2}d'$, $-e'$ may vary by $O(1)$ as the wavelength λ varies through the effective spectral range, while $-S_2$, $-S_3$,..., $-S_{10}$ vary only by $O(\mu^2)$ and can therefore be treated as constant in the fifth-order theory. That is, $a_1, a_2,..., a_7$ may vary, but $a_8, a_9,..., a_{16}$ remain effectively constant.

The variation of $a_1, a_2,..., a_7$ expresses the chromatic aberrations of the system.

The mean square image radius of the polychromatic image-patch is, in the fifth-order approximation, the weighted mean of

$$\rho_\lambda^{*2} = \frac{1}{\pi} \iint\limits_{u^2+v^2 \leqslant 1} (\xi_\lambda^{*2}+\eta_\lambda^{*2})\, du\, dv\dagger \qquad (1.94)$$

with respect to λ; we denote it by $(\overline{\rho_\lambda^{*2}})$. The mean square image radius over the whole field is then

$$\int_0^1 (\overline{\rho_\lambda^{*2}}) 2\Theta\, d\Theta = \overline{\int_0^1 \rho_\lambda^{*2}.2\Theta\, d\Theta} = \overline{E_\lambda^*}$$

to the same order of accuracy. Since

$$E_\lambda^* = f^2 \mu^{10} \sum_{r,s=1}^{16} t_{rs} a_r a_s,$$

where the t_{rs} (given by Table II) are independent of λ, we have

$$\overline{E_\lambda^*} = f^2 \mu^{10} \sum_{r,s=1}^{16} t_{rs} \overline{(a_r a_s)}. \qquad (1.95)$$

Because $a_8, a_9,..., a_{16}$ are effectively independent of λ, (1.95) can be written in the alternative form

$$\overline{E_\lambda^*} = f^2 \mu^{10}\Big[\sum_{p,q} t_{pq}\overline{(a_p a_q)} + \sum_{r,s} t_{rs} a_r a_s + 2\sum_{p,r} t_{pr}\bar{a}_p a_r \Big]$$

$$(p, q = 1, 2,..., 7;\ r, s = 8, 9,..., 16). \qquad (1.96)$$

If we define the *chromatism factors*

$$d_{pq} = \overline{(a_p-\bar{a}_p)(a_q-\bar{a}_q)} \quad (p, q = 1, 2,..., 7), \qquad (1.97)$$

so that $d_p = +\sqrt{d_{pp}}$ is the 'scatter' or r.m.s. deviation of a_p from its mean value, then it is easy to show that

$$\overline{(a_p a_q)} = d_{pq}+\bar{a}_p\bar{a}_q$$

and (1.96) can be written

$$\overline{E_\lambda^*} = f^2 \mu^{10}\Big[\sum_{r,s=1}^{16} t_{rs}\bar{a}_r\bar{a}_s + \sum_{p,q=1}^{7} t_{pq} d_{pq} \Big]. \qquad (1.98)$$

The quantities d_{pq} remain effectively constant (i.e. change by only $O(\mu^2)$) under the small variations of the design parameters of the system which are ordinarily called for in the process of balancing the fifth-degree monochromatic aberrations by means of controlled traces of lower-degree monochromatic aberrations. These variations, which can be expressed as changes $O(f\mu^4)$ in the spacings between surfaces, changes

---

† ξ_λ^*, η_λ^* are the fifth-order aberration displacements in λ-light, referred to the principal point of the λ_0-image-patch as origin. E^* is the corresponding value of E^*. Bars denote weighted λ-means throughout.

$O(f\mu^6)$ in surface figurings of type $\alpha r^2+\beta r^4$, and changes $O(f\mu^4)$ in the radii of curvature of spherical surfaces, also leave the Schwarzschild coefficients unchanged to fifth-order accuracy. Thus the d_{pq} provide a *chromatic contribution*

$$E_C^* = f^2\mu^{10}\sum_{p,q=1}^{7} t_{pq}d_{pq} \tag{1.99}$$

to $\overline{E_\lambda^*}$ which is left unchanged by the above process of aberration-balancing.†

The remaining part of $\overline{E_\lambda^*}$, namely the sum

$$E_M^* = f^2\mu^{10}\sum_{r,s=1}^{16} t_{rs}\overline{a_r}\,\overline{a_s}, \tag{1.100}$$

can be minimized by the procedure already used for monochromat anastigmats; it is only necessary to replace every a_r by $\overline{a_r}$ in the analysis of §§ 1.73 and 1.74.

The conclusion is that the error-balancing should increase the λ_0-values of a'', m'', b', f', c', d', e' on the surface S by

$$
\left.
\begin{aligned}
\Delta a'' &= -\mu^4[\tfrac{1}{6}S_2+\tfrac{2}{3}S_4+\tfrac{1}{12}S_6+\tfrac{9}{10}S_7+\tfrac{1}{3}S_9]-\overline{a''_{(0)}}\\
\Delta m'' &= -\mu^4[\tfrac{2}{3}S_5+\tfrac{1}{2}S_8+\tfrac{1}{2}S_{10}]-\overline{m''_{(0)}}\\
\Delta b' &= \mu^2[\tfrac{1}{2}S_4+\tfrac{4}{5}S_7+\tfrac{1}{4}S_9]-\overline{b'_{(0)}}\\
\Delta f' &= \mu^2[\tfrac{2}{3}S_5+\tfrac{3}{2}S_8+\tfrac{1}{2}S_{10}]-\overline{f'_{(0)}}\\
\Delta c' &= \mu^2[\tfrac{3}{4}S_6+S_9]-\overline{c'_{(0)}}\\
\Delta d' &= \mu^2[S_2+\tfrac{4}{3}S_4+\tfrac{1}{8}S_6+\tfrac{1}{6}S_9]-\overline{d'_{(0)}}\\
\Delta e' &= \mu^2[S_5+\tfrac{3}{4}S_{10}]-\overline{e'_{(0)}}
\end{aligned}
\right\} \tag{1.101}
$$

respectively, where $\overline{a''_{(0)}}$, $\overline{m''_{(0)}}$,..., $\overline{e'_{(0)}}$ denote the weighted λ-means of the initial values of a'', m'',..., e' on the surface S; $S_3 = 0$ since each (ξ, η)-origin is now at the centroid of the corresponding polychromatic image-patch. The best spherical field surface is obtained by setting

$$\epsilon(\Theta) = \frac{f\mu}{H}(2\Delta a''+2\Theta^2\Delta d'). \tag{1.102}$$

The mean square effective radius over the best spherical field surface is
$$E_4^* = E_C^*+f^2\mu^{10}[\tfrac{3}{50}S_7^2+\tfrac{1}{20}S_8^2+(\tfrac{1}{27}S_4^2+\tfrac{1}{27}S_4\,S_9+\tfrac{11}{216}S_9^2)+$$
$$+(\tfrac{11}{192}S_{10}^2+\tfrac{1}{36}S_{10}\,S_5+\tfrac{1}{54}S_5^2)+(\tfrac{1}{90}S_2^2+\tfrac{1}{90}S_2\,S_6+\tfrac{13}{1440}S_6^2)], \tag{1.103}$$

where E_C^* is the chromatic contribution (1.99).

† 'Finite' changes in the design parameters of the system, such as those considered in the more thoroughgoing optimization process of § 1.76 below, will of course alter the values of the d_{pq}.

1.76. *Illustrative example.* The general theory of §§ 1.71–1.75 can be used to find out what amount of axial undercorrection and what choice of neutral zone radius on the corrector plate of a Schmidt camera will minimize the r.m.s. effective radii of the polychromatic images over a given angular field. It is convenient here to use the refractive index n' of the plate to specify the wavelength λ of the light, instead of conversely, because the fifth-order aberration coefficients of the system are linear in n'.

We use the notation of Chapter III, §§ 2 and 3, except that here we write the sixth-order aberration function in the form $f\mu^6\Phi^*(u, v, \Theta; n')$, instead of in the form $R\mu^6\Phi^*(u, v, V; n')$ which is more convenient in Chapter III, and that the roles of u, v are interchanged. Since

$$V = \Theta[1 + O(\mu^2)],$$

it is permissible to write either V or Θ in the approximate formulae, and after allowing for the changes in notation we obtain from III (3.35), (3.36) the equation

$$f\mu^6\Phi^*(u, v, \Theta; n') = f\mu^6\left[c^2\Theta^2\left(\frac{1}{n'} + v\frac{\partial}{\partial v}\right) + 2k^{(0)}_{nn'\mu}\right](r^4 - 2r_0^2 r^2)$$

$$(1.104)$$

for the aberration function on the 'customary' receiving surface. Here $k_{nn'\mu}$ has been replaced by

$$k^{(0)}_{nn'\mu} = \frac{n' - n}{4\mu^2(n_0 - 1)} = O(1) \qquad (1.105)$$

and R is no longer scale-normalized to unity. n' denotes the refractive index of the plate in the wavelength under consideration, n denotes the value of n' (whether or not it belongs to the effective spectral range) for which the system is axially stigmatic, and n_0 denotes an arbitrary fixed value of n'. It is assumed that n', n and n_0 all differ by $O(\mu^2)$. The replacement of $k_{nn'\mu}$ by $k^{(0)}_{nn'\mu}$ is permissible since they differ by $O(\mu^2)$. By the 'customary' receiving surface is meant the sphere, concentric with the mirror, which passes through the point of axial stigmatism in n-light. In applying §§ 1.71–1.75 we use this surface as the reference surface S.

Table VI shows the aberrations of the system, set out after the manner of Table I. Since

$$\frac{f\mu}{H} = \frac{1}{2}[1 + O(\mu^2)],$$

the coefficients in $(f\mu/H)\Phi^*$ may be set equal to one-half those of Φ^* as given by (1.104) without invalidating the approximate formulae.

TABLE VI

Aberrations of the Schmidt camera

n	k	l	m	Coefficient of $\Theta^k v^l r^{2m}$ in $\frac{1}{2}\Phi^*$	Name of coefficient	$\Theta^k v^l r^{2m}$	Name of aberration
1	0	0	1	$-2r_0^2\, k_{nn'\mu}^{(0)}$	$\frac{1}{2}a''$	r^2	focus shift
2	1	1	0	0	$-m''$	Θv	
3	0	0	2	$k_{nn'\mu}^{(0)}$	$\frac{1}{4}b'$	r^4	primary spherical aberration
4	1	1	1	0	$-f'$	$\Theta v r^2$	
5	2	2	0	$-2r_0^2 c^2$	c'	$\Theta^2 v^2$	primary astigmatism
6	2	0	1	$-r_0^2 c^2/n_0$	$\frac{1}{2}d'$	$\Theta^2 r^2$	field curvature difference
7	3	1	0	0	$-e'$	$\Theta^3 v$	
8	0	0	3	0	$-S_7$	r^6	
9	1	1	2	0	$-S_8$	$\Theta v r^4$	
10	2	0	2	$c^2/2n_0$	$-S_4$	$\Theta^2 r^4$	lateral spherical aberration
11	2	2	1	$2c^2$	$-S_9$	$\Theta^2 v^2 r^2$	wings (Flügelfehler)
12	3	3	0	0	$-S_{10}$	$\Theta^3 v^3$	
13	3	1	1	0	$-S_5$	$\Theta^3 v r^2$	
14	4	0	1	0	$-S_2$	$\Theta^4 r^2$	
15	4	2	0	0	$-S_6$	$\Theta^4 v^2$	
16	5	1	0	0	$-S_3$	$\Theta^5 v$	

Let $\rho(n')$ be the effective spectral density distribution of the light, expressed in terms of n' as parameter. In a photographic system, ρ will depend on the characteristics of the emulsion used, as well as on those of the entering light. As before, we use bars to denote weighted means over the effective spectrum: that is, we write

$$\bar{g} = \frac{1}{L}\int g(n')\rho(n')\,dn', \qquad (1.106)$$

where $g(n')$ denotes any quantity which varies with n', $L = \int \rho(n')\,dn'$ and the integrations are over the effective spectral range. In particular, the weighted mean of n' itself is the quantity

$$\bar{n}' = \frac{1}{L}\int n'\rho(n')\,dn' \qquad (1.107)$$

and, by (1.105), the weighted mean of $k_{nn'\mu}^{(0)}$ is

$$\bar{k} = \overline{k_{nn'\mu}^{(0)}} = \frac{\bar{n}'-n}{4\mu^2(n_0-1)} = k_{n\bar{n}\mu}^{(0)}. \qquad (1.108)$$

Then it is easy to show that

$$\overline{(k_{nn'\mu}^{(0)})^2} = \kappa_\rho^2 + (k_{n\bar{n}'\mu}^{(0)})^2, \qquad (1.109)$$

where $\qquad \kappa_\rho^2 = \overline{(k_{nn'\mu}^{(0)}-\bar{k})^2} = \overline{(n'-\bar{n}')^2}/16\mu^4(n_0-1)^2. \qquad (1.110)$

PLATE I

Mechanical integrator (Maréchal, 1948) for the evaluation of diffraction integrals

From Table VI,

$$a_1 = -2r_0^2 k_{nn'\mu}^{(0)}, \qquad a_3 = k_{nn'\mu}^{(0)}, \qquad a_5 = -2r_0^2 c^2,$$

$$a_6 = -\frac{r_0^2 c^2}{n_0}, \qquad a_{10} = \frac{c^2}{2n_0}, \qquad a_{11} = 2c^2 \qquad (1.111)$$

and the remaining a_r are zero. It follows that

$$\bar{a}_1 = -2r_0^2 \bar{k}, \qquad \bar{a}_3 = \bar{k}, \qquad \bar{a}_5 = -2r_0^2 c, \qquad \bar{a}_6 = -\frac{r_0^2 c^2}{n_0}$$

$$(1.112)$$

and that the values of the chromatism factors d_{11}, d_{13}, d_{33} in (1.97) are here given by the equations

$$d_{11} = 4r_0^4 \kappa_\rho^2, \qquad d_{13} = -2r_0^2 \kappa_\rho^2, \qquad d_{33} = \kappa_\rho^2; \qquad (1.113)$$

all the other d_{pq} being equal to zero.

Applying § 1.73 with $\bar{a}_r$ in place of a_r, we find that the best spherical field surface in presence of chromatism is obtained by choosing $\epsilon(\Theta)$ to make $\bar{a}_1, \bar{a}_6$ satisfy the equations

$$\left.\begin{aligned} \bar{a}_1 &= -\tfrac{4}{3}\bar{a}_3 - \tfrac{3}{2}a_8 + \tfrac{1}{6}a_{14} + \tfrac{1}{12}a_{15} = -\tfrac{4}{3}\bar{k} \\ \bar{a}_6 &= -\tfrac{1}{2}\bar{a}_5 - \tfrac{4}{3}a_{10} - \tfrac{2}{3}a_{11} - a_{14} - \tfrac{1}{2}a_{15} = c^2\left(r_0^2 - \frac{2}{3}\frac{2n_0+1}{n_0}\right) \end{aligned}\right\}, \qquad (1.114)$$

that is, by moving the receiving surface forward by an amount $f\mu^4\epsilon(\Theta)$ from the customary receiving surface, where

$$\epsilon(\Theta) = \frac{2f\mu}{H}(\Delta\bar{a}_1 + \Theta^2 \Delta\bar{a}_6)$$

and $\Delta\bar{a}_1, \Delta\bar{a}_6$ denote the amounts which have to be added to the values (1.112) of $\bar{a}_1, \bar{a}_6$ on the customary field surface to bring them to the values (1.114). From (1.112), (1.114)

$$\left.\begin{aligned} \Delta\bar{a}_1 &= -\tfrac{4}{3}\bar{k} + 2r_0^2\bar{k} = 2(r_0^2 - \tfrac{2}{3})\bar{k} \\ \Delta\bar{a}_6 &= c^2\left(r_0^2\frac{n_0+1}{n_0} - \frac{2}{3}\frac{2n_0+1}{n_0}\right) \end{aligned}\right\};$$

thus the best spherical field surface is given by taking

$$\epsilon(\Theta) = \frac{2f\mu}{H}\left\{2(r_0^2 - \tfrac{2}{3})\left[\bar{k} + c^2\Theta^2\left(\frac{1}{2} + \frac{1}{2n_0}\right)\right] - \tfrac{2}{3}c^2\Theta^2\right\}. \qquad (1.115)$$

The value of $\overline{E_\lambda^*}$ in this surface is the $(\bar{a}_1, \bar{a}_6)$-minimized value of (1.98), which by § 1.73 is

$$f^2\mu^{10}\left[\sum_{4,\,9,\,12,\,13} t_{rs}^{(1)}\bar{a}_r\bar{a}_s + \sum_{3,\,5,\,8,\,10,\,11,\,14,\,15} t_{rs}^{(2)}\bar{a}_r\bar{a}_s + \sum_{p,\,q=1}^{7} t_{pq}d_{pq}\right]$$

$$= f^2\mu^{10}\left[\sum_{3,\,5,\,10,\,11} t_{rs}^{(2)}\bar{a}_r\bar{a}_s + \sum_{1,\,3} t_{pq}d_{pq}\right],$$

since the omitted terms are all zero,

$$= f^2\mu^{10}\left\{\frac{4}{9}\left[\bar{k}+c^2\left(\frac{1}{2}+\frac{1}{4n_0}\right)\right]^2 + \frac{1}{6}c^4[4(r_0^2-1)^2+1] + \frac{1}{27}c^4\left(1+\frac{1}{2n_0}\right)^2 + \right.$$

$$\left. +4\kappa_\rho^2[2(r_0^2-\tfrac{2}{3})^2+\tfrac{1}{9}]\right\}, \quad (1.116)$$

by (1.109), (1.110) and Tables II and IV.

From (1.116) it follows that for given f, μ, c (that is, for given focal length, focal ratio and angular field) the r.m.s. image radius over the best spherical field surface is least when

$$\bar{k} = -c^2\left(\frac{1}{2}+\frac{1}{4n_0}\right) \quad (1.117)$$

and when r_0 is chosen to minimize the expression

$$\tfrac{1}{6}c^4[4(r_0^2-1)^2+1]+4\kappa_\rho^2[2(r_0^2-\tfrac{2}{3})^2+\tfrac{1}{9}]. \quad (1.118)$$

(1.117) gives $\quad n-\bar{n}' = \tfrac{1}{4}\phi_0^2(n_0-1)(2n_0+1)/n_0,$

i.e. the corrector plate should be designed to give axial stigmatism for a 'fictitious' refractive index

$$n = \bar{n}'+\tfrac{1}{4}\phi_0^2(n_0-1)(2n_0+1)/n_0. \quad (1.119)$$

(1.118) is minimized by taking

$$r_0^2 = \frac{2}{3}+\frac{1}{3}\frac{1}{1+12\kappa_\rho^2/c^4}, \quad (1.120)$$

where, by (1.110), $\quad \dfrac{\kappa_\rho^2}{c^4} = \overline{(n'-\bar{n})^2}/\phi_0^4(n_0-1)^2. \quad (1.121)$

When r_0^2 and n are given their optimum values (1.119) and (1.120) the mean square image radius (1.116) over the best spherical field surface becomes

$$f^2\mu^{10}c^4\left\{\frac{1}{27}\left(1+\frac{1}{2n_0}\right)^2 + \frac{1}{6}+\frac{4}{3}\frac{\kappa_\rho^2}{c^4}\frac{c^4+4\kappa_\rho^2}{c^4+12\kappa_\rho^2}\right\}. \quad (1.122)$$

It has been shown (Linfoot 1951) that no improvement on the value (1.122) for $\overline{E_\lambda^*}$ can be obtained by dropping the restriction that a 'stigmatic index' n should exist and allowing quite general smooth variations in the plate profile, together with arbitrary smooth variations in the receiving surface. Under these wider conditions, the design given by (1.115), (1.119), and (1.120) remains the best in the mean square sense.

In a monochromat $\kappa_\rho^2 = 0$ by (1.121) and $r_0 = 1$, i.e. the 'neutral zone' should come at the edge of the working aperture on the corrector plate. In the general case, the best value of r_0 always lies between $\sqrt{\tfrac{2}{3}} = 0.81$ and 1. It is interesting that the two parameters $\bar{n}'$ and κ_ρ give all the information about the effective spectral distribution of the light which is relevant to the mean square optimization problem.

2. Diffraction images

2.1. *The aberration-free diffraction image*

In Fig. 3, $ABA'B'$ represents a circular aperture through which issues a train of spherical waves of wavelength λ.

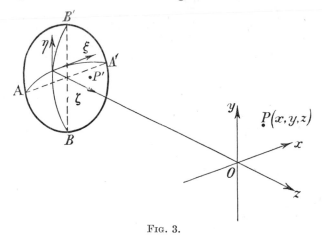

Fig. 3.

AA', BB', of length $2a$, are diameters of this aperture, C the pole of the wave-front S which momentarily fills it, O the centre of curvature of S. We call CO the axis of the wave-train and denote the distance CO by f.

Ox, Oy, Oz are axes of Cartesian coordinates (x, y, z) in the space near O; $C\xi$, $C\eta$, $C\zeta$ axes of Cartesian coordinates (ξ, η, ζ) in the space near C. It is assumed throughout that a/f is small, that a^2/f^2 is negligible in comparison with unity and that $\lambda/2\pi f$ is negligible in comparison with a^2/f^2.

By Huyghens's principle, the complex displacement at $P = (x, y, z)$ near C which results from waves of unit amplitude and zero phase on S is

$$D_\lambda(P) = \frac{i}{\lambda} e^{ikf} \iint\limits_S \frac{e^{-iks}}{s} \, dS, \qquad (2.1)$$

where s denotes the distance of P from the element dS located at $P' = (\xi, \eta, \zeta)$ on the wave-front filling the aperture and $k = 2\pi/\lambda$. Set

$$\xi = ar\cos\phi \qquad \eta = ar\sin\phi,$$
$$x = \rho\cos\psi \qquad y = \rho\sin\psi; \tag{2.2}$$

then
$$dS = a^2 r\, dr d\phi \tag{2.3}$$

(with an error which in the case of an f/5 pencil nowhere exceeds one part in 200) and hence

$$D_\lambda(P) = \frac{ia^2}{\lambda} e^{ikf} \int_0^1 \int_0^{2\pi} \frac{e^{-iks}}{s} r\, dr d\phi. \tag{2.4}$$

Now on the surface S

$$\zeta = f - \sqrt{(f^2 - a^2 r^2)} = f - f\left\{1 - \frac{1}{2}\frac{a^2 r^2}{f^2} - \frac{1}{8}\frac{a^4 r^4}{f^4} - \cdots\right\}$$
$$= \frac{a^2 r^2}{2f} + \frac{a^4 r^4}{8f^3} + \cdots. \tag{2.5}$$

Therefore

$$s^2 = PP'^2 = (x-\xi)^2 + (y-\eta)^2 + (z-\zeta+f)^2$$
$$= (x^2+y^2+z^2) + (\xi^2+\eta^2+\zeta^2) - 2(x\xi+y\eta+z\zeta) + 2f(z-\zeta) + f^2$$
$$= [(f+z)^2 + \rho^2] + [(f-\zeta)^2 + a^2 r^2] - f^2 - 2ar\rho\cos(\phi-\psi) - 2z\zeta$$
$$= CP^2 + OP'^2 - f^2 - 2ar\rho\cos(\phi-\psi) - 2z\zeta$$
$$= R'^2 - 2ar\rho\cos(\phi-\psi) - 2z\zeta \tag{2.6}$$

$$\text{(where } R' \text{ is written for } CP)$$

$$= R'^2 - 2ar\rho\cos(\phi-\psi) - z\left(\frac{a^2 r^2}{f} + \frac{a^4 r^4}{4f^3} + \cdots\right). \tag{2.7}$$

In an f/5 pencil, the error in replacing the last term of (2.7) by $za^2 r^2/f$ does not exceed $1/399$ of $za^2 r^2/f$.

If P is only a 'finite number' $O(1)$ of fringes away from focus laterally,[†] then $ar\rho/f = O(\lambda)$. If P is only a 'finite number' $O(1)$ of fringes away from focus longitudinally, then $az.ar/2f^2 = O(\lambda)$. Both these conditions are satisfied in the region we wish to investigate. Therefore in this region

$$\frac{2ar\rho}{f} = O(\lambda), \qquad \frac{1}{2}\frac{za^2\rho^2}{f^2} = O(\lambda), \tag{2.8}$$

where O means 'less than a moderate multiple of', say 5 or 10.

---

† That is to say, if the displacement of P from O would correspond to the appearance of only a 'finite' number $O(1)$ of fringes on the surface S seen under test in an interferometer. $ar/f = \lambda/2$ gives 'one fringe of lateral displacement'; $za^2/f^2 = 2\lambda$ gives 'one fringe of defocusing'.

From (2.7), (2.8),

$$s = R'\left[1 - \frac{2ar\rho}{R'^2}\cos(\phi-\psi) - \frac{z}{R'^2}\left(\frac{a^2r^2}{f^2} + \frac{a^4r^4}{4f^3} + \cdots\right)\right]^{\frac{1}{2}}$$

$$= R' - \frac{ar\rho}{R'}\cos(\phi-\psi) - \frac{za^2r^2}{2fR'} + O\left(\lambda\frac{a^2}{f^2}\right) + O\left(\frac{\lambda^2}{f}\right). \tag{2.9}$$

Both the error-terms here are negligible in comparison with λ. (In an f/5 pencil with $f = 1$ inch, $\lambda a^2/f^2 = \lambda/100$ and $\lambda^2/f = \lambda/50,000$.) Therefore in discussing (2.4) we may for present purposes set

$$s = R' - \frac{ar\rho}{R'}\cos(\phi-\psi) - \frac{za^2r^2}{2fR'},$$

$$ks = kR' - (f/R')[qr\cos(\phi-\psi) + \tfrac{1}{2}pr^2],$$

where the new variables p, q are defined by the equations

$$p = \frac{ka^2z}{f^2}, \qquad q = \frac{ka\rho}{f}. \tag{2.10}$$

In physical terms, $p/4\pi$ is the number of fringes of defocusing and q/π the number of fringes of lateral displacement of P relative to O. Substituting for s from (2.9) and noting that $R' = f[1+O(\lambda f/2\pi a^2)]$ in the region where $p/4\pi$, q/π are both $O(1)$, we now obtain the approximate formula

$$D_\lambda(P) = \frac{ia^2}{\lambda f}e^{ik(f-R')}\int_0^1\int_0^{2\pi} e^{i[\frac{1}{2}pr^2+qr\cos(\phi-\psi)]}r\,dr\,d\phi$$

$$= \frac{2\pi ia^2}{\lambda f}e^{ik(f-R')}\int_0^1 e^{\frac{1}{2}ipr^2}J_0(qr)r\,dr, \tag{2.11}$$

where J_0 is the Bessel function of order zero.

The integral on the right of (2.11) can be evaluated in terms of the functions

$$U_n(p,q) = \sum_{m=0}^\infty (-1)^m(p/q)^{n+2m}J_{n+2m}(q) \tag{2.12}$$

introduced by Lommel for this purpose; in fact†

$$2\int_0^1 J_0(qr)e^{\frac{1}{2}ipr^2}r\,dr = C(p,q)+iS(p,q), \tag{2.13}$$

† Watson, *Bessel Functions*, Cambridge, 1922, p. 541. A different evaluation, due to Zernike and Nijboer, is given below (equation (2.64)).

where

$$C(p,q) = \frac{\cos\frac{1}{2}p}{\frac{1}{2}p}\,U_1(p,q) + \frac{\sin\frac{1}{2}p}{\frac{1}{2}p}\,U_2(p,q)$$
$$S(p,q) = \frac{\sin\frac{1}{2}p}{\frac{1}{2}p}\,U_1(p,q) - \frac{\cos\frac{1}{2}p}{\frac{1}{2}p}\,U_2(p,q)$$

$$\left.\right\} . \tag{2.14}$$

Equation (2.11) therefore gives

$$D_\lambda(P) = \frac{\pi a^2}{\lambda f}\,e^{i[k(f-R')+\chi(p,q)+\pi/2]}\sqrt{(C^2+S^2)}, \tag{2.15}$$

where C, S are written for $C(p,q)$, $S(p,q)$ respectively,

$$\cos\chi = \frac{C}{\sqrt{(C^2+S^2)}}, \qquad \sin\chi = \frac{S}{\sqrt{(C^2+S^2)}} \tag{2.16}$$

and

$$\sqrt{(C^2+S^2)} = \frac{2}{p}\sqrt{\{U_1^2(p,q)+U_2^2(p,q)\}}. \tag{2.17}$$

The intensity $I_\lambda(z,\rho) = I(p,q)$ at P is then given by the equation

$$I_\lambda(z,\rho) = |D_\lambda(P)|^2$$
$$= \frac{\pi^2 a^4}{\lambda^2 f^2}(C^2+S^2)$$
$$= \frac{4\pi^2 a^4}{\lambda^2 f^2}\frac{1}{p^2}[U_1^2(p,q)+U_2^2(p,q)]. \tag{2.18}$$

(2.18) is valid, subject to the limitations already imposed by our approximations, for all p, q; but it is only convenient when $|q/p| > 1$. When $|q/p| < 1$ it may, as Lommel showed, be replaced with advantage by the equivalent formula†

$$I_\lambda(z,\rho) = \frac{4\pi^2 a^4}{\lambda^2 f^2}\frac{1}{p^2}[1+V_0^2(p,q)+V_1^2(p,q)-$$
$$-2V_0(p,q)\cos\{\tfrac{1}{2}(p+q^2/p)\}-2V_1(p,q)\sin\{\tfrac{1}{2}(p+q^2/p)\}], \tag{2.19}$$

where

$$V_n(p,q) = \sum_{m=0}^{\infty}(-1)^m(q/p)^{n+2m}J_{n+2m}(q). \tag{2.20}$$

Lommel, to whom this investigation is originally due,‡ used slightly different approximations in his argument from those made in the above modernized version;§ his parameters specifying the position of P

---

† When $|q/p| = 1$, (2.18) and (2.19) reduce to

$$I_\lambda(z,\rho) = \frac{\pi^2 a^4}{\lambda^2 f^2}\frac{1}{p^2}[J_0^2(p)-2J_0(p)\cos p+1].$$

‡ E. v. Lommel (1885). A very similar investigation was published almost simultaneously by H. Struve (1886).

§ Taken from Linfoot and Wolf (1953 a).

are not strictly identical with ours, and his handling of the error-terms is not quite precise enough for the purposes of the present section. His formulae have therefore been rederived here by a more accurate discussion.

In the geometrical focal plane, $p = 0$ and (2.18) reduces to Airy's well-known result

$$I_\lambda(0, \rho) = \frac{4\pi^2 a^4}{\lambda^2 f^2}\left(\frac{2J_1(q)}{q}\right)^2. \tag{2.21}$$

On the axis, $q = 0$ and (2.19) gives

$$I_\lambda(z, 0) = \frac{4\pi^2 a^4}{\lambda^2 f^2}\left(\frac{\sin \frac{1}{4}p}{\frac{1}{4}p}\right)^2. \tag{2.22}$$

Lommel's equations (2.18), (2.19) for the intensity distribution in space near focus formed the starting-point for the derivation by E. Wolf (1951 a) of expressions for the fraction of the total illumination which falls inside a given small circle about the (x, y)-origin in the receiving plane p = constant. We define

$$L_\lambda(z, \rho_0) = \frac{1}{\pi a^2}\int_0^{\rho_0}\int_0^{2\pi} I(z, \rho)\rho \, d\rho d\phi. \tag{2.23}$$

To the order of accuracy here in question, $L_\lambda(z, \rho_0)$ measures the fraction of the total illumination issuing from the aperture which reaches the inside of the circle $\rho = \rho_0$ in the given receiving plane. Then Wolf showed that

$$L_\lambda(z, \rho) = (q/p)^2\left[1 + \sum_{s=0}^{\infty}\frac{(-1)^s}{2s+1}(q/p)^{2s}Q_{2s}(q)\right] -$$

$$-\frac{4}{p}[Y_1(p, q)\cos\{\tfrac{1}{2}(p+q^2/p)\}+Y_2(p, q)\sin\{\tfrac{1}{2}(p+q^2/p)\}]$$
$$(|q/p| \leqslant 1) \quad (2.24)$$

$$= 1 - \sum_{s=1}^{\infty}\frac{(-1)^s}{2s+1}(p/q)^{2s}Q_{2s}(q) \quad (|q/p| \geqslant 1), \tag{2.25}$$

where

$$Y_n(p, q) = \sum_{s=0}^{\infty}(-1)^s(n+2s)(q/p)^{n+2s}J_{n+2s}(q), \tag{2.26}$$

$$Q_{2s}(q) = \sum_{i=0}^{2s}(-1)^i[J_i(q)J_{2s-i}(q)+J_{i+1}(q)J_{2s+1-i}(q)]. \tag{2.27}$$

When $p = 0$, (2.25) reduces to Rayleigh's formula

$$L_\lambda(0, \rho) = 1 - Q_0(q) = 1 - J_0^2(q) - J_1^2(q). \tag{2.28}$$

Figs. 4 and 5 show the distribution of $I_\lambda(z, \rho)$ and $L_\lambda(z, \rho)$ near focus in each meridional plane.† In Fig. 5 the curves $L_\lambda(z, \rho) = \text{const.}$, or $L(p, q) = \text{const.}$, can be regarded as analogues in a certain sense of the

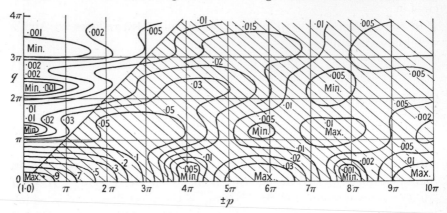

FIG. 4. Isophotes near focus of an aberration-free pencil. The intensity at the focus (0. 0) is normalized to unity. The scale-normalized coordinates (p, q) possess physical interpretations; $p/4\pi$ is the number of fringes of defocusing, q/π the number of fringes of lateral displacement of the point (z, ρ) from the geometrical focus O. The bisymmetrical diagram obtained by reflecting the figure in both the p- and q-axes shows the light distribution in any meridional section of the pencil; the p-axis is along the principal ray. The shaded area shows the region of the geometrical cone of rays. *After* Linfoot and Wolf (1953).

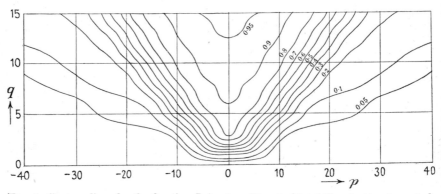

FIG. 5. Contour lines for the fraction $L_\lambda(z, \rho) = L(p, q)$ of total illumination in a circle of radius ρ about the origin in the plane $z = \text{const.}$ *After* Wolf (1951 a).

rays of the geometrical theory. Their form near the geometrical focus $(p, q) = (0, 0)$ agrees well with that postulated by Dennis Taylor (1894) on experimental grounds for the cone of light near focus. The comparison

† Fig. 4, constructed from tables given in Lommel's paper (1885), is substantially identical with the figure of Zernike and Nijboer (1949), reproduced as Fig. 10 below, which was obtained from the expansion (2.64).

is rather rough and ready, since Taylor's observations were made in polychromatic light. Nevertheless, his value of just below $\pm 0\cdot 2$ mm. for the permissible focal tolerance of an f/15 pencil is in good accordance with Figs. 4 and 5. It is the tubular elongation of the bright central nucleus of the diffraction image, visible in Fig. 4 and exceeding what we could expect on the basis of more elementary considerations, which explains the excellent performance of 6- or 8-inch refracting telescopes in spite of their considerable secondary spectrum.

2.2. Effect of central obstruction

To allow for the effect of a central obstruction of radius $a' = \epsilon a$, we subtract from $D_\lambda(P)$ in (2.11) the complex quantity

$$D'_\lambda(P) = \frac{2\pi i a'^2}{\lambda f} e^{ik(f-R')} \int_0^1 e^{\frac{1}{2}ip'r^2} J_0(q'r) r \, dr, \qquad (2.29)$$

in which

$$p' = \frac{ka'^2 z}{f^2} = \epsilon^2 p, \qquad q' = \frac{ka'\rho}{f} = \epsilon q. \qquad (2.30)$$

The intensity at P is then the squared modulus of the quantity

$$D_\lambda^{(\epsilon)}(P) = D_\lambda(P) - D'_\lambda(P)$$

$$= \frac{2\pi i a^2}{\lambda f} e^{ik(f-R')} \left[\int_0^1 e^{\frac{1}{2}ipr^2} J_0(qr) r \, dr - \epsilon^2 \int_0^1 e^{\frac{1}{2}ip'r^2} J_0(q'r) r \, dr \right]. \qquad (2.31)$$

Now, by (2.13), (2.14),

$$\int_0^1 e^{\frac{1}{2}ipr^2} J_0(qr) r \, dr = \frac{1}{p} e^{\frac{1}{2}ip} [U_1(p,q) - i U_2(p,q)],$$

$$\int_0^1 e^{\frac{1}{2}ip'r^2} J_0(q'r) r \, dr = \frac{1}{p'} e^{\frac{1}{2}ip'} [U_1(p',q') - i U_2(p',q')], \qquad (2.32)$$

where U_1, U_2 are Lommel functions. Therefore (2.31) can be written in the form

$$D_\lambda^{(\epsilon)}(P) = \frac{ika^2}{f} e^{ik(f-R')} \left[\frac{1}{p} e^{\frac{1}{2}ip} (U_1 - i U_2) - \frac{1}{p} e^{\frac{1}{2}i\epsilon^2 p} (U'_1 - i U'_2) \right], \qquad (2.33)$$

in which U_1, U_2, U'_1, U'_2 stand for $U_1(p,q)$, $U_2(p,q)$, $U_1(p',q')$, $U_2(p',q')$ respectively, and the intensity $I_\lambda^{(\epsilon)}(P) = |D_\lambda^{(\epsilon)}(P)|^2$ is given by the equation

$$I_\lambda^{(\epsilon)}(P) = \frac{k^2 a^4}{f^2 p^2} | e^{\frac{1}{2}ip} (U_1 - i U_2) - e^{\frac{1}{2}i\epsilon^2 p} (U'_1 - i U'_2) |^2$$

$$= \frac{\pi^2 a^4}{\lambda^2 f^2} \{ M^2(p,q) - 2\epsilon^2 N(p,q;p',q') + \epsilon^4 M^2(p',q') \}, \qquad (2.34)$$

where

$$M^2(p, q) = \left(\frac{2}{p}\right)^2 (U_1^2 + U_2^2)$$

$$M^2(p', q') = \left(\frac{2}{p'}\right)^2 (U_1'^2 + U_2'^2)$$

$$N(p, q; p', q') = \frac{4}{pp'}[(U_1 U_1' + U_2 U_2')\cos \tfrac{1}{2}(1-\epsilon^2)p +$$
$$+ (U_2 U_1' - U_1 U_2')\sin \tfrac{1}{2}(1-\epsilon^2)p]$$

$$\left.\right\} \quad (2.35)$$

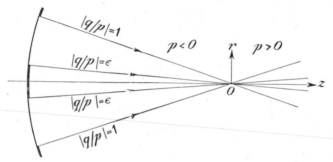

Fig. 6. Meridional section of centrally obstructed pencil.

On the axis of the converging pencil, $q = 0$ and (2.34) gives for the intensity the expression

$$I_\lambda^{(\epsilon)}(z, 0) = \frac{4\pi^2 a^4}{\lambda^2 f^2}\left(\frac{\sin \tfrac{1}{4}p(1-\epsilon^2)}{\tfrac{1}{4}p}\right)^2. \qquad (2.36)$$

Thus the central obstruction increases the distance between the zeros along the axis of the pencil by a factor $1/(1-\epsilon^2)$ but they remain equally spaced—at least in the range where our approximations are valid, namely the part of the axis where $p/4\pi$ does not become large compared with unity.

In the geometrical focal plane $p = 0$ and the expression (2.34) for the intensity reduces to

$$I_\lambda^{(\epsilon)}(0, \rho) = \frac{4\pi^2 a^4}{\lambda^2 f^2}\left[\frac{2J_1(q)}{q} - \epsilon^2 \frac{2J_1(\epsilon q)}{\epsilon q}\right]^2. \qquad (2.37)$$

The zeros of this function give, in q-units, the radii of the 'Airy dark rings' corresponding to a centrally obstructed aperture. The expressions (2.36) and (2.37) were given (with a different normalization) many years ago by Steward (1925).

Figs. 7 and 8 show the light distribution near focus for the two selected values 0·25 and 0·707 of the linear obstruction ratio ϵ; Fig. 4 shows the corresponding distribution for the unobstructed aperture. To interpret these three figures, we note that each of them represents one-quarter of a bisymmetrical pattern, obtained by reflecting it in the p and q axes. This bisymmetrical pattern shows the isophotes (lines of equal intensity)

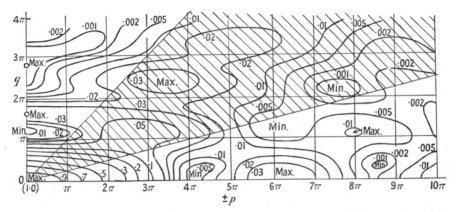

Fig. 7. Isophotes near focus of an aberration-free pencil with central obstruction ratio $\epsilon = 0.25$. The intensity at the geometrical focus is normalized to unity. Reflection of the figure in both coordinate axes gives a diagram of the isophotes in any meridional section. The shaded area gives the position of the hollow cone of rays. *After* Linfoot and Wolf (1953).

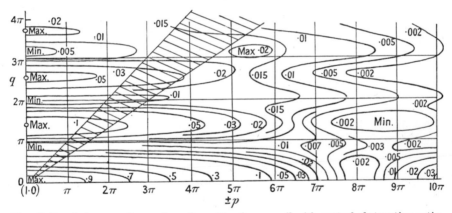

Fig. 8. Isophotes near focus of an aberration-free pencil with central obstruction ratio $\epsilon = 0.707$. The intensity at the geometrical focus is normalized to unity. Reflection of the figure in both coordinate axes gives a diagram of the isophotes in any meridional section. The shaded area gives the position of the hollow cone of rays. *After* Linfoot and Wolf (1953).

near focus in any meridional section of the pencil. The use of (p, q)-coordinates in the diagrams is equivalent to scale-normalizing the cylindrical Cartesian coordinates (p, z) in accordance with equations (2.10). The intensity at the geometrical focal point $(0, 0)$ is normalized to unity in each figure.

The shaded areas in the bisymmetrical patterns show where the geometrical light-cones meet the meridional (p, q)-plane in each case. In the unobstructed case (Fig. 4) the rays fill a solid cone, with axis lying along the p-axis, and the lines $|q/p| = 1$ lie in its surface. In the centrally obstructed cases the cone is hollow; its axis lies along the p-axis and its 'body' lies between the two conical surfaces traced out when the lines $|q/p| = \epsilon$ and $|q/p| = 1$ (see Fig. 6) are rotated about the p-axis.

In Fig. 7, $\epsilon = 0\cdot25$. This value is of special interest because it corresponds to the greatest central obstruction which is regarded as tolerable by users of visual reflecting telescopes. A comparison of Figs. 4 and 7 shows how small is the effect of this obstruction on the relative intensities in different parts of the image. An increase in the intensity of the first Airy bright ring is the most important change.

In Fig. 8, $\epsilon = 0\cdot707$ and half the area of the aperture is obstructed. The central nucleus of the image is drawn out to approximately twice its former length along the axis and its cross-section is correspondingly reduced. The difference between the diffraction image and the ray theoretic image near focus is very striking; no trace of a hollow-cone structure appears in the former.

From Fig. 8 it can be inferred that a large central stop on the objective of a refracting telescope not only increases resolving power by decreasing the lateral diameter of the bright central nucleus of the image but also, by elongating the nucleus in the axial direction, reduces the disturbing effects of chromatism on its colour composition at best focus.

2.21. *Boivin's series.* In a paper on diffraction by concentric arrays of ring-shaped apertures, A. Boivin (1952) gave the following 'multiplication formulae' for the Lommel functions:

$$\left.\begin{array}{l}U_n(\alpha^2 p, \alpha q) = \sum_{m=0}^{\infty} \dfrac{(\alpha^2-1)^m p^m}{2^m m!}\, U_{n-m}(p, q) \\[4mm] V_n(\alpha^2 p, \alpha q) = \sum_{m=0}^{\infty} \dfrac{(\alpha^2-1)^m p^m}{2^m m!}\, V_{n+m}(p, q)\end{array}\right\}; \qquad (2.38)$$

here α may be any real number. Taken together with Lommel's recurrence relations

$$\left.\begin{array}{l}U_n(p, q)+U_{n+2}(p, q) = (p/q)^n J_n(q) \\[2mm] V_n(p, q)+V_{n+2}(p, q) = (q/p)^n J_n(q)\end{array}\right\}, \qquad (2.39)$$

these formulae can be used for the computation of U_n, V_n in ranges of the arguments which fall outside Lommel's tables.

They can be applied, as Boivin showed, to discuss the three-dimensional diffraction images formed by a zone plate.

2.3. *Diffraction theory of aberrations*

2.31. *The diffraction integral.* Fig. 9 represents an oblique pencil of light emerging from the exit pupil of an optical system and coming to an approximate focus on the smooth receiving surface S in the image-layer. O' is the axial point of the exit pupil of radius H', $O'P'$ the principal ray of the emerging pencil, P' its intersection with the receiving surface.

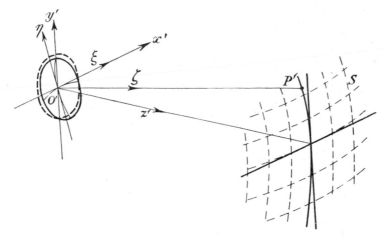

FIG. 9. Wave-front of an oblique pencil.

(x', y', z') and (ξ, η, ζ) are two sets of rectangular Cartesian coordinates, both with origin at O'; in the first set $O'z'$ lies along the optic axis and $O'y'$ in the meridional plane containing P'; in the second set $O'\zeta$ lies along the principal ray and $O'\eta$ in meridional plane containing P'; the axes $O'x'$ and $O'\xi$ coincide.

We denote by W' the wave-front which cuts all the rays of the pencil orthogonally and which passes through O'. Thus, in the notation of § 1.3, O' is itself the principal point of W' and the sphere centred on P' and passing through O' is the reference sphere W_0 of W'.

As in § 1, the rays of the pencil imprint on W' and on W_0 two systems of coordinate numbers u, v and if (as is here supposed) the angular field radius of the system is $O(\mu)$, the scale-normalized Cartesian coordinates $X = x'/H'$, $Y = y'/H'$ of a point on W' or on W_0 satisfy the relation

$$X = u + O(\mu^2), \qquad Y = v + O(\mu^2); \tag{2.40}$$

the error-terms $O(\mu^2)$ are smooth functions of u, v and the off-axis angle parameter Θ. We also have on W' and W_0,

$$\xi/H' = u + O(\mu^2), \qquad \eta/H' = v + O(\mu^2). \tag{2.41}$$

In the case where the distance between W' and W_0 may amount to several wavelengths, we can calculate the intensity distribution in the space near P' (that is, the diffraction image) in the following way. With P' as origin we set up a system (x, y, z) of rectangular Cartesian coordinates, taking the positive z-axis along the principal ray $O'P'$ produced and the positive y-axis pointing away from the optic axis $O'z'$ in the meridional plane $P'O'z'$.

We apply Huyghens's principle, integrating over the reference sphere W_0. Because of the distortion of the wave-fronts, the phase of the wave displacements is not the same at all points of W_0; it is the same at all points of W', on which we take the amplitude to be equal to 1. If the retardation of W' behind W_0 is measured by the smooth aberration function $\phi(u, v; \Theta)$, the wave displacement at the point of coordinate numbers (u, v) on W_0 is represented with sufficient accuracy by the complex number† $\exp\left\{-\dfrac{2\pi i}{\lambda}\phi(u, v; \Theta)\right\}$.

Applying Huyghens's principle, we obtain in place of (2.1) the equation

$$D_\lambda(P) = \frac{i}{\lambda}e^{ikf'}\iint\limits_{W_0} \frac{e^{-iks}}{s}e^{-ik\phi(u,v;\Theta)}\,dS \tag{2.42}$$

for the complex displacement at the point $P = (x, y, z)$ near P', where $k = 2\pi/\lambda$ as usual, $f' = O'P'$, and s now denotes the distance of P from the element dS located at the point of coordinate numbers (u, v) on W_0.

When P is within $O(1)$ fringes of P' both laterally and longitudinally we obtain, by repeating the reasoning of § 2.1,

$$s = R' - \frac{x\xi + y\eta}{R'} - \frac{z(\xi^2 + \eta^2)}{2f'R'} + O\left(\lambda\frac{H'^2}{f'^2}\right) + O(\lambda^2/f'), \tag{2.43}$$

where R' now stands for $O'P$. Assuming as before that H'^2/f^2 and $\lambda f/2\pi H'^2$ are both negligible in comparison with unity, we obtain the approximate formula

$$D_\lambda(P) = \frac{i}{\lambda R'}e^{ik(f'-R')}\iint\limits_{W_0} \exp\left\{ik\left[\frac{x\xi + y\eta}{R'} + \frac{z(\xi^2 + \eta^2)}{2f'R'} - \phi(u, v; \Theta)\right]\right\}dS. \tag{2.44}$$

---

† The approximation here consists in supposing that the change in amplitude between W' and W_0 may be neglected. This is evidently true when W' and W_0 lie everywhere within a few wavelengths of each other.

In systems of moderate aperture and field, further approximations can be made without too great a loss of accuracy. $R' = O'P$ differs from $f' = O'P'$ by an amount which, when P is within $O(1)$ fringes of P', is negligible in comparison with f'. Further, the error in replacing $\iint_{W_n} \dots dS$ by $\iint_{\xi^2+\eta^2<H'^2} \dots d\xi d\eta$ is negligible in the present order of approximation. We therefore define

$$D_\lambda^*(P)$$
$$= \frac{i}{\lambda f'} e^{ik(O'P'-O'P)} \iint_{\xi^2+\eta^2<H'^2} \exp\left\{ik\left[\frac{x\xi+y\eta}{f'} + \frac{z(\xi^2+\eta^2)}{2f'^2} - \phi(u,v;\Theta)\right]\right\} d\xi d\eta$$

$$(2.45)$$

and can then say that $|D_\lambda^*(P)|^2$ gives an approximate value for the intensity at the point $P = (x, y, z)$ of the diffraction image in terms of the aberration function $\phi(u, v; \Theta)$, the oblique focal distance f', the radius H' of the exit pupil and the wavelength λ. On setting

$$\xi = H'r\sin\chi, \qquad \eta = H'r\cos\chi,$$

$$x = \rho\sin\omega, \qquad y = \rho\cos\omega, \qquad (2.46)$$

and
$$p = kH'^2z/f'^2, \qquad q = kH'\rho/f' \qquad (2.47)$$

(2.45) becomes

$$D_\lambda^*(P) = \frac{ikH'^2}{2\pi f'} e^{ik(O'P'-O'P)} \times$$

$$\times \int_0^1 \int_0^{2\pi} \exp\{\tfrac{1}{2}ipr^2 + iqr\cos(\chi-\omega) - ik\phi(u, v; \Theta)\}r\, dr d\chi. \quad (2.48)$$

The parameters p and q have here the same meaning as in the special case ($\Theta = 0$, $f' = f$, $H' = a$) of § 2.1; namely, $p/4\pi$ is the number of fringes of defocusing and q/π the number of fringes of lateral displacement of P relative to P'.

In discussing the images of point sources, it is convenient to omit the factor $\dfrac{ikH'^2}{2f'} e^{ik(O'P'-O'P)}$ in (2.48), and to set

$$d_\lambda^*(P) = \frac{1}{\pi} \int_0^1 \int_0^{2\pi} \exp\{\tfrac{1}{2}ipr^2 + iqr\cos(\chi-\omega) - ik\phi(u, v; \Theta)\}r\, dr d\chi. \quad (2.49)$$

Then $|d_\lambda^*(P)|^2$ expresses the intensity as a fraction of that at the centre of the aberration-free image. We call it the normalized intensity at P. Its maximum under the condition $p = 0$ is the so-called Strehl definition of the image in the receiving surface S.

2.32. *Nijboer's classification of the aberrations.* The usual classification of the aberrations is obtained by writing the aberration function as a sum of terms of the form $\Theta^k v^l r^{2m}$ (compare equation (1.91)), that is, terms of the form $\Theta^k r^{2m+l} \cos^l \chi$, where χ is the 'azimuthal angle' of the point (ξ, η) with respect to the meridional plane.

A considerable improvement in the formalism of aberration theory was made by B. R. A. Nijboer (1942) when he proposed classifying the aberrations on the basis of a different expansion

$$\phi(u, v; \Theta) = \sum b_{lnm} \Theta^{2l+m} r^n \cos m\chi \qquad (2.50)$$

of the aberration function, where the integers $l, m, n \geqslant 0$ and $n-m \geqslant 0$ is even.† The degree $2l+m+n$ of the single term $b_{lnm} \Theta^{2l+m} r^n \cos m\chi$ is always even; the degree $N = 2l+m+n-1$ of the corresponding aberration is odd. The number of aberrations of (odd) degree N is $\frac{1}{8}(N+1)(N+7)$, since this is the number of integers n, l, m satisfying the conditions

$$2l+m+n-1 = N; \qquad l, m, n \geqslant 0;$$

$$l+m+n > 0; \qquad n-m \geqslant 0 \text{ even};$$

the case $n = m = 0$ does not represent an aberration in the accepted sense of the term and is therefore excluded.

Table VII displays the aberration terms of the second, fourth, sixth, and eighth degrees. Those of the second degree represent only a 'misplacement' of the image; they are the 'Gauss' errors of § 1. Those of the fourth degree correspond to the Seidel errors, except that the Seidel astigmatism corresponding to (022) is now referred to the best-focus setting instead of appearing as a sagittal focal line. The classification of the sixth-degree terms (which give rise to the fifth-degree errors) differs from Schwarzschild's in three cases, namely (122), (042), and (033), each of which is a linear combination of two Schwarzschild aberrations.

An inspection of Table VII shows that the terms with $n = 1, m = 1$ all represent bodily displacements of the image away from the axis; their sum represents a bodily displacement of the image of amount proportional to

$$b_{011} \Theta + b_{111} \Theta^3 + b_{211} \Theta^5 + b_{311} \Theta^7 + ...,$$

that is to say a *distortion*. The aberrations resulting from the individual terms may be called first-degree distortion (plate-scale error), third-degree distortion (Seidel distortion), fifth-degree distortion and so on.

---

† In the present account of Nijboer's work there are some minor changes in notation; in particular Nijboer's p is here replaced by $\frac{1}{2}p$ and r is scale-normalized.

PLATE II

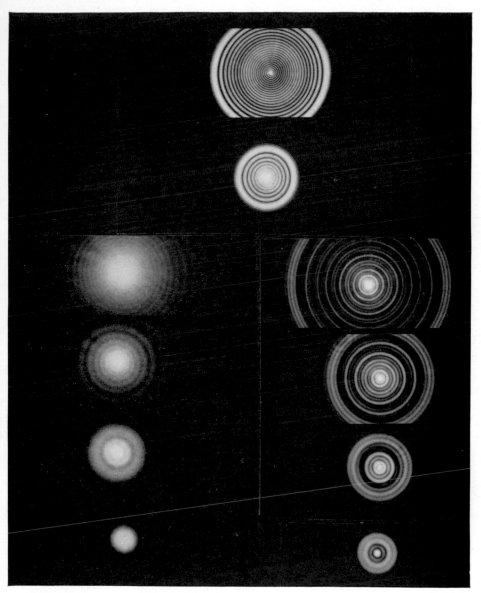

(a) *Top*. Images in presence of primary spherical aberration of amount 16λ, at marginal focus and at circle of least confusion. (b) *Bottom left*. Images in plane of paraxial focus, in presence of primary spherical aberration of amounts 17·5λ, 8·4λ, 3·72λ, 1·4λ. (c) *Bottom right*. Images in plane of least confusion, in presence of primary spherical aberration of amounts 17·5λ, 8·4λ, 3·72λ, 1·4λ. Scale three times that of (b). *After* Nienhuis (1948)

TABLE VII

Aberration terms (Nijboer)

n \ m	0	1	2	3	4	
1		$\Theta r \cos\chi$ (011)					Second-
2	r^2 (020)						degree ($N=1$)
1		$\Theta^3 r \cos\chi$ (111)					Fourth-
2	$\Theta^2 r^2$ (120)		$\Theta^2 r^2 \cos 2\chi$ (022)				degree
3		$\Theta r^3 \cos\chi$ (031)					($N=3$)
4	r^4 (040)						
1		$\Theta^5 r \cos\chi$ (211)					
2	$\Theta^4 r^2$ (220)		$\Theta^4 r^2 \cos 2\chi$ (122)				Sixth-
3		$\Theta^3 r^3 \cos\chi$ (131)		$\Theta^3 r^3 \cos 3\chi$ (033)			degree
4	$\Theta^2 r^4$ (140)		$\Theta^2 r^4 \cos 2\chi$ (042)				($N=5$)
5		$\Theta r^5 \cos\chi$ (051)					
6	r^6 (060)						
1		$\Theta^7 r \cos\chi$ (311)					
2	$\Theta^6 r^2$ (320)		$\Theta^6 r^2 \cos 2\chi$ (222)				
3		$\Theta^5 r^3 \cos\chi$ (231)		$\Theta^5 r^3 \cos 3\chi$ (133)			Eighth-
4	$\Theta^4 r^4$ (240)		$\Theta^4 r^4 \cos 2\chi$ (142)		$\Theta^4 r^4 \cos 4\chi$ (044)		degree
5		$\Theta^3 r^5 \cos\chi$ (151)		$\Theta^3 r^5 \cos 3\chi$ (053)			($N=7$)
6	$\Theta^2 r^6$ (160)		$\Theta^2 r^6 \cos 2\chi$ (062)				
7		$\Theta r^7 \cos\chi$ (071)					
8	r^8 (080)						

(The numbers in brackets indicate the values of the three indices l, n, m.)

The terms with $n = 2$, $m = 0$ all represent malfocusing; their sum represents a misplacement of the receiving surface by an amount proportional to

$$b_{020}+b_{120}\,\Theta^2+b_{220}\,\Theta^4+\dots.$$

The individual terms may be called focus error, primary field-curvature error, secondary field-curvature error and so on.

In the remaining cases, the *shape* of the geometrical image corresponding to a single aberration term depends only on the values of n, m, while the value of l determines the manner in which its *size* varies as Θ increases, i.e. as the object point moves away from the axis. Thus the sum of the terms with $m = 0$, $n = 4$ represents primary spherical aberration of amount proportional to

$$b_{040}+b_{140}\,\Theta^2+b_{240}\,\Theta^4+\dots;$$

we may call the aberrations corresponding to the individual terms primary spherical aberration of the third, fifth, seventh,... degrees. The second of these is Schwarzschild's 'lateral spherical aberration'.

The aberrations corresponding to the terms r^6, $\Theta^2 r^6$,... we call secondary spherical aberration of the fifth, seventh,... degree respectively, and so on.

To discuss the geometrical or the diffraction image of a particular object point, we collect together for each pair of values of n, m the terms of different degrees and write (2.50) in the form

$$\phi(u, v; \Theta) = \sum_{nm} f_{nm}(\Theta) r^n \cos m\chi, \tag{2.51}$$

where $n \geqslant m \geqslant 0$, $n-m$ is even, and the coefficients

$$f_{nm}(\Theta) = \Theta^m \sum_l b_{lnm} \Theta^{2l}; \tag{2.52}$$

in (2.52), l satisfies the inequalities $l \geqslant 0$, $l+m+n > 0$. The result, together with the names assigned to the aberrations, is shown in Table VIII.

It will be seen that field-surface error and distortion may be regarded as degenerate cases of spherical aberration and coma respectively.

Schwarzschild's 'wings' (Flügelfehler) $\Theta^2 r^4 \cos^2 \chi$ here appear as a linear combination of fifth-degree primary spherical aberration and fifth-degree secondary astigmatism; his 'arrows' (Pfeilfehler) as a linear

TABLE VIII
Names of the Aberrations

n \ m	0	1	2	3†	
1		distortion ($r \cos \chi$)			
2	field surface error (r^2)		primary astigmatism ($r^2 \cos 2\chi$)		
3		primary coma ($r^3 \cos \chi$)		primary trefoil ($r^3 \cos 3\chi$)	
4	primary spherical aberration (r^4)		secondary astigmatism ($r^4 \cos 2\chi$)		etc.
5		secondary coma ($r^5 \cos \chi$)		secondary trefoil ($r^5 \cos 3\chi$)	
6	secondary spherical aberration (r^6)		tertiary astigmatism ($r^6 \cos 2\chi$)		
		etc.			

† The names trefoil, tetrafoil,... seem to provide a convenient means of referring to the aberration-forms $r^n \cos 3\chi$, $r^n \cos 4\chi$,..., respectively.

combination of fifth-degree primary trefoil and fifth-degree primary coma.

By restricting the discussion to receiving surfaces lying in the image-layer of an optical system and by retaining only leading terms in the aberration function, we avoid the complications which can otherwise arise through interaction in certain cases between the coefficients of aberration terms of different orders of magnitude.

Nijboer went on to show that in the diffraction theory of aberrations the formalism is further improved if the set of functions $r^n \cos m\chi$, in terms of which $\phi(u, v; \Theta)$ is to be expanded, is 'orthogonalized' by introducing in place of the simple powers r^n the polynomials

$$R_n^m(r) = \sum_{k=0}^{\frac{1}{2}(n-m)} (-1)^k \frac{(n-k)! \, r^{n-2k}}{k! \, \{\frac{1}{2}(n+m)-k\}! \, \{\frac{1}{2}(n-m)-k\}!}, \qquad (2.53)$$

first used by F. Zernike (1934) in his classic paper on the knife-edge test and the phase-contrast method. The effect of the change, as will be seen in more detail in § 2.33, is to add to each aberration $r^n \cos m\chi$ certain 'balancing' amounts of the lower aberrations $r^{n-2} \cos m\chi$, $r^{n-4} \cos m\chi, \ldots$ of the same type. $R_n^m(r) \cos m\chi$ is a polynomial in v and r^2 (see Table X), while $R_n^m(r)$ itself is a polynomial in r of degree n (see Table IX), possessing the further representations

$$R_n^m(r) = \frac{1}{\{\frac{1}{2}(n-m)\}! \, r^m} \left(\frac{d}{dr^2}\right)^{\frac{1}{2}(n-m)} \left[(r^2)^{\frac{1}{2}(n+m)}(r^2-1)^{\frac{1}{2}(n-m)} \right] \qquad (2.54)$$

and

$$R_n^m(r) = (-1)^{\frac{1}{2}(n-m)} \binom{\frac{1}{2}(n+m)}{m} r^m \times$$

$$\times F\left(\frac{n+m}{2}+1, \, -\frac{n+m}{2}, \, -\frac{n-m}{2}, \, m+1, \, r^2\right) \qquad (2.55)$$

in the second of which F is a hypergeometric function.

On setting $m = 0$ in (2.54) and recalling Rodrigues' formula for the Legendre polynomials P_n, we observe that

$$R_{2n}^0(r) = P_n(2r^2-1). \qquad (2.56)$$

The R_n^m possess the orthogonality property

$$\int_0^1 R_n^m(r) R_{n'}^m(r) r \, dr = \begin{cases} 0 & (n \neq n'), \\ \dfrac{1}{2n+2} & (n = n'), \end{cases} \qquad (2.57)$$

TABLE IX

The Zernike polynomials $R_n^m(r)$ for $m, n \leq 8$

m\n	0	1	2	3	4	5	6	7	8
0	1		$2r^2-1$		$6r^4-6r^2+1$		$20r^6-30r^4+12r^2-1$		$70r^8-140r^6+90r^4-20r^2+1$
1		r		$3r^3-2r$		$10r^5-12r^3+3r$		$35r^7-60r^5+30r^3-4r$	
2			r^2		$4r^4-3r^2$		$15r^6-20r^4+6r^2$		$56r^8-105r^6+60r^4-10r^2$
3				r^3		$5r^5-4r^3$		$21r^7-30r^5+10r^3$	
4					r^4		$6r^6-5r^4$		$28r^8-42r^6+15r^4$
5						r^5		$7r^7-6r^5$	
6							r^6		$8r^8-7r^6$
7								r^7	
8									r^8

TABLE X

The circle polynomials $R_n^m(r)\cos m\chi$ for $m, n \leq 4$

m\n	0	1	2	3	4
0	1		$2r^2-1$		$6r^4-6r^2+1$
1		v		$3vr^2-2v$	
2			v^2-u^2		$20v^3r^2-15vr^4-16v^3+12vr^2$
3				$4v^3-3vr^2$	
4					$16v^5-20v^3r^2+5vr^4$

which we state here without proof.† From this it follows at once that the set of polynomials

$$R_n^m(r) \frac{\cos}{\sin} m\chi \qquad (n \geqslant m \geqslant 0,\ n-m \text{ even})\ddagger \qquad (2.58)$$

is orthogonal over the unit circle, i.e. that the integral

$$\frac{1}{\pi} \int_0^1 \int_0^{2\pi} R_n^m(r) \frac{\cos}{\sin} m\chi \cdot R_{n'}^{m'}(r) \frac{\cos}{\sin} m'\chi r\, dr d\chi$$

$$= \frac{1}{\pi} \int_0^{2\pi} \frac{\cos}{\sin} m\chi \frac{\cos}{\sin} m'\chi\, d\chi \cdot \int_0^1 R_n^m(r) R_{n'}^{m'}(r) r\, dr$$

vanishes unless $m = m'$ and $n = n'$; in the last case its value is $1/(n+1)$. It can also be shown that the set is *complete*, so that any smooth aberration function can be expanded as a series of functions of the set. Because the optical wave distortions are symmetrical about the meridional plane, the aberration function is an even function of χ and only terms $R_n^m(r) \cos m\chi$ occur in its expansion, which accordingly takes the form

$$\phi(u, v; \Theta) = \sum_{lmn} a_{lnm} \Theta^l R_n^m(r) \cos m\chi \qquad (n \geqslant m \geqslant 0,\ n-m \text{ even}). \quad (2.59)$$

Of importance later is the evaluation

$$\int_0^1 R_n^m(r) J_m(qr) r\, dr$$

$$= \sum_{s=0}^{\infty} \frac{(-1)^s (\tfrac{1}{2}q)^{m+2s}}{(m+s)!\, s!\, \{\tfrac{1}{2}(n-m)\}!} \int_0^1 r^{2s} \left(\frac{d}{dr^2}\right)^{\tfrac{1}{2}(n-m)} [(r^2)^{\tfrac{1}{2}(n+m)}(r^2-1)^{\tfrac{1}{2}(n-m)}] r\, dr$$

$$= \frac{(-1)^{\tfrac{1}{2}(n-m)}}{q} \sum_{k=0}^{\infty} \frac{(-1)^k (\tfrac{1}{2}q)^{n+2k+1}}{k!\,(n+k+1)!}$$

$$= (-1)^{\tfrac{1}{2}(n-m)} \frac{J_{n+1}(q)}{q}, \qquad (2.60)$$

where J_n are Bessel functions.

Returning now to (2.49), we first consider once more the aberration-free case $\phi = 0$, in which

$$d_\lambda^*(P) = \int_0^1 e^{\tfrac{1}{2}ipr^2} J_0(qr) r\, dr. \qquad (2.61)$$

---

† The proof given in Nijboer's thesis depends on the differential equation satisfied by $R_n^m(r)$, which is easily found from (2.55) and the known properties of the hypergeometric function.

‡ When $m = 0$ the cosine terms only are included.

From Bauer's formula[†]

$$e^{iz\cos\theta} = \sqrt{\left(\frac{\pi}{2z}\right)} \sum_{n=0}^{\infty} (2n+1)i^n J_{n+\frac{1}{2}}(z) P_n(\cos\theta) \qquad (2.62)$$

we find, using (2.56),

$$e^{\frac{1}{2}ipr^2} = e^{\frac{1}{2}ip}e^{\frac{1}{2}ip(2r^2-1)} = e^{\frac{1}{2}ip}\sqrt{\left(\frac{2\pi}{p}\right)} \sum_{n=0}^{\infty} (2n+1)i^n J_{n+\frac{1}{2}}(\tfrac{1}{4}p) R_{2n}^0(r). \qquad (2.63)$$

Substituting in (2.61) and using (2.60), we obtain for $d_\lambda^*(P)$ the expansion

$$d_\lambda^*(P) = e^{\frac{1}{2}ip}\sqrt{\left(\frac{2\pi}{p}\right)} \sum_{n=0}^{\infty} (2n+1)(-i)^n J_{n+\frac{1}{2}}(\tfrac{1}{4}p)\frac{J_{2n+1}(q)}{q}. \qquad (2.64)$$

On setting $p = 0$ or $q = 0$ in (2.64), we obtain once more the well-known expressions

$$\left(\frac{\sin\tfrac{1}{4}p}{\tfrac{1}{4}p}\right)^2 \quad \text{and} \quad \left(\frac{2J_1(q)}{q}\right)^2 \qquad (2.65)$$

for the (normalized) intensity distribution along the principal ray and in the geometrical focal plane respectively.

2.321. *Physical interpretation of the classification by circle polynomials.* The expansion in terms of circle polynomials corresponds in an interesting way with the balancing of small aberrations of the same generic type against each other to obtain maximum Strehl definition.[‡] We can write the expansion (2.59) in the form

$$\phi(u, v; \Theta) = \sideset{}{'}\sum_{nm} g_{nm}(\Theta) R_n^m(r) \cos m\chi, \qquad (2.66)$$

where

$$g_{nm}(\Theta) = \sum_l a_{lnm} \Theta^l, \qquad (2.67)$$

where the dash indicates that the terms for which $m = 0$ are provided with a factor $\tfrac{1}{2}$, and where l, m, n are subject to the restrictions

$$l, m, n \geqslant 0; \quad l+m+n \geqslant 0; \quad n-m \geqslant 0 \text{ even}. \qquad (2.68)$$

Then in the first place it is evident[§] that

$$\frac{1}{\pi}\int_0^1\int_0^{2\pi} [\phi(u, v; \Theta) - g_{00}(\Theta)]r\,dr\,d\chi = 0, \qquad (2.69)$$

---

† Watson, l.c., p. 368.   ‡ See § 2.31 for the meaning of this term.
§ (2.57) gives, in particular,

$$\int_0^1 R_n^0(r)r\,dr = 0 \quad (n \geqslant 1).$$

so that the term with $m = n = 0$ represents the mean retardation of the wave-front behind the reference sphere. Writing

$$V(u, v; \Theta) = \phi(u, v; \Theta) - g_{00}(\Theta) \tag{2.70}$$

and using the orthogonality relations

$$\frac{1}{\pi} \int_0^1 \int_0^{2\pi} R_n^m(r) \cos m\chi \, . \, R_{n'}^{m'}(r) \cos m'\chi \left\{ \begin{array}{l} = \dfrac{\delta_{nn'} \delta_{mm'}}{2n+2} \quad (n \geqslant 1) \\[2mm] = 1 \quad (n = 0) \end{array} \right. \tag{2.71}$$

we obtain

$$\frac{1}{\pi} \int_0^1 \int_0^{2\pi} V(u, v; \Theta) r \, dr d\chi = 0 \tag{2.72}$$

and

$$\frac{1}{\pi} \int_0^1 \int_0^{2\pi} [V(u, v; \Theta)]^2 r \, dr d\chi = \sideset{}{'}\sum_{\substack{n,m \\ n>0}} \frac{g_{nm}^2(\Theta)}{2n+2}. \tag{2.73}$$

(2.73) is the 'Parseval equation' for the orthogonal set of functions $R_n^m(r) \cos m\chi$.

By (2.49), the normalized intensity at the point P' (i.e. $p = q = 0$) in the diffraction image is

$$|d_\lambda^*(P')|^2 = \frac{1}{\pi^2} \left| \int_0^1 \int_0^{2\pi} e^{-ikV(u,v;\Theta)} r \, dr d\chi \right|^2.$$

When the aberrations are so small that $V(u, v; \Theta)$ is small compared with $\lambda/2\pi$, this yields the approximate equation

$$|d_\lambda^*(P')|^2 = \frac{1}{\pi^2} \left| \int_0^1 \int_0^{2\pi} [1 - \tfrac{1}{2} k^2 V^2(u, v; \Theta)] r \, dr d\chi - ik \int_0^1 \int_0^{2\pi} V(u, v; \Theta) r \, dr d\chi \right|^2$$

$$= \left(1 - \frac{k^2}{2\pi^2} \int_0^1 \int_0^{2\pi} [V(u, v; \Theta)]^2 r \, dr d\chi \right)^2, \quad \text{by (2.72),}$$

$$= \left(1 - \frac{k^2}{2\pi} \sideset{}{'}\sum_{\substack{n,m \\ n>0}} \frac{g_{nm}^2(\Theta)}{2n+2} \right)^2, \tag{2.74}$$

or

$$|d_\lambda^*(P')|^2 = 1 - \frac{k^2}{\pi^2} \int_0^1 \int_0^{2\pi} [V(u, v; \Theta)]^2 r \, dr d\chi \tag{2.75}$$

$$= 1 - \frac{4\pi}{\lambda^2} \sideset{}{'}\sum_{\substack{n,m \\ n>0}} \frac{g_{nm}^2(\Theta)}{2n+2}. \tag{2.76}$$

By (2.46), (2.47)

$$\tfrac{1}{2}pr^2+qr\cos(\chi-\omega)-k[\tfrac{1}{2}g_{00}(\Theta)+g_{11}(\Theta)v+g_{20}(\Theta)(r^2-\tfrac{1}{2})]$$

$$= \tfrac{1}{2}[p-2kg_{20}(\Theta)]r^2-\frac{k}{f'}(x\xi+y\eta)-kg_{11}(\Theta)[\eta/H'+O(\mu^2)]-$$

$$-\tfrac{1}{2}k[g_{00}(\Theta)-g_{20}(\Theta)]$$

$$= \frac{k}{f'}\left[z-2\left(\frac{f'}{H'}\right)^2 g_{20}(\Theta)\right]\frac{\xi^2+\eta^2}{2f'}+\frac{k}{f'}\left[x\xi+\left\{y-\frac{f'}{H'}g_{11}(\Theta)\right\}\eta\right]-$$

$$-\tfrac{1}{2}k[g_{00}(\Theta)-g_{20}(\Theta)]+O(\mu^2 g_{11}(\Theta)). \qquad (2.77)$$

From (2.49) and (2.77) it follows that, whatever other aberration terms may be present, the effect of the terms in $g_{11}(\Theta)$ and $g_{20}(\Theta)$ is merely a bodily displacement of the normalized intensity distribution $|d^*_\lambda(P')|^2$ relative to the (x,y,z)-coordinate system, namely a shift $2(f'/H')^2 g_{20}(\Theta)$ along the principal ray towards the exit pupil together with a shift $(f'/H')g_{11}(\Theta)$ in the positive y-direction. (2.74) shows that if g_{11}, g_{20} are varied, the other g_{nm} remaining fixed, the intensity at P' is greatest when g_{11}, g_{20} are both zero. In other words, when the aberrations are small the physical meaning of the equations $g_{11}=g_{20}=0$ is that the three-dimensional diffraction image has its point of maximum intensity at the (x,y,z)-origin P'; (2.74) or (2.76) then measures the Strehl definition at the most favourable focal setting.

By Table VIII, the introduction of the circle polynomials leaves the term in $r\cos\chi$ unchanged and merely adds a phase-shifting constant to the term in r^2.

We now consider the effect of the introduction of circle polynomials on the aberrations which represent changes in the image itself and not merely changes in its position. We consider the aberrations separately, supposing in each case that $\phi(u,v;\Theta)$ is represented by a single term in the expansion (2.66).

Spherical aberration. Primary spherical aberration, represented according to (2.51) by the aberration term $f_{40}(\Theta)r^4$, corresponds in the new classification to the aberration function

$$\tfrac{1}{2}g_{40}(\Theta)R^0_4(r) = g_{40}(\Theta)(3r^4-3r^2+\tfrac{1}{2}). \qquad (2.78)$$

It follows from (2.74) that when $g_{40}(\Theta)$ is small the added term in r^2 provides the amount of focal adjustment needed to make P' coincide with the brightest point of the diffraction image, namely the point midway between the paraxial and marginal focal points.† For any

† The term $\tfrac{1}{2}$ has no effect on the intensities, and a middle term $-6r^2$ on the right of (2.80) would correspond to the marginal focal setting, since it would give $\partial\phi/\partial r = 0$ for $r = 1$.

departure from this focal setting would express itself by the appearance of a non-zero term $\frac{1}{2}g_{20}(\Theta)R_2^0(r)$ in the expansion of the aberration function, and this would reduce the Strehl definition (2.74).

Secondary spherical aberration, formerly represented by $f_{60}(\Theta)r^6$, now appears as

$$\tfrac{1}{2}g_{60}(\Theta)R_6^0(r) = g_{60}(\Theta)(10r^6 - 15r^4 + 6r^2 - \tfrac{1}{2}), \qquad (2.79)$$

and here it follows from (2.74), in the same way as before, that the added terms in r^4 and r^2 provide primary spherical aberration and focus shift in the amounts which (provided g_{60} is small) make the Strehl definition a maximum.†

Coma. Primary coma, represented according to (2.51) by $f_{31}(\Theta)vr^2$, now corresponds to the aberration function

$$g_{31}(\Theta)R_3^1(r)\cos\chi = g_{31}(\Theta)(3vr^2 - 2v). \qquad (2.80)$$

The added term in v represents a lateral shift of the image which, when $g_{31}(\Theta)$ is small, is of the amount needed to bring its brightest point to the origin P' of (x, y, z)-coordinates. Any small change in the amount of shift or of the focal setting, or of both together, would introduce terms $g_{11}R_1^1(r)\cos\chi$ or $\frac{1}{2}g_{20}R_2^0(r)$ or both into the aberration function, and this by (2.74) would decrease the Strehl definition $|d_\lambda^*(P')|^2$.

Secondary coma appears, in the new classification, already offset by that amount of primary coma which (for small aberrations) maximizes the intensity at the brightest point of the image, and with that brightest point at the origin of (x, y, z)-coordinates.

Astigmatism. Primary astigmatism, customarily represented by a term $f_{22}(\Theta)v^2$ corresponding to a sagittal focal line, is represented in the new classification by the function

$$g_{22}(\Theta)R_2^2(r)\cos 2\chi = g_{22}(\Theta)(v^2 - u^2). \qquad (2.81)$$

This means that the receiving surface now passes through the midpoint of astigmatic separation, which for small amounts of astigmatism is the brightest point of the image, and it is no longer necessary to consider astigmatism and field curvature together, as in the classical Seidel theory. The introduction of circle polynomials causes no change in this case, since $R_2^2(r) = r^2$. Secondary astigmatism appears accompanied by the optimum amount of 'balancing' primary astigmatism.

---

† The balancing of spherical aberration of different degrees so as to maximize Strehl definition was first worked out by Richter (1925).

Finally, consider the case where

$$\phi(u, v; \Theta) = g_{nm}(\Theta) R_n^m(r) \cos m\chi,\tag{2.82}$$

that is to say ϕ is represented by a single term of the expansion (2.66), and where $(2\pi/\lambda)\phi(u, v; \Theta)$ is small. Using (2.74) in the same way as before, we see that this term represents the aberration of type $r^n \cos m\chi$ accompanied by those amounts of the lower aberrations

$$r^{n-2s} \cos m\chi \quad (s = 0, 1, ..., \tfrac{1}{2}(n-m))\tag{2.83}$$

which raise the intensity at the brightest point of the diffraction image to its greatest possible value and also bring that point to the origin of coordinates; in a word, which maximize the Strehl definition of the three-dimensional image. It is also interesting to see, from the same application of (2.74), that the aberrations (2.83) are the *only* ones which can be effective in raising the Strehl definition of an image suffering from $r^n \cos m\chi$; for example, that a reduction of Strehl definition caused by 'trefoil' cannot be alleviated by the introduction of any type of spherical aberration or of astigmatism.

2.33. *The diffraction patterns associated with a single aberration.* In the presence of a single aberration, we can write

$$\phi(u, v; \Theta) = \frac{\lambda}{2\pi} \beta_{lnm} R_n^m(r) \cos m\chi,$$

where, according to (2.66) and (2.67),

$$\beta_{lnm} = \frac{2\pi}{\lambda} a_{lnm} \Theta^l.\tag{2.84}$$

Equation (2.49) then becomes

$$d_\lambda^*(P) = \frac{1}{\pi} \int_0^1 \int_0^{2\pi} \exp\{\tfrac{1}{2}ipr^2 + iqr\cos(\chi-\omega) - i\beta_{lnm} R_n^m(r) \cos m\chi\} r \, dr d\chi.\tag{2.85}$$

(2.85) can be evaluated as an infinite series by expanding both

$$\exp\{iqr\cos(\chi-\omega)\} \quad \text{and} \quad \exp\{-i\beta_{lnm} R_n^m(r) \cos m\chi\}$$

according to the well-known formula†

$$e^{iz\cos\phi} = \sum_{\nu=-\infty}^{\infty} J_\nu(z) i^\nu e^{i\nu\phi}.\tag{2.86}$$

Multiplying the two expansions and integrating the product term by term, we find

$$d_\lambda^*(P) = 4 \sum_{\nu=0}^{\infty}{}' i^\nu \cos m\nu\omega \int_0^1 e^{\frac{1}{2}ipr^2} J_\nu(\beta_{lnm} R_n^m(r)) J_{m\nu}(qr) r \, dr,\tag{2.87}$$

† Watson (1922) p. 14.

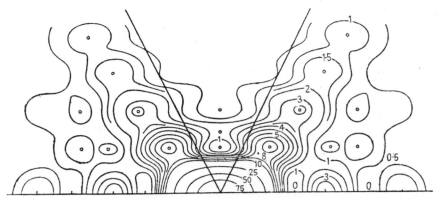

Fig. 10. Isophotes in a meridional plane near focus of aberration-free image. The intensity at focus is normalized to 100. The straight lines indicate the boundary of the geometrical shadow. Axial maxima and minima are indicated by short strokes, others by small circles. *After* Zernike and Nijboer (1949).

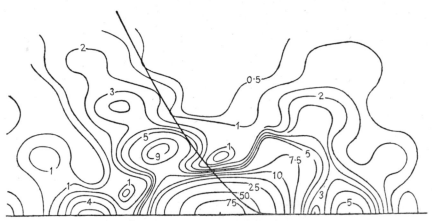

Fig. 11. Isophotes, as in Fig. 10, in presence of primary spherical aberration of amount $\beta_{l40} = \frac{1}{2}$ ($\phi = 0{\cdot}48\lambda r^4$). The thick line indicates the geometrical caustic. Strehl definition 0·95. *After* Zernike and Nijboer (1949).

where the dash denotes that the term in $\nu = 0$ is to be taken with a factor $\frac{1}{2}$. Replacing J_n by its power series expansion and rearranging according to powers of β_{lnm}, we obtain

$$d_\lambda^*(P) = 2 \int\limits_0^1 e^{\frac{1}{2}ipr^2} J_0(qr) r \, dr -$$

$$- 2i\beta_{lnm}\, i^m \cos m\omega \int\limits_0^1 e^{\frac{1}{2}ipr^2} R_n^m(r) J_m(qr) r \, dr +$$

$$+ B_2(i\beta_{lnm})^2 - B_3(i\beta_{lnm})^3 + B_4(i\beta_{lnm})^4 - \dots, \quad (2.88)$$

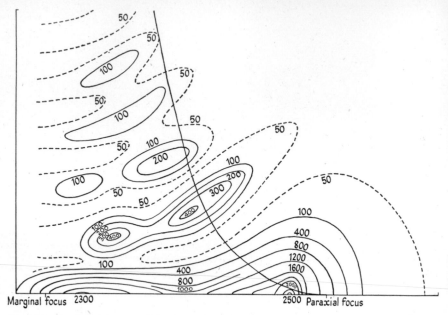

Marginal focus 2300   2500 Paraxial focus

FIG. 12. Isophotes in a meridional plane in presence of primary spherical aberration of amount $\beta_{l40} = \pi$ ($\phi = 3\lambda r^4$). The thick line indicates the geometrical caustic. *After* Maréchal.

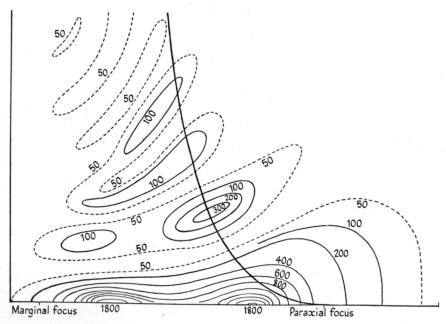

Marginal focus   1800   1800   Paraxial focus

FIG. 13. Isophotes in a meridional plane in presence of primary spherical aberration of amount $\beta_{l40} = \frac{4}{3}\pi$ ($\phi = 4\lambda r^4$). *After* Maréchal.

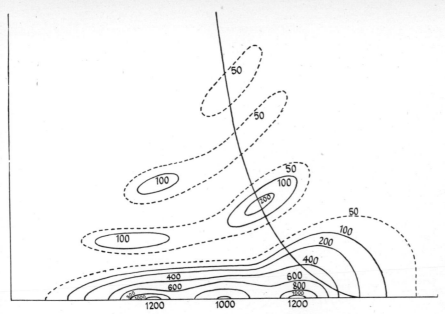

FIG. 14. Isophotes in a meridional plane in presence of primary spherical aberration of amount $\beta_{l40} = 2\pi$ $(\phi = 6\lambda r^4)$. *After* Maréchal.

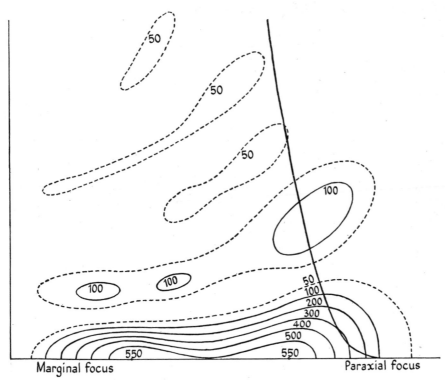

Marginal focus   Paraxial focus

FIG. 15. Isophotes in a meridional plane in presence of primary spherical aberration of amount $\beta_{l40} = \frac{10}{3}\pi$ $(\phi = 10\lambda r^4)$. *After* Maréchal.

where each B_ν is a linear sum† of terms

$$\cos m\nu'\omega \int_0^1 e^{\frac{1}{2}ipr^2}(R_n^m(r))^\nu J_{m\nu}(qr)r\,dr \quad (\nu' = \nu, \nu-2,\dots \geqslant 0). \quad (2.89)$$

Nijboer found that when both $\frac{1}{2}p$ and β_{lnm} are $O(1)$, about four terms of the expansion (2.88) give the intensity distributions in the diffraction

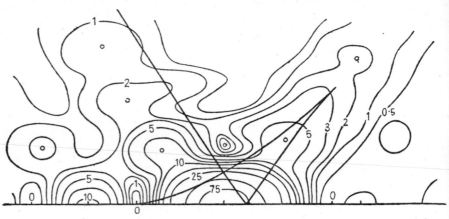

FIG. 16. Spherical aberration $\beta_{l60} = \frac{1}{2}$ (secondary spherical aberration $1\cdot6\lambda r^6$ balanced against primary spherical aberration $2\cdot4\lambda r^4$). *After* Zernike and Nijboer (1949).

images with sufficient accuracy for the drawing of isophotes. The intensity distribution along the principal ray may be found by setting $q = 0$ in (2.87), which then becomes

$$d_\lambda^*(P) = 2\int_0^1 e^{\frac{1}{2}ipr^2}J_0(\beta_{lnm}R_n^m(r))r\,dr. \quad (2.90)$$

The intensity in the plane $p = 0$, which for a small aberration is the plane of maximum Strehl definition, can be found from the equation

$$d_\lambda^*(P) = 4\sum_{\nu=0}^\infty{}' i^\nu \cos m\nu\omega \int_0^1 J_\nu(\beta_{lnm}R_n^m(r))J_{m\nu}(qr)r\,dr, \quad (2.91)$$

obtained on setting $p = 0$ in (2.87).

Figs. 11–15 show the isophotes in meridional sections of images suffering from amounts up to 10λ of primary spherical aberration; those for the aberration-free image are reproduced in Fig. 10 for comparison. Figs. 12–15 were obtained with the help of M. Maréchal's ingenious

† The actual sums may be found in Nijboer's thesis or in Wolf (1951 b), p. 103; Nijboer's p becomes $\frac{1}{2}p$ in the present notation.

mechanical integrator,† a photograph of which is reproduced as Plate I; to obtain the isophotes from the expansion (2.88) for such large values of β_{l40} would involve very heavy computations. Fig. 16, constructed from (2.88), shows the effect of a fairly small amount of 'balanced' secondary spherical aberration. In Plate II are reproduced photographs, due to Nienhuis, illustrating the appearance in selected focal planes of

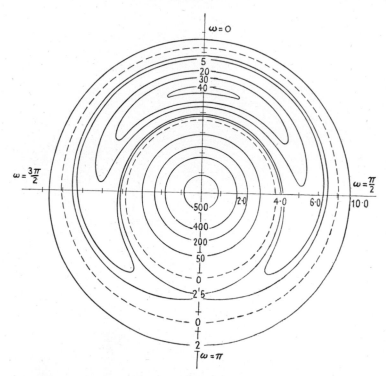

FIG. 17. Primary coma ($\beta_{l31} = \frac{1}{2}$; $\phi = 0{\cdot}24\lambda(r^3 - \frac{2}{3}r)\cos\chi$); isophotes in the plane $p = 0$. 1,000 units represents the intensity at the centre of the aberration-free image. The dotted curves are lines of zero intensity. *After* Nijboer.

images suffering from amounts up to $17{\cdot}5\lambda$ of primary spherical aberration.

The isophotes in the plane $p = 0$ corresponding to various amounts up to $17{\cdot}5\lambda$ of primary coma are shown in Figs. 17–21.‡ The last two, due to Kingslake (1948), were obtained by a method (incorrectly stated to be applicable only in the plane $p = 0$) which is equivalent to the use

† A. Maréchal (1948). I am indebted to Prof. Maréchal for the unpublished diagrams here redrawn as Figs. 12, 13, 14, 15, and 26.

‡ Fig. 17, previously unpublished, was kindly supplied by Dr. Nijboer.

of the equation

$$\frac{1}{\pi}\int\limits_0^1\int\limits_0^{2\pi}\exp\{\tfrac{1}{2}ipr^2+iqr\cos(\chi-\omega)-i\beta h(r)\cos\chi\}r\,dr\,d\chi$$

$$=\int\limits_0^1 e^{\frac{1}{2}ipr^2}J_0[\sqrt{\{\beta^2h^2(r)-2q\beta rh(r)\cos\omega+q^2r^2\}}].2r\,dr.\quad(2.92)$$

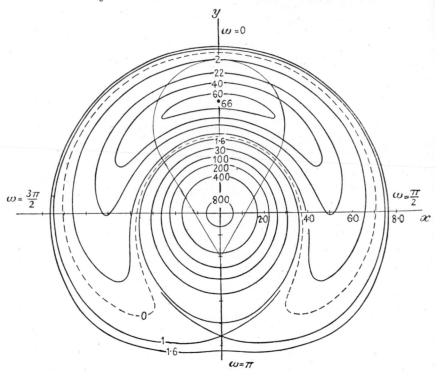

Fig. 18. Primary coma ($\beta_{l31}=1$; $\phi=0.48\lambda(r^3-\tfrac{2}{3}r)\cos\chi$); isophotes in the plane $p=0$. Strehl definition 0·879. The dotted curve is a line of zero intensity. The boundary of the geometrical coma flare is also shown. *After* Nijboer (1947).

Plate III shows photographs (after Kingslake (1948)) in the plane $p=0$ of images suffering from primary coma $Fr^3\cos\chi$ of amounts $F=0$, 0·64λ, 1·4λ, 2·3λ, 3·2λ, 4·3λ, 5·3λ, 6·4λ, 7·7λ, respectively. Plate IV shows photographs of primary coma $-\phi=2\lambda(r^3-\tfrac{2}{3}r)\cos\chi$ at focal settings corresponding approximately to the values $p=0$, 10, 20, 30, 40, 50.†

Figs. 22–24 show the isophotes in the mean focal plane for amounts

† In Dr. Kingslake's paper, the focal settings are given as 0·1 mm. apart in an f/5·6 pencil, which for λ = 5 × 10⁻⁵ cm. would give the p-values 0, 10, 20, 30, 40, 50 for the six focal settings shown.

$\pm0{\cdot}08\lambda$, $\pm0{\cdot}16\lambda$, $\pm0{\cdot}64\lambda$ respectively of primary astigmatism; Fig. 25 shows the isophotes in the second case when the focal setting is shifted to the plane through the horizontal focal line. Plate V shows primary

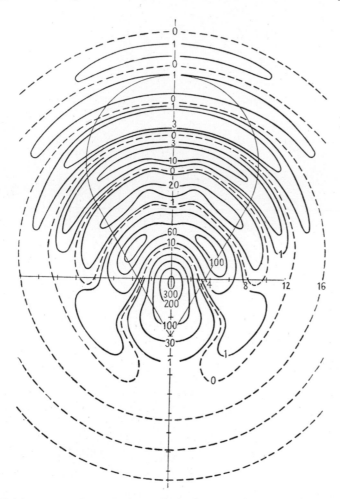

FIG. 19. Primary coma ($\beta_{l31} = 3$; $\phi = 1{\cdot}4\lambda(r^3 - \tfrac{2}{3}r)\cos\chi$); isophotes in the plane $p = 0$. Strehl definition 0·306. The dotted curves are lines of zero intensity. The boundary of the geometrical coma flare is also shown. *After* Nienhuis (1948).

astigmatism of amounts $\pm1{\cdot}4\lambda$, $\pm2{\cdot}7\lambda$, $\pm3{\cdot}5\lambda$, $\pm6{\cdot}5\lambda$, in the mean focal plane in each case.

Fig. 26 shows isophotes from a diffraction image combining primary spherical aberration (2λ), primary coma ($\pm1\lambda$) and primary astigmatism ($\pm1\lambda$).

From (2.88) may be deduced an interesting property, first noticed by Nijboer, of small aberrations in the plane $p = 0$ through the point of maximum intensity. When m is even, (2.88) gives

$$|d_\lambda^*(P)|^2 = \left(2 \int_0^1 J_0(qr)r \, dr\right)^2 + O(\beta_{lnm}^2),$$

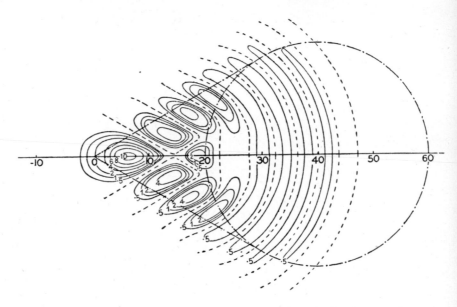

Fig. 20. Primary coma ($\phi = 3{\cdot}2\lambda r^3\cos \chi$); isophotes in the plane $p = 0$.
After Kingslake (1948).

while, when m is odd, it gives

$$|d_\lambda^*(P)|^2 = \left(2 \int_0^1 J_0(qr)r \, dr\right)^2 + O(\beta_{lnm}).$$

Thus the presence of a first-order amount of coma causes a first-order disturbance in the intensity distribution of the ideal image, while the presence of a first-order amount of astigmatism only causes a second-order disturbance of the intensities. In particular, the Strehl definition is much more seriously impaired by small amounts of coma than by small amounts of astigmatism. This provides a further reason, in addition to the asymmetry of the comatic image, why the practical tolerance for off-axis coma is so much tighter than that for astigmatism in highly corrected systems such as microscope objectives.

3. Images of coherent or partially coherent object surfaces

3.1. *Relevance of the ikonal function*

In the imaging of point sources and of self-luminous object surfaces by an optical system, no phase relationships exist between wave-fronts belonging to pencils of rays originating in different object points. The

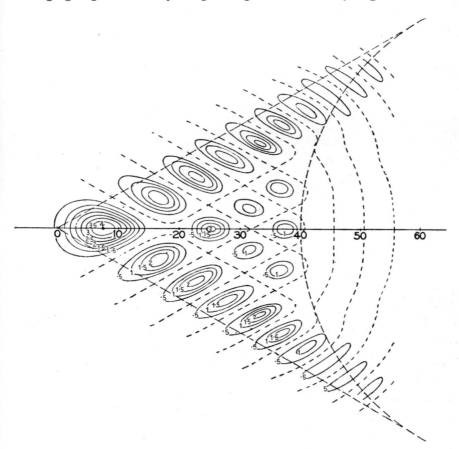

FIG. 21. Primary coma ($\phi = 6\cdot4\lambda r^3\cos\chi$); isophotes in the plane $p = 0$.
After Kingslake (1948).

aberration function defined in § 1.3 then provides a sufficient basis for the investigation of the structure of the diffraction images.

In the imaging of coherently or partially coherently lit objects, there are phase relationships between wave-fronts originating in different object points, and we therefore need to take account, for each value of the wavelength λ, not only of the shapes of the wave-fronts W in the different pencils but also of the optical-path distance between every W and the object point P in which it originated.

This could be done quite simply by calculating the optical-path distance between P and the principal point P' of the image on a given receiving surface, and subtracting the optical distance between P' and

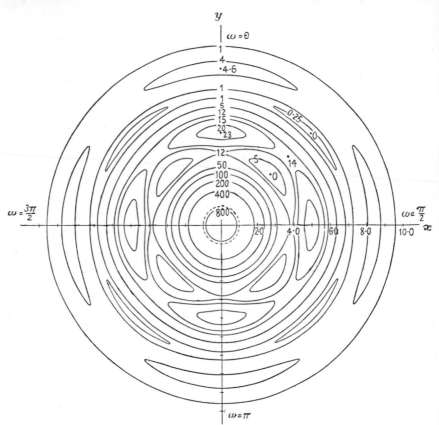

Fig. 22. Primary astigmatism at mean focus ($\beta_{l22} = \frac{1}{2}$, $\phi = 0.08\lambda r^2 \cos 2\chi$). Strehl definition 0·959. *After* Nijboer (1942).

the principal point of W. The result is the optical distance between P and the wave-front W.

However, it is usually more convenient in analytical discussions to obtain the same result by way of an ikonal function $e(u, v; \Theta)$, defined as the optical-path distance between P and the point where the (u, v)-ray is cut by a sphere of fixed radius centred on P'. A convenient value for the fixed radius is the distance between the centre of the exit pupil and the axial point of the receiving surface.

The ikonal function $e(u, v; \Theta)$, which is very similar to one proposed by Wolf (1952), depends on the optical system, the object surface and the receiving surface; and the aberration function $\phi(u, v; \Theta)$ is connected with it by the simple relation

$$\phi(u, v; \Theta) = e(u, v; \Theta) - e(0, 0; \Theta). \tag{3.1}$$

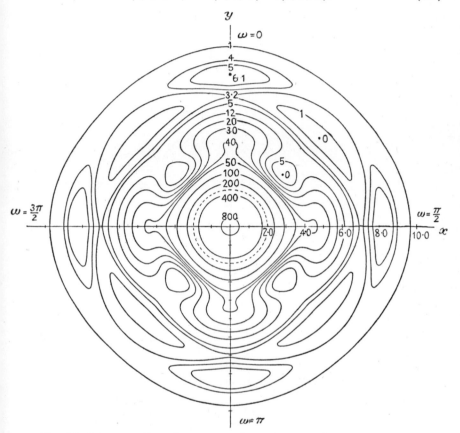

FIG. 23. Primary astigmatism at mean focus ($\beta_{l_{22}} = 1$, $\phi = 0.16\lambda r^2 \cos 2\chi$). Strehl definition 0·840. *After* Nijboer (1949).

To prove (3.1) it is sufficient to observe that, for fixed P, P' and W, the difference $e(u, v; \Theta) - \phi(u, v; \Theta)$ is the optical distance along the (u, v)-ray from P to the wave-front W, and is therefore constant as u, v vary. The value of the constant is seen to be $e(0, 0; \Theta)$ on setting $u = v = 0$ and remembering that $\phi(0, 0; \Theta) = 0$.

In the same way as the aberration function $\phi(u, v; \Theta)$ of an anastigmat may be written in the form $f\mu^6 \Phi(u, v; \Theta)$, where (see § 1.6)

$$f\mu^6 \Phi(u, v; \Theta) = f\mu^6 \Phi^*(u, v; \Theta) + O(f\mu^8) \tag{3.2}$$

and $(f\mu/H)\Phi^*(u, v; \Theta)$ is of the form (1.47), so the ikonal function $e(u, v; \Theta)$ of the system may be written in the form $f\mu^6 E(u, v; \Theta)+\text{const.}$, where

$$f\mu^6 E(u, v; \Theta) = f\mu^6 E^*(u, v; \Theta)+O(f\mu^8) \tag{3.3}$$

FIG. 24. Primary astigmatism at mean focus ($\beta_{l22} = 4$, $\phi = 0.64\lambda r^2\cos 2\chi$). Strehl definition 0.066. *After* Nienhuis (1948).

and the sixth-degree polynomial $E^*(u, v; \Theta)$ is given by an equation of the form

$$\frac{f\mu}{H} E^*(u, v; \Theta) = h''\Theta^2+\tfrac{1}{2}a''r^2-m''\Theta v+$$
$$+a'\Theta^4+\tfrac{1}{4}b'r^4-f'\Theta vr^2+c'\Theta^2v^2+\tfrac{1}{2}d'\Theta^2r^2-e'\Theta^3v-$$
$$-S_1\Theta^6-S_2\Theta^4r^2-S_3\Theta^5v-S_4\Theta^2r^4-$$
$$-S_5\Theta^3vr^2-S_6\Theta^4v^2-S_7r^6-S_8\Theta vr^4-$$
$$-S_9\Theta^2v^2r^2-S_{10}\Theta^3v^3, \tag{3.4}$$

analogous to (1.47). Fig. 2 shows the separate types of aberration.

Alternatively we may write, in agreement with the notation of (1.52),

$$\frac{f\mu}{H} E^*(u, v; \Theta) = \sum_{n=1}^{19} a_n \sigma_n = \sum c_{klm} \Theta^k v^l r^{2m}, \qquad (3.5)$$

where the non-negative integers k, l, m now satisfy, in place of (1.53), the conditions

$$l \leqslant k; \qquad k-l \text{ even}; \qquad k+l+2m = 2, 4 \text{ or } 6. \qquad (3.6)$$

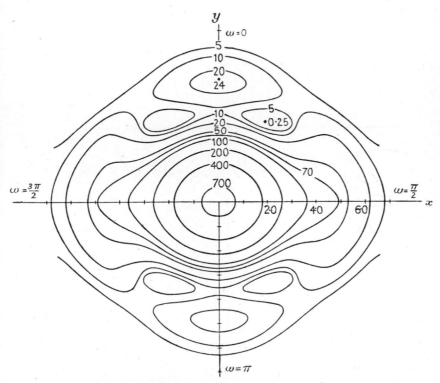

FIG. 25. Primary astigmatism in the focal plane through the horizontal focal line ($\phi = 0.32\lambda r^2 \sin^2 \chi$). *After* Nijboer (1942).

In the simpler case of an aplanat or of a general centred system, $e(u, v; \Theta)$ takes the form $f\mu^4 E(u, v; \Theta) + O(f\mu^6)$, where

$$f\mu^4 E(u, v; \Theta) = f\mu^4 E^*(u, v; \Theta) + O(f\mu^6) \qquad (3.7)$$

and

$$\frac{f\mu}{H} E^*(u, v; \Theta) = h''\Theta^2 + \tfrac{1}{2}a''r^2 - m''\Theta v +$$

$$+ a'\Theta^4 + \tfrac{1}{4}b'r^4 - f'\Theta v r^2 + c'\Theta^2 v^2 + \tfrac{1}{2}d'\Theta^2 r^2 - e'\Theta^3 v. \qquad (3.8)$$

The dominant term in (3.7) is now of the fourth order, and the sixth-degree expressions are all absorbed into the error-term.

If we impose the condition that the coefficients h'', a' in (3.8) shall be $O(1)$, the position of the receiving surface within the image-layer of thickness $O(f\mu^2)$ is thereby fixed to within $O(f\mu^4)$, i.e. is uniquely determined to the Seidel order of accuracy, except for a parallel bodily shift

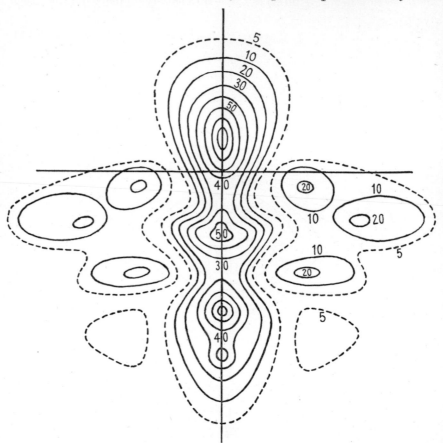

Fig. 26. Combined aberrations (primary spherical aberration 2λ, primary coma $\pm\lambda$, primary astigmatism $\pm\lambda$). *After* Maréchal.

along the axis (overall focal adjustment) of amount $O(f\mu^2)$. For, a change $O(f\mu^2)$ in the focal setting of an off-axis point, due to a change in form or tilt of the receiving surface through a given axial point, would involve changes comparable with $1/\mu^2$ in the values of the coefficients h'', a' of (3.8).

For similar reasons, the coefficients h'', a', S_1 in (3.4) cannot all be $O(1)$ for more than one position of the receiving surface within the image layer of an anastigmat, overall focal adjustments of amount $O(f\mu^4)$ excepted.

Whether even one receiving surface exists for which h'', a', S_1 are all $O(1)$ depends on the ikonal properties of the anastigmat under consideration.

3.2. *Partial coherence*

The theory of partial coherence, first investigated by van Cittert (1934), was greatly improved by Zernike (1938) and later by Hopkins (1951 a, b; 1953). The account which follows is largely based on Hopkins's treatment.

When discussing interference at a single point P, it is necessary to distinguish between disturbances at P which originate in the same element of the primary light source and those which originate in different elements of the source.

In the first case, the phase relations are constant and the disturbances at P are said to be coherent. The disturbances are then combined by adding the complex displacements at P. In the second case the phase relations are random and the disturbances are said to be incoherent. The disturbances are then combined by adding the intensities at P.

In general, the disturbances at two different points P_1 and P_2 will be neither coherent nor incoherent. Coherent light from any given element of the primary source may reach P_1 and P_2, but these disturbances will be incoherent with light reaching P_1 and P_2 from any other element of the source. The disturbances at P_1 and P_2 are *partially coherent* and some means of measuring partial coherence is needed for their adequate description.

A measure of partial coherence should make it possible, given the intensities I_1, I_2 at two points P_1, P_2, to state how the disturbances propagated from these points to a third point P must be combined to calculate the intensity at P.

Suppose light from an extended primary source L to reach two points P_1, P_2, either directly or through an optical system, and let an emission element e_m of the source give rise to complex displacements u_{m1}, u_{m2} at P_1, P_2 respectively. u_{m1}, u_{m2} are then coherent, but not necessarily in phase.

Suppose further that P is a point reached, either directly or through an optical system S, by light from P_1 and P_2 (see Fig. 27). Let f_1 be the complex displacement which would be produced at P by a complex displacement of unit amplitude and zero phase at P_1, and similarly for f_2 and P_2. Then f_1, f_2 express the imaging properties of the paths $P_1 P, P_2 P$.

Since u_{m1} and u_{m2} are coherent, the complex displacement produced at P, *via* P_1 and P_2, by the element e_m of the source is equal to $u_{m1} f_1 + u_{m2} f_2$

and the intensity at P due to the element e_m is

$$\delta I_P = (u_{m1}f_1 + u_{m2}f_2)(\bar{u}_{m1}\bar{f}_1 + \bar{u}_{m2}\bar{f}_2)$$
$$= |u_{m1}|^2|f_1|^2 + |u_{m2}|^2|f_2|^2 + 2\mathbf{R}(u_{m1}\bar{u}_{m2}f_1\bar{f}_2), \qquad (3.9)$$

where bars denote complex conjugates and $\mathbf{R}$ the real part.

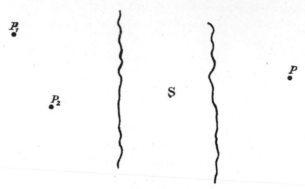

FIG. 27.

Since the different emission elements e_m of the source are mutually incoherent, we must sum the intensities (3.9) to obtain the intensity at P due to the whole source. Therefore this intensity

$$I_P = \left(\sum_m |u_{m1}|^2\right)|f_1|^2 + \left(\sum_m |u_{m2}|^2\right)|f_2|^2 + 2\mathbf{R}\left\{\left(\sum_m u_{m1}\bar{u}_{m2}\right)f_1\bar{f}_2\right\}$$
$$= I_1|f_1|^2 + I_2|f_2|^2 + 2\mathbf{R}\left\{\left(\sum_m u_{m1}\bar{u}_{m2}\right)f_1\bar{f}_2\right\}, \qquad (3.10)$$

where
$$I_1 = \sum_m |u_{m1}|^2, \qquad I_2 = \sum_m |u_{m2}|^2$$

are the total intensities at P_1, P_2 due to the whole of L. The form of the result is the same whether L is one-, two-, or three-dimensional.

The complex quantity

$$J_{12} = \sum_m u_{m1}\bar{u}_{m2} \qquad (3.11)$$

is called the *mutual intensity* of P_1 and P_2; when P_1 and P_2 coincide, it reduces to the ordinary intensity:

$$J_{11} = \sum_m |u_{m1}|^2 = I_1, \qquad J_{22} = \sum_m |u_{m2}|^2 = I_2. \qquad (3.12)$$

If we now define

$$\gamma_{12} = \frac{J_{12}}{\sqrt{(J_{11}J_{22})}} = \frac{1}{\sqrt{(I_1 I_2)}}\sum_m u_{m1}\bar{u}_{m2}, \qquad (3.13)$$

equation (3.10) can be written in the form

$$I_P = I_1|f_1|^2 + I_2|f_2|^2 + 2\sqrt{(I_1 I_2)}\mathbf{R}(\gamma_{12}f_1\bar{f}_2). \qquad (3.14)$$

We call γ_{12} the phase coherence factor between P_1 and P_2.† If f_1 and f_2 are known for the paths $P_1 P$ and $P_2 P$ (that is, if the properties of the system $\mathbf{S}$ are known), a knowledge of I_1, I_2 and γ_{12} is sufficient to enable I_P to be calculated by (3.14). The modulus $|\gamma_{12}|$ will be shown to measure the *degree of coherence* of the vibrations and its argument their 'effective phase difference'. From (3.12), (3.13) and the inequalities‡

$$\left| \sum_m u_{m1} \bar{u}_{m2} \right|^2 \leqslant \left(\sum_m |u_{m1}||u_{m2}| \right)^2 \leqslant \sum_m |u_{m1}|^2 \sum_m |u_{m2}|^2,$$

we obtain

$$|\gamma_{12}| \leqslant 1. \tag{3.15}$$

Physical interpretation of γ_{12}. The physical meaning of different values which γ_{12} may take is easily seen by considering P_1 and P_2 to be

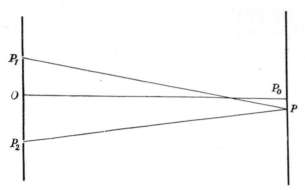

FIG. 28. Young's experiment.

two pinholes in an opaque screen and $\mathbf{S}$ to be absent, as in Young's experiment (Fig. 28). Let P_0 be a point on the receiving screen T equidistant from P_1 and P_2. Then when P is at P_0, $f_1 = f_2$ and (3.14) becomes

$$I_P = |f_1|^2 \{ I_1 + I_2 + 2\sqrt{(I_1 I_2)} \mathbf{R}(\gamma_{12}) \}. \tag{3.16}$$

If P is moved from P_0, in a direction parallel to the line $P_1 P_2$, through a small distance x, then the value of $P_1 P - P_2 P$ changes from 0 to $t = (P_1 P_2 / OP)x$ (with negligible error), $f_2 = f_1 e^{ikt}$ and

$$I_P = |f_1|^2 \{ I_1 + I_2 + 2\sqrt{(I_1 I_2)} \mathbf{R}(\gamma_{12} e^{-ikt}) \}. \tag{3.17}$$

If $\gamma_{12} = 0$, it follows from (3.17) that I_P remains effectively constant as t varies and no fringes are formed. This is the case of mutual incoherence between P_1 and P_2.

† This name was proposed by Hopkins; Zernike called it the *complex degree of coherence*.

‡ Hardy, Ingham and Polya, *Inequalities*, C.U.P. 1934, (1.3.1) and (1.3.2).

If $\gamma_{12} \neq 0$, (3.17) shows that, as t increases, I_P varies sinusoidally between the values

$$I_{\max} = |f_1|^2\{I_1 + I_2 + 2\sqrt{(I_1 I_2)}|\gamma_{12}|\} \tag{3.18}$$

and
$$I_{\min} = |f_1|^2\{I_1 + I_2 - 2\sqrt{(I_1 I_2)}|\gamma_{12}|\}. \tag{3.19}$$

These variations constitute the interference fringes; the 'fringe visibility' is defined as

$$\frac{I_{\max} - I_{\min}}{I_{\max} + I_{\min}} = \frac{2\sqrt{(I_1 I_2)}}{I_1 + I_2}|\gamma_{12}|. \tag{3.20}$$

When the intensities of illumination of the two pinholes are made equal, $I_1 = I_2$ and the fringe visibility (3.20) is simply $|\gamma_{12}|$. This shows that $|\gamma_{12}|$ is identical with Zernike's *degree of coherence*. Complete coherence is the case $|\gamma_{12}| = 1$.

Returning to (3.17), we see that in the general case $\gamma_{12} \neq 0$, γ_{12} complex, the values of t which maximize I_P are

$$t = \frac{\lambda}{2\pi}\arg\gamma_{12} + n\lambda \quad (n = 0, \pm 1, \pm 2,...).$$

The interference bands are shifted sideways, so that the central maximum of the band $n = 0$ no longer agrees with P_0, as it would if P_1, P_2 were lit coherently and cophasally. The amount of shift is the same as would result, in the coherent case, from a phase retardation $\arg\gamma_{12}$ of P_2 relative to P_1. We may therefore call $\arg\gamma_{12}$ the *effective phase retardation* of P_2 relative to P_1. It reduces to an ordinary phase retardation when P_1, P_2 are mutually coherent, i.e. when $|\gamma_{12}| = 1$.

If the dimensions of the source are small compared with the wavelength λ, the amplitude ratios $|u_{m1}/u_{m2}|$ and the phase differences $\arg(u_{m1} \bar{u}_{m2})$ are approximately the same for all the emission elements e_m; hence we can write $u_{m1} = au_{m2}$, $I_1 = |a|^2 I_2$, where the complex number a is independent of m, and (3.13) gives

$$|\gamma_{12}| = \frac{1}{|a|I_2}\left|\sum_m au_{m2}\bar{u}_{m2}\right| = \frac{1}{|a|I_2}|aI_2| = 1.$$

Thus *light from a small primary source gives coherent illumination*, although the source itself may consist of many independent emission elements. An easy extension of the above argument shows that the same result holds for small secondary sources.

Partial coherence is of great importance in the theory of the microscope. Self-luminous objects are the only ones which are fully incoherent; in all other cases there is partial coherence between the light issuing from neighbouring points of the object surface. As a result, the resolving power of an aberration-free objective, and the tolerance for aberrations of different types, are fundamentally dependent on the character of the illumination. We shall return to this topic in § 3.7.

3.3. *Calculation of γ_{12} from given illumination data*

Let $w_1(Q)$, $w_2(Q)$ be the complex displacements which would be caused at P_1, P_2 respectively by a point source of unit flux situated at the point Q occupied by the emission element e_m and represented by a complex displacement of unit amplitude and zero phase. Then the flux of e_m is $|a_m|^2$, where

$$a_m = \frac{u_{m1}}{w_1(Q)} = \frac{u_{m2}}{w_2(Q)}, \tag{3.21}$$

and (3.13) can be written

$$\gamma_{12} = \frac{1}{\sqrt{(I_1 I_2)}} \sum_m |a_m|^2 w_1(Q)\overline{w_2(Q)}, \tag{3.22}$$

where

$$I_1 = \sum_m |a_m|^2 |w_1(Q)|^2, \qquad I_2 = \sum_m |a_m|^2 |w_2(Q)|^2. \tag{3.23}$$

If the source L is a self-luminous surface, with flux density $l(Q)$ at the point Q, and if QP_1, QP_2 make only small angles with the normal at Q to the surface, the sum of the quantities $|a_m|^2$ over the emission elements contained in an element of area $d\sigma$ situated at Q is $l(Q)\,d\sigma$ and (3.22), (3.23) take the form

$$\gamma_{12} = \frac{1}{\sqrt{(I_1 I_2)}} \iint_L l(Q)w_1(Q)\overline{w_2(Q)}\,d\sigma, \tag{3.24}$$

where

$$I_1 = \iint_L l(Q)|w_1(Q)|^2\,d\sigma, \qquad I_2 = \iint_L l(Q)|w_2(Q)|^2\,d\sigma \tag{3.25}$$

are the intensities at P_1 and P_2.

Plane illuminated by an extended plane source. Suppose in particular that the primary source L is represented by a flux distribution $l(\xi, \eta)$ occupying a finite region of a plane (ξ, η) and directly illuminating a parallel plane (x, y), as shown in Fig. 29. The complex displacements $w_1(Q)$, $w_2(Q)$ at P_1, P_2 in the (x, y)-plane are here given by the equations

$$w_1(Q) = \frac{e^{-ikR_1}}{R_1}, \qquad w_2(Q) = \frac{e^{-ikR_2}}{R_2}, \tag{3.26}$$

where Q is the point (ξ, η),

$$R_1 = QP_1, \qquad R_2 = QP_2 \tag{3.27}$$

and $k = 2\pi/\lambda$. Whence, by (3.24), (3.25),

$$\gamma_{12} = \frac{1}{\sqrt{(I_1 I_2)}} \int\int_L \mathcal{U}(\xi, \eta) \frac{e^{ik(R_2 - R_1)}}{R_1 R_2} d\xi d\eta, \tag{3.28}$$

where
$$I_1 = \int\int_L \frac{\mathcal{U}(\xi, \eta)}{R_1^2} d\xi d\eta, \qquad I_2 = \int\int_L \frac{\mathcal{U}(\xi, \eta)}{R_2^2} d\xi d\eta \tag{3.29}$$

are the intensities at P_1 and P_2.

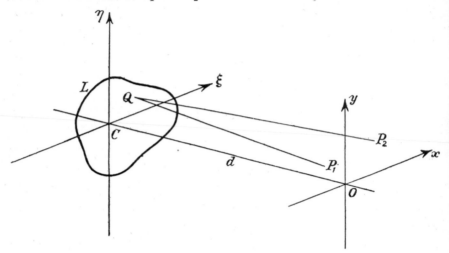

FIG. 29. Plane illuminated by extended plane source.

To obtain a picture of the way in which γ_{12} depends on the relative positions of P_1 and P_2, consider the case where the angles subtended by QC at O (see Fig. 29) and by OP_1, OP_2 at C are always small, and suppose the source L replaced by a transparent layer, filling the same region of the (ξ, η)-plane, which transmits a variable fraction $\tau(\xi, \eta)$ of the light falling on it. Let a point source and a lens of negligible aberrations be placed behind this layer in such a way that the geometric image of the source is formed at P_2. The complex displacement $D_\lambda(P_1)$ at a neighbouring point P_1 of the diffraction image centred at P_2 may then be calculated by applying Huyghens's principle to the absorbing surface. We obtain

$$D_\lambda(P_1) = C \int\int_L \sqrt{\{\tau(\xi, \eta)\}} e^{i\phi(\xi, \eta)} \frac{e^{-ikR_1}}{R_1} d\xi d\eta, \tag{3.30}$$

where C is a normalizing constant and the phase $\phi(\xi, \eta)$ on the screen can be immediately determined by moving P_1 to the special position P_2. As this is the geometric image, the waves all arrive there in the same phase, so that $\phi(\xi, \eta) - kR_2$ is a constant. Therefore (3.30) can be written in the form

$$D_\lambda(P_1) = C' \int\int \sqrt{\{\tau(\xi, \eta)\}} \frac{e^{ik(R_2-R_1)}}{R_2} d\xi d\eta. \qquad (3.31)$$

This agrees with (3.28) for an appropriate choice of C' if $\sqrt{\{\tau(\xi, \eta)\}}$ is a constant multiple of $l(\xi, \eta)/R_2$ i.e. if $(1/R_2)\sqrt{\{\tau(\xi, \eta)\}}$ is a constant multiple of $(1/R_2^2)l(\xi, \eta)$; in other words, if the *amplitudes* contributed at P_2 by the different parts of the transmitting screen are proportional to the *intensities* contributed at P_2 by the corresponding parts of the light source L. Thus the phase-coherence factor between any point P_1 and a given point P_2 is equal to the complex displacement at P_1 in the diffraction pattern associated with an aperture coincident with the source, the diffraction pattern being centred on P_2 and the complex displacement at P_2 being normalized to unity.

In particular, a uniformly bright plane circular source of radius $d \tan \alpha$ small compared with d gives, near the origin in the (x, y)-plane, the complex coherence distribution

$$\gamma_{12} = \frac{2J_1(z)}{z}, \qquad z = \frac{2\pi}{\lambda}P_1P_2 \sin \alpha, \qquad (3.32)$$

where J_1 is the Bessel function of order 1.

(3.24) and (3.25) were derived on the assumption that, for all positions of Q in the radiating surface L, the lines QP_1, QP_2, make only small angles with the normal at Q to the surface. When this assumption is not satisfied, account has to be taken of the effects of the obliquity between the joins QP_1, QP_2 and the normal at Q to the radiating surface. This can be done by introducing an obliquity factor $\sqrt{(\cos \theta)}$ on the Huyghens wavelets emitted by a surface element $d\sigma$, where $\theta = 0$ corresponds to the point of the wavelet on the normal from $d\sigma$. Further, if P_1, P_2 are points on a receiving surface S', we need to replace the complex displacements $w_1(Q)$, $w_2(Q)$ by displacement densities $w_1(Q)\sqrt{(\cos \theta'_1)}$, $w_2(Q)\sqrt{(\cos \theta'_2)}$ on S', where θ'_1, θ'_2 are the respective obliquities of QP_1, QP_2 with the normals to S' at P_1, P_2.

The effect of the change on (3.29) is to replace these equations by

$$I_1 = \int\int_L l(\xi, \eta) \frac{\cos^2\theta_1}{R_1^2} d\xi d\eta, \qquad I_2 = \int\int_L l(\xi, \eta) \frac{\cos^2\theta_2}{R_2^2} d\xi d\eta, \qquad (3.33)$$

in which θ_1, θ_2 denote the angles of obliquity between QP_1, QP_2 and the normal to the (ξ, η)-plane, and to insert a factor $\cos \theta_1 \cos \theta_2$ under the integral sign in (3.28). In a practical case, where $l(\xi, \eta)$ is smooth except for a possible sharp cut-off at the edge of L, γ_{12} is effectively zero unless P_2 is near to P_1, so that $\cos\theta_1\cos\theta_2$ can be replaced by $\cos^2\theta_1$ and the modified form of (3.28) can be written

$$\gamma_{12} = \frac{1}{I_1} \iint_L \frac{l(\xi,\eta)\cos^2\theta_1}{R_1^2} e^{ik(R_2-R_1)}\, d\xi d\eta. \tag{3.34}$$

(3.33) and (3.34) show that when P_2 is near to P_1 the phase-coherence factor γ_{12} is the weighted mean of $e^{ik(R_2-R_1)}$ as Q ranges over the source L, the weighting being according to the luminosity contributions at P_1 from the different parts of L.† It follows that if the distance $P_1 P_2$ does not exceed $\lambda/8$, the real part of γ_{12} cannot fall below $\cos\frac{1}{4}\pi$ and consequently $|\gamma_{12}| \geqslant 0.707$. Hence the (x,y)-plane can never be incoherently illuminated by L.

In the case (3.32), corresponding to a circular source of radius $d\tan\alpha$, the degree of coherence $|\gamma_{12}| = 2J_1(z)/z$ falls to 0.880 when $z=1$, i.e. when

$$P_1 P_2 = \frac{\lambda}{2\pi}\operatorname{cosec}\alpha = \frac{0.16\lambda}{\sin\alpha}; \tag{3.35}$$

here α is the angular radius of the source seen from a point in the opposing region of the (x,y)-plane. Regarding this as a tolerable departure from perfect coherence, we can say that *the diameter of the coherence-patches corresponding to a source of angular radius α is $0.32\lambda/\sin\alpha$*. This rule of thumb is useful in estimating the size of source needed in diffraction experiments.

The degree of coherence $|\gamma_{12}| = 2J_1(z)/z$ decreases steadily to zero as z increases from 0 to 3.83; for this value of z, corresponding to

$$P_1 P_2 = \frac{0.61\lambda}{\sin\alpha},$$

there is mutual incoherence. A further increase of z reintroduces a small amount of partial coherence, which never exceeds 0.14 and vanishes again at the next root of $J_1(z)$, namely $z = 7.02$. Since γ_{12} changes sign as z passes through each root of $J_1(z)$, the positions of bright and dark fringes are interchanged after each disappearance.

In the present context, Michelson's method of measuring the small angular diameters of stars appears in a new light. The stellar source, of angular radius α, illuminates the plane of the outer mirrors M_1, M_2 of the interferometer. The visibility of the fringes observed is determined by $|\gamma_{12}|$ in this plane, and the large interferometer attachment carried by

† (3.11) and (3.13) give the same result more directly.

PLATE III

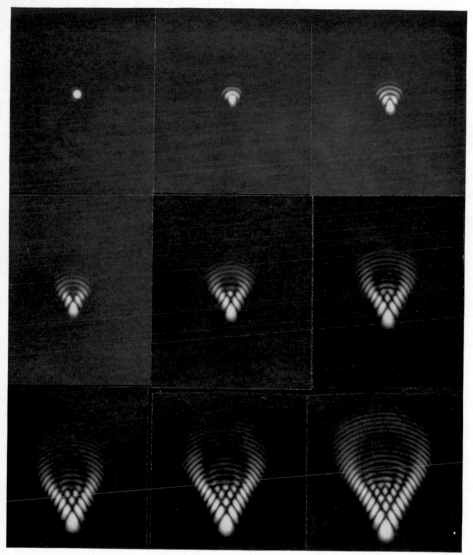

Primary coma $-\phi = Fr^3 \cos\chi$ of amounts $F = 0$, $0\cdot64\lambda$, $1\cdot4\lambda$, $2\cdot3\lambda$, $3\cdot2\lambda$, $4\cdot3\lambda$, $5\cdot3\lambda$, $6\cdot4\lambda$, $7\cdot7\lambda$, photographed in the focal plane $p = 0$. *After* Kingslake (1948)

the 100-inch telescope of the Mt. Wilson observatory provided a means of determining those values of $P_1 P_2$, up to 20 feet, for which $\gamma_{12} = 0$. Thus in the case of α Orionis (Betelgeuse) incoherence was found to occur first for a pair of points 121 inches apart. This corresponds to a circular diffraction pattern of which the first dark ring has a radius of 121 inches. Such a pattern would be formed by a circular aperture subtending an angle of 0·047 seconds.

3.4. Small sources

Suppose that P_1 is at O, the origin of the (x, y)-plane in Fig. 29, and that P_2 is the point (x, y), Q being the point (ξ, η) as before. Then

$$R_2^2 - R_1^2 = (x-\xi)^2 + (y-\eta)^2 - \xi^2 - \eta^2$$

$$= r^2 - 2(x\xi + y\eta),$$

where $r^2 = x^2 + y^2$. Whence

$$R_2 - R_1 = \frac{r^2}{R_1 + R_2} - \frac{2}{R_1 + R_2}(x\xi + y\eta). \tag{3.36}$$

For small values of x and y, such as make $r^2/2d \ll \lambda/2\pi$, it is sufficiently accurate to write (3.36) as

$$R_2 - R_1 = -\frac{x\xi + y\eta}{d} \tag{3.37}$$

and (3.34) then becomes

$$\gamma_{12} = \frac{1}{\sqrt{(I_1 I_2)}} \int\int_L \frac{l(\xi, \eta)}{d^2} e^{-ik(x\xi + y\eta)/d} \, d\xi d\eta$$

$$= \frac{1}{G} \int\int_L l(\xi, \eta) e^{-ik(x\xi + y\eta)/d} \, d\xi d\eta, \tag{3.38}$$

where

$$G = \int\int_L l(\xi, \eta) \, d\xi d\eta. \tag{3.39}$$

In this case γ_{12} is, apart from a constant factor and a change of scale, simply the Fourier transform of $l(\xi, \eta)$.

When L is very small, however, γ_{12} may differ appreciably from zero for positions of P_2 in which $r^2/2d$ is no longer small compared with $\lambda/2\pi$. Then the term $r^2/(R_1 + R_2)$ in (3.36) must be retained, and (3.38) replaced by

$$\gamma_{12} = e^{\frac{1}{2}ikr^2/d} \frac{1}{G} \int\int_L l(\xi, \eta) e^{-ik(x\xi + y\eta)/d} \, d\xi d\eta. \tag{3.40}$$

In the special case where L is a uniformly lit circular disk of radius $a \ll d$, (3.38) may be used provided $a \gg \sqrt{(\lambda d)}$. For then

$$\left(\frac{\lambda}{2\pi}\frac{3 \cdot 83}{\sin \alpha}\right)^2 \frac{1}{2d} \ll \frac{\lambda}{2\pi},$$

where α is the angular radius of the source seen from O, and both the phase coherence factor γ_{12} and the function

$$2J_1\left(\frac{2\pi}{\lambda}r\sin\alpha\right)\bigg/\left(\frac{2\pi}{\lambda}r\sin\alpha\right) \tag{3.41}$$

which represents it when $r^2/2d \ll \lambda/2\pi$ are effectively zero outside this region.

But if $a = O\{\sqrt{(\lambda d)}\}$, γ_{12} is appreciably different from zero for points P_2 whose distance from P_1 is comparable with $\sqrt{(\lambda d/\pi)}$. We must then use (3.40), which gives the approximate equation

$$\gamma_{12} = e^{\frac{1}{2}ikr^2/d}\frac{2J_1(z)}{z} \quad (z = kr\sin\alpha), \tag{3.42}$$

valid in the domain $r \ll d$. The cruder approximation $\gamma_{12} = 2J_1(z)/z$ given by (3.38) would only remain valid in the domain $r \ll \sqrt{(\lambda d/\pi)}$.

When the source is vanishingly small ($\alpha \to 0$), (3.42) becomes

$$\gamma_{12} = e^{\frac{1}{2}ikr^2/d}; \tag{3.43}$$

i.e. the points P_1 and P_2 are coherently illuminated ($|\gamma_{12}| = 1$) and the illumination at P_2 is advanced in phase by $kr^2/2d$ relative to that at P_1. This is obvious a priori, since P_1 and P_2 are now illuminated by a point source whose distance from P_2 exceeds by $r^2/2d$ its distance from P_1.

3.5. Propagation of γ_{12}

Suppose the phase-coherence factor γ_{12} and the intensity distribution $l(P)$ both to be known on a surface S, and suppose that the light from S illuminates a second surface S', either directly or through an optical system. Then the phase-coherence factor γ'_{12} and the intensity distribution $l(P')$ on S' can be calculated in the following way from those on S.

First suppose that S' is directly illuminated by S and the line joining any point P of S to any point P' of S' makes only small angles with the surface normals at its ends. Let $(dS)_1$, $(dS)_2$ be two elements of S, situated at the movable points P_1, P_2 respectively (see Fig. 30) and small compared with the wavelength λ. Let u_{m1} be the complex displacement at P_1 due to the emission element e_m of the primary source, u_{m2} that at P_2.

Then, by Huyghens's principle, the disturbances at P'_1 and P'_2 on S' are respectively

$$u'_{m1} = \frac{ik}{2\pi} \int_S \frac{u_{m1}}{R_{11}} e^{-ikR_{11}} (dS)_1, \qquad u'_{m2} = \frac{ik}{2\pi} \int_S \frac{u_{m2}}{R_{22}} e^{-ikR_{22}} (dS)_2, \qquad (3.44)$$

where $R_{11} = P_1 P'_1$, $R_{22} = P_2 P'_2$. In the first integral, P_1 runs over the whole of the surface S; in the second, P_2.

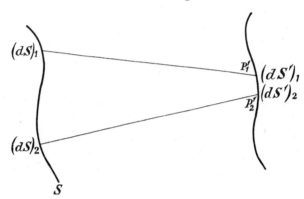

FIG. 30.

The phase coherence factor between P'_1, P'_2 is by definition

$$\gamma'_{12} = \frac{1}{\sqrt{(I'_1 I'_2)}} \sum_m u'_{m1} \bar{u}'_{m2}. \qquad (3.45)$$

Hence, by (3.44),

$$\sqrt{(I'_1 I'_2)}\gamma'_{12} = \frac{k^2}{4\pi^2} \sum_m \int_S \int_S \frac{u_{m1} \bar{u}_{m2}}{R_{11} R_{22}} e^{ik(R_{22} - R_{11})} (dS)_1 (dS)_2$$

$$= \frac{k^2}{4\pi^2} \int_S \int_S \left(\sum_m u_{m1} \bar{u}_{m2}\right) \frac{e^{ik(R_{22} - R_{11})}}{R_{11} R_{22}} (dS)_1 (dS)_2$$

$$= \frac{k^2}{4\pi^2} \int_S \int_S \sqrt{(I_1 I_2)}\gamma_{12} \frac{e^{ik(R_{22} - R_{11})}}{R_{11} R_{22}} (dS)_1 (dS)_2. \qquad (3.46)$$

(3.46) expresses the mutual intensity $\sqrt{(I'_1 I'_2)}\gamma'_{12}$ on the surface S' in terms of the mutual intensity $\sqrt{(I_1 I_2)}\gamma_{12}$ on S. When $P'_2 = P'_1 = P'$, the mutual intensity $\sqrt{(I'_1 I'_2)}\gamma'_{12}$ reduces to the ordinary intensity at P'. Therefore this intensity is obtained on taking $P'_2 = P'_1 = P'$ in (3.46).

    The presence of a diaphragm between S and S' can be allowed for by limiting the integrations over S to those parts which can be seen from P'_1, P'_2 respectively, provided that the effects of diffraction at the edge of the diaphragm are to be disregarded. To take account of this diffraction, it is necessary to make the transition from S to S' in two stages, first from S to the plane of the diaphragm, then from the part of this plane occupied by the diaphragm aperture to S'.

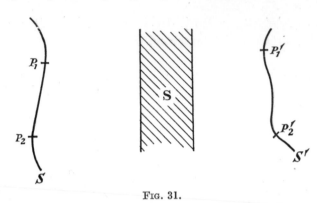

Fig. 31.

Essentially the same method can be used in the more general case where the light from S reaches S' through an optical system $\mathbf{S}$ and the obliquities on S are not restricted to be small. Let $d_\lambda(P, P')\, dS$ denote, for light of wavelength λ, the complex displacement density at P' on S' which would be caused by a complex displacement density l throughout the surface element dS ($\ll \lambda$) situated at P on S. $d_\lambda(P, P')\, dS$ describes the optical properties of the system $\mathbf{S}$ with respect to the surface S.

Then a coherent displacement density $D(P)$ on S causes a complex displacement density

$$D'(P') = \int_S d_\lambda(P, P')D(P)\, dS \tag{3.47}$$

at P'. (3.47) is equally valid for all positions of P' in or behind the exit pupil of $\mathbf{S}$. To discuss the general case, suppose that the intensity and coherence distributions on S are described by the mutual intensity distribution J_{12}.†

Let $D_m(P)$ denote the complex displacement density at P on S due to the emission element e_m of the primary source and $D'_m(P')$ that at P' on S', the light in the second case having reached P' via $\mathbf{S}$. Then by (3.11) the mutual intensity J_{12} between the points P_1, P_2 on S is given by the equation

$$J_{12} = \sum_m D_m(P_1)\overline{D_m(P_2)} \tag{3.48}$$

† $I_1 = J_{11}$ expresses the intensity distribution, $\gamma_{12} = J_{12}/\sqrt{(J_{11} J_{22})}$ the phase-coherence distribution, in terms of the mutual intensity distribution J_{12}.

PLATE IV

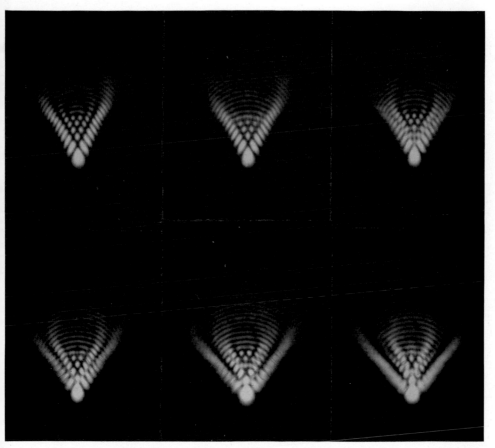

Primary coma $-\phi = 2\lambda(r^3 - \frac{2}{3}r)\cos\chi$ at focal settings corresponding approximately to the values $p = 0$, 10, 20, 30, 40, 50. *After* Kingslake (1948)

and the mutual intensity J'_{12} between P'_1, P'_2 on S' by the equations

$$J'_{12} = \sum_m D'_m(P'_1)\overline{D'_m(P'_2)}$$

$$= \sum_m \int_S d_\lambda(P_1, P'_1)D_m(P_1)\,(dS)_1 \int_S \overline{d_\lambda(P_2, P'_2)}\,\overline{D_m(P_2)}\,(dS)_2,$$

by (3.47),

$$= \int_S \int_S \sum_m D_m(P_1)\overline{D_m(P_2)}d_\lambda(P_1, P'_1)\overline{d_\lambda(P_2, P'_2)}\,(dS)_1(dS)_2$$

$$= \int_S \int_S J_{12}\,d_\lambda(P_1, P'_1)\overline{d_\lambda(P_2, P'_2)}\,(dS)_1(dS)_2, \qquad (3.49)$$

by (3.48). This is the generalization of (3.46). To express it in terms of phase-coherence factors we write it

$$\sqrt{(I'_1 I'_2)}\gamma'_{12} = \int_S \int_S \sqrt{(I_1 I_2)}\gamma_{12}\,d_\lambda(P_1, P'_1)\overline{d_\lambda(P_2, P'_2)}\,(dS)_1(dS)_2, \quad (3.50)$$

where the intensities

$$I_1 = J_{11} = \sum_m |D_m(P_1)|^2, \qquad (3.51)$$

$$I'_1 = J'_{11} = \int_S \int_S J_{12}\,d_\lambda(P_1, P'_1)\overline{d_\lambda(P_2, P'_1)}\,(dS)_1(dS)_2 \qquad (3.52)$$

and similarly for I_2, I'_2.

Equation (3.52) provides a means of evaluating the intensity distribution in the diffraction image, by an optical system $\mathbf{S}$ of known $d_\lambda(P, P')$, of a partially coherent object surface S. In this case S' lies in the image-layer (in the sense of § 1) of S with respect to the system.

The approximate evaluation of $d_\lambda(P, P')$ takes an essentially different form according as P' is not or is near to the image of P in $\mathbf{S}$.

In the first case, it is permissible to ignore the aberrations of $\mathbf{S}$ and to suppose that the rays issuing from P and passing through $\mathbf{S}$ emerge as a stigmatic pencil whose vertex $P*$ is the ideal image of P. Then if P' lies inside this pencil, we may take $d_\lambda(P, P')$ to be a constant multiple of

$$\frac{ie^{-ik[PP']}}{P'P*}\sqrt{(\cos\theta)},$$

where $[PP']$ denotes the optical distance along the ray from P through $\mathbf{S}$ to P' and θ the angle which this ray makes at P with the forward normal to the surface element dS. If P' is outside the pencil, $d_\lambda(P, P')$

is taken as zero. (3.49) then gives, for points P_1', P_2' in the illuminated part of S',

$$J_{12}' = \text{const.} \times \int (dS)_1 \int (dS)_2\, J_{12}\frac{e^{i([P_2 P_2'] - [P_1 P_1'])}}{R_1' R_2'}\sqrt{(\cos\theta_1 \cos\theta_2)}, \quad (3.53)$$

where $\qquad R_1' = P_1' P_1^*, \qquad R_2' = P_2' P_2^*.$

In the first integral, $(dS)_1$ runs over those parts of S which can send rays to P_1'; in the second, $(dS)_2$ runs over those parts of S which can send rays to P_2'. From (3.53) and the definition of γ_{12} it follows that

$$\gamma_{12}' = \frac{1}{\sqrt{(I_1' I_2')}} \int (dS)_1 \int (dS)_2 \sqrt{(I_1 I_2)}\gamma_{12}\frac{e^{ik(R_{22} - R_{11})}}{R_1' R_2'}\sqrt{(\cos\theta_1 \cos\theta_2)}, \quad (3.54)$$

where $\qquad R_{11} = [P_1 P_1'], \qquad R_{22} = [P_2 P_2'].$ $\qquad (3.55)$

(3.54) reduces to (3.46) in the special case where **S** is a 'null' system (giving $P_1^* = P_1$, $P_2^* = P_2$) and all the obliquities are small.

In the second case, when P' is near to the image of P in S, a wave-front starting from P and passing through **S** emerges as a converging, near-spherical wave-front W with its approximate centre of curvature near P'. In this case, $d_\lambda(P, P')$ may be evaluated by applying Huyghens's principle to the wave-front W in the same way as in § 2, but taking account of the variation in amplitude resulting from the obliquity factor $\sqrt{(\cos\theta)}$. When all the obliquities are small, $d_\lambda(P, P')$ agrees with the complex displacement at the point P' in the diffraction image by **S** of a unit source of zero phase situated at P.

3.6. *Coherence in the image of a light source*

Suppose the lens system **S** images the self-luminous surface S on to the receiving surface S' in the image-layer of **S**, all the obliquities being small.

Let e_m be an emission element, of flux l_m, situated at P on S and let P' be the principal point of the image-patch of P on S'. The light from e_m produces at the points P_1', P_2' near P' the complex displacements u_{m1}', u_{m2}', where

$$u_{m1}' \bar{u}_{m2}' = l_m d_\lambda(P, P_1')\overline{d_\lambda(P, P_2')}. \quad (3.56)$$

The mutual intensity J_{12}' of the points P_1', P_2' is then given by the equation

$$J_{12}' = \sum_m u_{m1}' \bar{u}_{m2}'$$

$$= \sum_m l_m d_\lambda(P, P_1')\overline{d_\lambda(P, P_2')}. \quad (3.57)$$

If there is a finite flux density $l(P)$ at every point P of the surface S, the

sum of the l_m over sources lying in a surface element dS situated at P
is $l(P) dS$ and (3.57) becomes

$$J'_{12} = \int\limits_S l(P) d_\lambda(P, P'_1)\overline{d_\lambda(P, P'_2)} \, dS. \qquad (3.58)$$

From (3.58) and from the remark at the end of § 3.5 it is clear that
$\gamma_{12} = J'_{12}/\sqrt{(I'_1 I'_2)}$ can only differ appreciably from zero when the distance $P'_1 P'_2$ is comparable with the size of the diffraction images (including aberrations) by **S** of point sources on S.

Therefore, in investigating phase coherence on S', it is sufficient to
consider an arbitrary fixed point Q on S, together with the principal
point Q' of its geometrical image patch on S', and to obtain an approximate evaluation of J'_{12} for any two points P'_1, P'_2 near Q'.

In (3.58), the only appreciable contributions to the integral on the
right come from that part of the domain of integration which is near Q.
For if P is not near Q, the distances $P'P'_1$ and $P'P'_2$ on S' will be large
compared with the size of the diffraction images of a point source and
consequently $d_\lambda(P, P'_1)\overline{d_\lambda(P, P'_2)}$ will be negligibly small. Let $\delta(Q)$ denote
a neighbourhood of Q which images into a neighbourhood $\delta'(Q')$ large
compared with the diffraction spread at Q', but which is small enough
to allow the use of the approximate equation

$$l(P) = l(Q) \qquad (3.59)$$

for all P in $\delta(Q)$. The statement that $l(Q)$ is slowly varying near Q is to
be interpreted as meaning that such a neighbourhood exists. Then
(3.58) can be replaced by the approximate equation

$$J'_{12} = l(Q) \int\limits_{\delta(Q)} d_\lambda(P, P'_1)\overline{d_\lambda(P, P'_2)} \, dS. \qquad (3.60)$$

The aberrations of **S**, which evidently play a part in determining the
values of $d_\lambda(P, P'_1)$ and $d_\lambda(P, P'_2)$, are most conveniently described in
terms of an ikonal function $e(u, v; P)$ similar to that in § 3.1;† we define
$e(u, v; P)$ as the net optical distance along the (u, v)-ray from P to a
sphere $M_{P'}$, of fixed radius, centred at the principal point P' of the
P-image patch on S'. For the value of the fixed radius we choose the
distance from the axial point of the exit pupil to the axial point of S'.

$e(u, v; P)$ is a slowly varying function of P in a practical case, so that
it is permissible to write

$$e(u, v; P) = e(u, v; Q) \qquad (3.61$$

for all P in $\delta(Q)$.

† A new notation is required because the (u, v)-coordinates are no longer oriented
with special reference to the azimuth of the point P.

We obtain an explicit expression for $d_\lambda(P, P'_1)$ by supposing a unit source of zero phase to be situated at P and applying Huyghens's principle to the surface $M_{P'}$, on which the displacement due to the unit source is, apart from a constant factor, $\exp\{-ik\,e(u, v; P)\}$ at the point P^* where it is met by the (u, v)-ray from P.

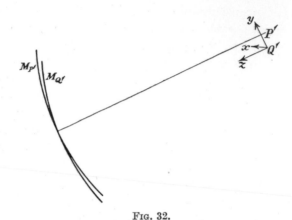

FIG. 32.

The application gives

$$d_\lambda(P, P'_1) = C'\frac{k\sin\alpha}{\pi}\iint_A \exp\{-ik[e(u, v; Q)+P^*P'_1]\}\,du\,dv, \quad (3.62)$$

where the double integral is over the (u, v)-region A corresponding to the clear aperture of S (the circle $u^2+v^2 \leqslant 1$ if S is free from vignetting) and $e(u, v; P)$ has been replaced by $e(u, v; Q)$ in accordance with (3.61); C' is a (complex) constant independent of P, P'_1, and Q.

In the space near Q' we introduce Cartesian coordinates (x, y, z) with origin at Q' and positive z-direction along the normal at Q' to the surface S' pointing towards S (see Fig. 32). Let P', P'_1, P'_2 have the respective coordinates (x, y, z), (x_1, y_1, z_1), (x_2, y_2, z_2) in this system. Thus P'_1 has a displacement relative to P' of components (x_1-x, y_1-y, z_1-z) and it follows by a calculation similar to that at the beginning of § 2.1 that

$$P^*P'_1 = R-[(x_1-x)u+(y_1-y)v]\sin\alpha-\tfrac{1}{2}(z_1-z)(u_1^2+v_1^2)\sin^2\alpha,$$

to a sufficient approximation, where $\sin\alpha \ll 1$ denotes the numerical aperture of the pencils emerging from S and R the radius of the sphere $M_{P'}$. If, as is here supposed, S' has radii of curvature everywhere at least comparable with R in size, the last term on the right can be neglected, for the positions of P', P'_1 under consideration, and (3.62) becomes

$$d_\lambda(P, P'_1) = C'\frac{k\sin\alpha}{\pi}e^{-ikR}\iint\limits_A \exp\{-ik\,e(u_1, v_1; Q)\}\times$$

$$\times e^{ik\sin\alpha[(x_1-x)u_1+(y_1-y)v_1]}\,du_1\,dv_1. \quad (3.63)$$

Substituting in (3.60) from this and the corresponding equation for $d_\lambda(P, P'_2)$, we obtain

$$J'_{12} = |C'|^2\frac{k^2\sin^2\alpha}{\pi^2}l(Q)\iint\limits_A du_1\,dv_1\iint\limits_A du_2\,dv_2\int\limits_{\delta(Q)}dS\times$$

$$\times e^{ik\sin\alpha[(x_1-x)u_1+(y_1-y)v_1]}e^{-ik\sin\alpha[(x_2-x)u_2+(y_2-y)v_2]}\times$$

$$\times\exp\{ik[e(u_2, v_2; Q)-e(u_1, v_1; Q)]\}$$

$$= |C'|^2k^2\sin^2\alpha\,l(Q)\iint\limits_A \tau_Q(u_2, v_2)e^{-ik\sin\alpha[u_2(x_2-x_1)+v_2(y_2-y_1)]}\,du_2\,dv_2\times$$

$$\times\iint\limits_{\delta(Q)}dS\iint\limits_A du_1\,dv_1\,\bar\tau_Q(u_1, v_1)e^{ik\sin\alpha[(x-x_1)(u_2-u_1)+(y-y_1)(v_2-v_1)]}, \quad (3.64)$$

where $\tau_Q(u, v)$ is written for $\exp\{ik\,e(u, v; Q)\}$.

The inner integrations over $\delta(Q)$ and A can be replaced by

$$m^2\iint\limits_\Gamma dx\,dy\iint\limits_A du_1\,dv_1\,\bar\tau_Q(u_1, v_1)e^{ik\sin\alpha[(x-x_1)(u_2-u_1)+(y-y_1)(u_2-u_1)]}, \quad (3.65)$$

where Γ is the region of S' traced out by P' when P runs over $\delta(Q)$ and is large compared with the size of the diffraction image of a point source at Q, while m is the linear magnification from S to S'. Also the clear aperture A includes a circle round the point (u_2, v_2) of radius $\gg\lambda/(2\pi\sin\alpha)$ provided that (u_2, v_2) is not very close to the edge of A. Thus we obtain, with the above proviso, the approximate evaluation

$$m^2\int\limits_{-\infty}^{\infty}\!\!\int dx\,dy\,e^{ik\sin\alpha[(x-x_1)u_2+(y-y_1)v_2]}\times$$

$$\times\int\limits_{-\infty}^{\infty}\!\!\int \bar\tau_Q(u_1, v_1)e^{-ik\sin\alpha[(x-x_1)u_1+(y-y_1)v_1]}\,du_1\,dv_1$$

$$= m^2\int\limits_{-\infty}^{\infty}\!\!\int dx'\,dy'\,e^{ik\sin\alpha(x'u_2+y'v_2)}\int\limits_{-\infty}^{\infty}\!\!\int \bar\tau_Q(u_1, v_1)e^{-ik\sin\alpha(x'u_1+y'v_1)}\,du_1\,dv_1,$$

on introducing the new variables $x' = x-x_1$, $y' = y-y_1$,

$$= \frac{4\pi^2m^2}{k^2\sin^2\alpha}\bar\tau_Q(u_2, v_2), \quad (3.66)$$

by the two-dimensional form of Fourier's inversion theorem.† Substitution from (3.66) into (3.64) now gives the approximate evaluation

$$J'_{12} = |C''|^2 l(Q) \iint_A |\tau_Q(u_2, v_2)|^2 e^{-ik \sin \alpha[u_2(x_2-x_1)+v_2(y_2-y_1)]} \, du_2 \, dv_2, \quad (3.67)$$

where $C'' = 2mC'$.

If the lens system **S** introduces 'smooth' changes of amplitude, as well as of phase, in the wave-fronts passing through it, the argument is unaffected; we have merely to redefine $\tau_Q(u, v)$ as

$$\sqrt{\{j(u, v; Q)\}} \exp\{ik\, e(u, v; Q)\},$$

where $j(u, v; Q)$ is the intensity transmission factor corresponding to the object point Q. Therefore (3.67) holds in this more general case also. From it we obtain the desired evaluation

$$\gamma_{12} = \frac{J'_{12}}{\sqrt{(J'_{11} J'_{22})}} = \frac{1}{I} \iint_A |\tau_Q(u, v)|^2 e^{-ik \sin \alpha[u(x_2-x_1)+v(y_2-y_1)]} \, du\, dv, \quad (3.68)$$

where

$$I = \iint_A |\tau_Q(u, v)|^2 \, du\, dv. \quad (3.69)$$

Since $\tau_Q(u, v)$ enters here only through its squared modulus $j(u, v; Q)$, we have the interesting result that γ_{12} is unaffected by the aberrations of **S**; in particular a small amount of defocusing‡ leaves γ_{12} unaltered.

An even more striking result follows from the observation that the value of γ_{12} given by (3.68) is identical with that which would result if the clear aperture of **S** were self-luminous, with flux-density distribution $|\tau_Q(u, v)|^2$.

Such a flux-density distribution in the clear aperture is obtained on placing a source of uniform brightness close to **S** on the side opposite to S'. We infer that *the coherence when S' is illuminated through **S** is the same whether a uniformly bright source is imaged on to S' or placed just behind **S***. This theorem, under slightly less general hypotheses, was first given by Zernike (1938). Since (3.68) is here established for sources of non-uniform brightness, provided $l(Q)$ varies only slowly§ as Q ranges over S, we can deduce the physically more appropriate formulation: *the coherence when a source of non-uniform, slowly varying brightness is imaged on to S' is the same as that given by a uniformly bright source just behind **S***.

---

† An accurate treatment of this and the next step involves analytical refinements which seem out of place in the present context.

‡ i.e. a focus shift which is small compared with the effective focal length of **S**.

§ In the sense explained above.

As will be seen in the next section, this result has important consequences in microscopy. In the arrangement known as critical illumination, and represented in Fig. 33, the source is imaged on to the partly
transparent object from behind by a condenser. The idea behind this
method of transillumination was that different parts of the object should
be illuminated by different parts of the source, and it was presumed that
the use of a highly corrected condenser must be of advantage for the
resolving power. Zernike's theorem proves on the contrary that this
has no influence, for by (3.68) the presence of aberrations (including
defocusing) in the condenser does not alter the coherence in the object
surface and by (3.52) the resolution in the image surface depends only
on this coherence and on the optical properties of the micro-objective.
If the harmful effect of stray light is disregarded, the condenser may
even be replaced by a diffusion disk subtending the same angle at the
object surface; in most practical cases, however, the effect of stray light
on resolution is appreciable.

3.7. *Transillumination in the microscope*

In the ordinary use of the microscope, the object or slide is not self-
luminous but consists of a thin slice of more or less transparent substance
mounted in Canada balsam between thin glass plates and lit from behind
or 'transilluminated'. Its optical properties when set up for observation
in the object plane S of the micro-objective M (see Fig. 33) can be
represented, for light of wavelength λ, by a complex function

$$E(x,y) = |E(x,y)| \exp\left\{\frac{2\pi i}{\lambda} \phi(x,y)\right\} \qquad (3.70)$$

of the coordinates (x,y) in this plane. $|E(x,y)|$ then measures the
amplitude factor and $\phi(x,y)$ the phase retardation in wavelengths which
the specimen imprints on the wave-fronts passing through it at the
point (x,y).

The image of the point $P = (x,y)$ in the object plane S of the micro-
objective M is the point $P' = (x',y')$ in its image surface S'. (We leave
the aberrations of M out of account for the moment.) O and O' are the
axial points of S, S' respectively.

The observer sees through the eyepiece (not shown in Fig. 33) a well-
defined circular region $x'^2 + y'^2 \leqslant r'^2$ of the image surface; the corresponding region $x^2 + y^2 \leqslant r^2$ of the object plane is the *field* of the
microscope.

Critical illumination. In this commonly used form of transillumination
the edge of the field-stop aperture L is imaged on to the object plane S

by a condenser C (see Fig. 33) and a uniformly bright source Σ is placed close behind L. The size of L is adjusted so that its image on S just covers the field.

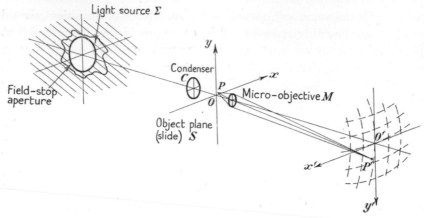

FIG. 33. Microscope with critical illumination.

If Σ is taken as actually filling the aperture L and obliquity factors are neglected, the phase-coherence factor between two neighbouring points P_1, P_2 of the field is, by (3.32) and Zernike's theorem,

$$\gamma_{12} = \frac{2J_1(z)}{z},\qquad (3.71)$$

where $z = (2\pi/\lambda)P_1 P_2 \sin\beta$ and $\sin\beta$ is the numerical aperture at which the condenser is working. This numerical aperture can be adjusted by means of an iris diaphragm (the *condenser stop*) built into the condenser mounting.

To take account of the fact that Σ is behind and not in the aperture L, we should first calculate γ_{12} in the plane of the aperture L, directly illuminated by Σ, and then apply § 3.5 to deduce the value of γ_{12} in S. Because the angle subtended by the condenser aperture at a point of L is small, the coherence patches on L are small compared with the Airy disks corresponding to this angle, and it is easy to deduce from this that the effect of the partial coherence in L on the values of γ_{12} in S is small.

Köhler illumination. An arrangement which is photometrically an improvement on critical illumination is shown in Fig. 34. A condensing lens C' placed close behind the field-stop aperture L images the source Σ into the 'back focal plane' of the condenser C, so that the rays from each emission element e_m of Σ emerge from C as a parallel beam. C images the edge of L on to the object plane as before, but the condenser diaphragm is now transferred to the Σ'-plane. Through every point P of the field passes a cone of rays, each ray of the cone originating in a different point of Σ. When the condenser diaphragm is fully opened, the cone of rays which can pass, via C, through a point P anywhere in the field should fill the aperture of the micro-objective M. The source Σ should be large enough for its image Σ' by C' to fill the fully opened condenser diaphragm.

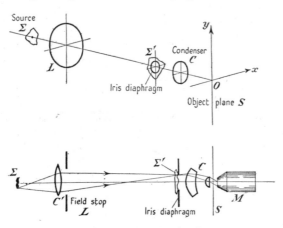

FIG. 34. Köhler illumination.

An important practical advantage of Köhler's arrangement is that irregularities in the brightness distribution on Σ do not cause irregularities in the intensity of the field illumination.

It remains to consider the coherence properties in the object plane. The wave-fronts after passing through L and C emerge approximately plane, but loaded with heavy aberrations.†

The light from an emission element e_m situated at (ξ, η) in the primary source Σ reaches two neighbouring points $P_1 = (x_1, y_1)$, $P_2 = (x_2, y_2)$ in the field surface S with a phase difference

$$\delta_{12} = k[p_m(x_2 - x_1) + q_m(y_2 - y_1)],$$

where (p_m, q_m) are the first two direction cosines of the small region of the near-flat wave-front which crosses the (x, y)-plane near P_1, P_2. The heavy aberrations on the wave-front only cause small changes in the values of p_m and q_m.

From (3.11) and (3.13), the phase-coherence factor γ_{12} between neighbouring points P_1, P_2 is simply the weighted mean, over the emission

† Wave-front curvature due to a small error in the position of C may be included among these aberrations.

elements e_m, of $e^{i\delta_{12}}$, the weighting being according to the respective intensity contributions of the e_m near P_1 and P_2.

Only those elements e_m whose images by C' lie in the aperture of the iris diaphragm (Fig. 34) send light to P_1 and P_2, and they may be specified by the inequality

$$p_m^2 + q_m^2 \leqslant \sin^2\beta, \tag{3.72}$$

where β is (to a sufficient approximation) the angular semi-aperture of the pencils of rays passing, via the condenser, through P_1 and P_2.

When the effective part of the source Σ is uniformly bright, so that the iris diaphragm is filled by a uniformly bright area of the image Σ', we can replace sums by integrals and, neglecting obliquity factors, obtain the approximate equation

$$\gamma_{12} = \iint\limits_{p^2+q^2 \leqslant \sin^2\beta} \exp\{ik[p(x_2-x_1)+q(y_2-y_1)]\}\, dp\, dq$$

$$= \frac{2J_1(z)}{z}, \tag{3.73}$$

where
$$z = \frac{2\pi}{\lambda} P_1 P_2 \sin\beta.$$

Thus the coherence is, within the limits of accuracy of our approximations, the same with Köhler illumination as with critical illumination. In view of this result it seems unfortunate that critical and Köhler illumination are often designated as 'incoherent' and 'coherent' respectively.

3.71. *Condenser aperture and resolving power in the microscope.* From (3.71) and (3.73) we can find an expression for the light intensity in the image by the micro-objective M of two pinholes a small distance apart in the object plane under critical or Köhler illumination.

Let $\sin\alpha$ be the numerical aperture of M and $\sin\beta = s \sin\alpha$ that of the condenser. If the aberrations of M are negligible, we can introduce a system of coordinate numbers x', y' to identify the points P' in the image surface S' of M by assigning to the geometrical image of the point (x, y) in the object plane S the coordinate numbers $x' = x$, $y' = y$.

A unit source at $P_1 = (x_1, y_1)$ or at $P_2 = (x_2, y_2)$ in the plane S gives at an arbitrary point P' of coordinate numbers $x' = x$, $y' = y$ in S' an intensity proportional to

$$\left(\frac{2J_1(z_1)}{z_1}\right)^2 \quad \text{or} \quad \left(\frac{2J_1(z_2)}{z_2}\right)^2 \tag{3.74}$$

respectively, where

$$z_1 = \frac{2\pi}{\lambda} \sin \alpha \sqrt{\{(x-x_1)^2+(y-y_1)^2\}}, \qquad z_2 = \frac{2\pi}{\lambda} \sin \alpha \sqrt{\{(x-x_2)^2+(y-y_2)^2\}}$$

$$(3.75)$$

and the factor of proportionality is the same in both cases.

By (3.71) and (3.73), the phase-coherence factor between P_1 and P_2 in the object plane is

$$\gamma_{12} = \frac{2J_1(sz_{12})}{sz_{12}}, \qquad (3.76)$$

where

$$sz_{12} = \frac{2\pi}{\lambda} \sin \beta \; P_1 P_2, \qquad z_{12} = \frac{2\pi}{\lambda} \sin \alpha \; P_1 P_2,$$

and if P_1, P_2 are neighbouring points the illumination intensity may be taken to be the same for both.

It then follows from (3.14) that at the points P' of coordinate numbers $x' = x$, $y' = y$ in S' the intensities are proportional to the quantity

$$I(z_1, z_2) = \left(\frac{2J_1(z_1)}{z_1}\right)^2 + \left(\frac{2J_1(z_2)}{z_2}\right)^2 + 2\frac{2J_1(sz_{12})}{sz_{12}} \frac{2J_1(z_1)}{z_1} \frac{2J_1(z_2)}{z_2}. \quad (3.77)$$

Some interesting conclusions follow from (3.77). If sz_{12} is a zero of J_1, the product term vanishes and P_1, P_2 are incoherently illuminated. In particular, this will be so if $s = 1$ and $P_1 P_2$ is equal to the resolution limit conventionally defined as the radius of the first dark ring in the Airy pattern of M. At this separation of $P_1 P_2$

$$I(z_1, z_2) = \left(\frac{2J_1(z_1)}{z_1}\right)^2 + \left(\frac{2J_1(z_2)}{z_2}\right)^2 \qquad (3.78)$$

and the intensity distribution in S' is the same as if P_1, P_2 were self-luminous.

When the aperture of the condenser is very small ($s \to 0$), (3.77) gives

$$I(z_1, z_2) = \left(\frac{2J_1(z_1)}{z_1} + \frac{2J_1(z_2)}{z_2}\right)^2; \qquad (3.79)$$

in this case the points are coherently and cophasally illuminated.

In the case where each of the incoherently illuminated points P_1, P_2 has its image centred on the first Airy dark ring in the image of the other point, (3.78) gives an intensity 0·736 at the point of S' midway between P_1', P_2', compared with 1·000 at P_1' or P_2'. The corresponding separation

$$P_1 P_2 = \frac{3 \cdot 83\lambda}{2\pi \sin \alpha} = \frac{0 \cdot 61\lambda}{\sin \alpha}$$

is the well-known Rayleigh limit of resolution for an objective of numerical aperture $\sin \alpha$ working in light of wavelength λ. It is easy to calculate, for different values of s, the least separation ρ_{12} of P_1, P_2 which gives the same intensity drop of 26·4 per cent. at the mid-point. The result is shown in Fig. 35, from which it will be seen that suitably arranged critical or Köhler illumination can give a slightly better resolution of

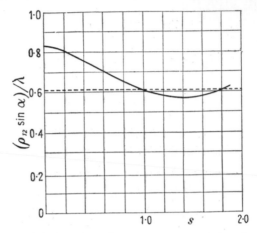

FIG. 35. Effect of condenser aperture on the resolution of two luminous pinholes of equal brightness. *After* Hopkins and Barham (1950).

two equal pinholes than that obtained by incoherent illumination, while axial illumination gives, in this case, only about three-quarters of the resolution obtainable with two equal self-luminous point sources.

3.72. *Images of transilluminated objects.* In microscopy we usually have to deal with the more general case of a transilluminated extended object imaged by an objective **S** of small aberrations (see Fig. 36). By (3.52), the intensity distribution in the image surface S' depends only on the values of the mutual intensities on the emitting side of the object plane S and on the distribution function $d_\lambda(P_1, P_2')$ of the micro-objective **S**.

We set up in S a system of Cartesian coordinates (X, Y) with origin at the axial point O of S, and in the exit pupil of S a set of scale-normalized coordinates (u, v), so that the positive u- and X-directions are parallel and likewise the positive v- and Y-directions. The ray issuing from the point $Q = (X_0, Y_0)$ in S and passing through the point (u, v) of the exit pupil will be called the (u, v)-ray through Q. Those (u, v)-rays, and only those, for which $u^2 + v^2 < 1$ pass through **S**, and their intersections with

PLATE V

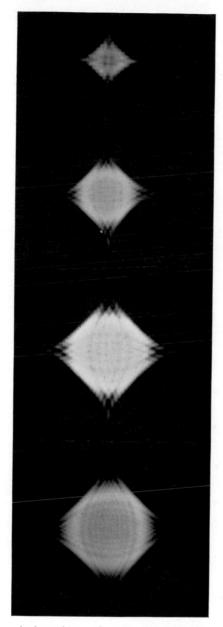

Astigmatism of amounts $\pm 1\cdot4\lambda$, $\pm 2\cdot7\lambda$, $\pm 3\cdot5\lambda$, $\pm 6\cdot5\lambda$, with the receiving surface at mean focus. *After* Zernike and Nienhuis

the receiving surface S' form the geometrical image-patch of Q on S'. The intersection Q' of the principal ray ($u = v = 0$) through Q is called the principal point of the Q-image patch.

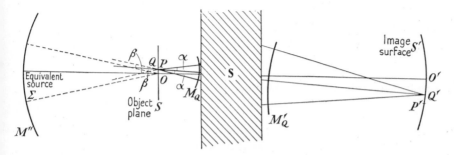

FIG. 36. Imaging of transilluminated object.

We suppose the working field of **S** to be of small angular radius (its radius is less than $3°$ in most practical cases). Then for any point Q in the working field, the (u, v)-rays with $u^2 + v^2 < 1$ form, to a sufficient approximation, a right circular cone of semi-angle α, where $\sin \alpha$† is the N.A. (numerical aperture) of the objective **S**. The principal ray through Q is the axis of this cone and the (u, v)-ray through Q makes with the principal ray an angle θ, where, to a sufficient approximation,

$$\sin \theta = r \sin \alpha \quad (r^2 = u^2 + v^2). \qquad (3.80)$$

Spherical wave-fronts issuing from Q and passing through **S** are converted into near-spherical wave-fronts centred approximately on Q'. We construct the two reference spheres M_Q, M'_Q, centred on Q, Q' and respectively passing through the axial points of the entry and exit pupils of **S**.

We denote by $\delta(Q)$ a small circular patch of the object surface, lying in the working field and centred on Q.‡ The radius of $\delta(Q)$ is small compared with that of the working field but large compared with the Airy disk diameter $1\cdot22\lambda/\sin\alpha$ corresponding to the numerical aperture of **S**. In a microscope with a working-field diameter of 500 Airy disks we might take the diameter of $\delta(Q)$ as about 30 Airy disk diameters. If Q is too close to the edge of the working field, it does not possess a neighbourhood $\delta(Q)$ with the above properties.

---

† Or $N \sin \alpha$ in the case of an immersion objective. In this case the object space may be supposed to have the refractive index N.

‡ A small square, with sides parallel to the axes of coordinates, would serve equally well.

The objective **S** is assumed to have the properties of a good micro-objective. Its aberration function

$$\phi(u, v; P) = e(u, v; P) - e(0, 0; P)$$

(see equation (3.1)) is supposed $\leqslant \lambda$ (say) all over the working field. We further suppose that, for a proper choice of the receiving surface S' in the image-layer of S (see § 3.1)

$$e(u, v; P) - e(u, v; Q) \ll \lambda/2\pi \tag{3.81}$$

for all P in $\delta(Q)$. Thus we may use throughout $\delta(Q)$ the approximation

$$\exp\{ik\,e(u, v; P)\} = \exp\{ik\,e(u, v; Q)\}. \tag{3.82}$$

It will appear later from the analysis,† and is in any case a familiar fact of experience, that when critical or Köhler illumination is used the parts of S outside $\delta(Q)$ do not contribute appreciably to the intensity distribution in the immediate vicinity of Q' in the image surface S'. It is therefore convenient, in a discussion of this distribution, to make use of the coordinates

$$x = X - X_0, \qquad y = Y - Y_0, \tag{3.83}$$

obtained on moving the (X, Y)-origin to the point Q.

The principal ray through any point $P = (x, y)$ in the field area, after passing through **S**, intersects the receiving surface S' in a point P' to which we assign the coordinate numbers $x' = x$, $y' = y$.

The structure of the object can be represented by a complex transmission function $E(X, Y)$ in the region $X^2 + Y^2 \leqslant a^2$ which represents the working field; outside this circle we define $E(X, Y)$ as zero. In terms of x, y the transmission function may be written as

$$E_Q(x, y) = \begin{cases} E(x + X_0, y + Y_0) & (x + X_0)^2 + (y + Y_0)^2 \leqslant a^2 \\ 0 & \text{elsewhere.} \end{cases} \tag{3.84}$$

The mutual intensity between the two points

$$P_1 = (x_1, y_1) \quad \text{and} \quad P_2 = (x_2, y_2)$$

on the emitting side of S is then

$$E_Q(x_1, y_1)\overline{E_Q(x_2, y_2)}J_{12}, \tag{3.85}$$

where J_{12} is the mutual intensity between P_1 and P_2 on the receiving side. In a practical case, the intensity J_{11} of the illumination is usually arranged to be constant over the working field. Variation in this intensity can in any case be covered analytically by keeping J_{11} constant and supplementing $E(X, Y)$ with an appropriate real multiplying factor CI_{11}.

† See (3.92) and (3.94).

Therefore it is permissible in the present discussion to assume $J_{11} = 1$ everywhere. The illumination is then sufficiently described by the phase-coherence factor $\Gamma_{12} = J_{12}/\sqrt{(J_{11} J_{22})}$.

With coherent or Köhler illumination the value of Γ_{12} for any two points P_1, P_2 of the working field is given by the approximate equation

$$\Gamma_{12} = \frac{2J_1(sz)}{sz}, \tag{3.86}$$

where $sz = (2\pi/\lambda)P_1 P_2 \sin\beta$ and λ is the wavelength in the object space of refractive index N.

A uniformly bright source, filling a region Σ of a spherical surface M'' of very large radius centred at O, would provide uniform illumination with the same Γ_{12} if the region Σ is the inside of a circle centred on the optic axis and subtending an angular radius β at O. We call it an *equivalent primary source* for the given illumination; in the immersion case $(N > 1)$ the whole of the space between S and this fictitious source is supposed to be filled with material of refractive index N.

The (u, v)-rays through O, produced backwards, define a set of coordinate numbers (u, v) on M''; when $\sin\beta > \sin\alpha$ the coordinate numbers of a point corresponding to a ray which would meet the plane of the exit pupil of $\mathbf{S}$ in a point (u, v) with $u^2 + v^2 > 1$ (and therefore cannot actually pass through S) are still defined as (u, v). Σ is thus the region $u^2 + v^2 \leqslant s^2$ on M''; the radius of the sphere M'' is supposed large compared with the linear diameter of the working field of $\mathbf{S}$.

A surface element $d\sigma$ at the point of coordinate numbers (u, v) on M'' emits a flux $\gamma(u, v) d\sigma$, where

$$\gamma(u, v) = \begin{cases} 1 & (u^2 + v^2 \leqslant s^2) \\ 0 & (u^2 + v^2 > s^2) \end{cases} \tag{3.87}$$

is the normalized flux density. The wave-fronts issuing from $d\sigma$ are sensibly plane when they pass through the small field area on S. The complex displacement which they create at a point (u_1, v_1) on M_Q can be regarded as due to a Fraunhofer diffraction by the field area. It is therefore approximately proportional to $\epsilon_Q(u_1 - u, v_1 - v)\sqrt{\{\gamma(u, v) d\sigma\}}$, where the function

$$\epsilon_Q(u, v) = \frac{k \sin\alpha}{2\pi} \int\!\!\!\int_{-\infty}^{\infty} E_Q(x, y)e^{-ik \sin\alpha(ux + vy)}\, dx\, dy, \tag{3.88}$$

defined for all u, v, represents sufficiently well in the region $u^2 + v^2 \leqslant 1$ that part of the diffraction spectrum of $E_Q(x, y)$ under axial illumination which could pass through the objective.

From this we can calculate, approximately, the complex displacement at the point (u_1, v_1) on M'_Q; it is proportional to

$$\exp\{-ik\,e(u_1, v_1; Q)\}\epsilon_Q(u_1-u, v_1-v)\sqrt{\{\gamma(u, v)\,d\sigma\}} \qquad (3.89)$$

since the optical distance along the (u_1, v_1)-ray between M_Q and M'_Q differs from $e(u_1, v_1; Q)$ only by a constant.

The displacement distribution (3.89) on M'_Q produces at the point P' of coordinate numbers $x' = x$, $y' = y$ on S' a complex displacement proportional to

$$\sqrt{\{\gamma(u, v)\,d\sigma\}} \iint\limits_{u_1^2+v_1^2<1} \exp\{-ik\,e(u_1, v_1; Q)\}\epsilon_Q(u_1-u, v_1-v) \times$$
$$\times e^{ik\sin\alpha(u_1 x + v_1 y)}\,du_1\,dv_1 \qquad (3.90)$$
$$= \sqrt{\{\gamma(u, v)\,d\sigma\}}\phi_Q(u, v; x, y),$$

where $\phi_Q(u, v; x, y)$ denotes the value of the surface integral. The corresponding intensity is proportional to

$$\gamma(u, v)|\phi_Q(u, v; x, y)|^2\,d\sigma, \qquad (3.91)$$

and here $d\sigma$ is approximately proportional to $du\,dv$ as (u, v) runs over Σ. Summing over all the elements of the equivalent source Σ and remembering that $\gamma(u, v) = 0$ outside the circle $u^2+v^2 \leqslant s^2$, we obtain for the total intensity at P' near Q' the equation

$$I'(x, y) = \int\limits_{-\infty}^{\infty}\!\!\int \gamma(u, v)|\phi_Q(u, v; x, y)|^2\,du\,dv, \qquad (3.92)$$

where

$$\phi_Q(u, v; x, y) = \iint\limits_{u_1^2+v_1^2<1} \exp\{-ik\,e(u_1, v_1; Q)\}\epsilon_Q(u_1-u, v_1-v) \times$$
$$\times e^{ik\sin\alpha(u_1 x + v_1 y)}\,du_1\,dv_1. \qquad (3.93)$$

Since $k\sin\alpha \gg 1$, we can apply Fourier's integral inversion formula to the right-hand side of (3.93), treating it as though the domain of integration were infinite, and obtain, with the use of (3.88), the approximate equation

$$\phi_Q(u, v; x, y) = \frac{k\sin\alpha}{2\pi} \iint\limits_{\delta(Q)} E_Q(x_1, y_1)F(x-x_1, y-y_1) \times$$
$$\times e^{ik\sin\alpha(ux_1 + vy_1)}\,dx_1\,dy_1, \qquad (3.94)$$

where the complex function

$$F(x, y) = \frac{k\sin\alpha}{2\pi} \iint\limits_{u_1^2+v_1^2<1} \exp\{-ik\,e(u_1, v_1; Q)\}e^{ik\sin\alpha(xu_1 + yv_1)}\,du_1\,dv_1 \qquad (3.95)$$

is, except for a constant factor, simply $d_\lambda(Q, P')$.

The writing of $\iint_{\delta(Q)}$ instead of $\iint_{-\infty}^{\infty}$ in (3.94) is justified as an approximation because the circle $\delta(Q)$ is large compared with an Airy disk, and the
writing of $d_\lambda(P_1, P')$ in the form $F(x-x_1, y-y_1)$ in (3.94) is possible
because $e(u, v; P)$ is effectively independent of P in the circle $\delta(Q)$, which
is small compared with the working field.

To express these results in terms of the coordinates X, Y in S and the
corresponding system of coordinate numbers X, Y in S', we first note
that $\epsilon_Q(u, v)$ is related to the spectral function

$$\epsilon(u, v) = \frac{k \sin \alpha}{2\pi} \iint E(X, Y) e^{-ik \sin \alpha(uX + vY)} \, dX dY \qquad (3.96)$$

by the equation

$$\epsilon_Q(u, v) = \epsilon(u, v) e^{ik \sin \alpha(uX_0 + vY_0)}, \qquad (3.97)$$

which follows at once from (3.88) on changing variables under the integral
sign.

(3.92), (3.93), and (3.94) then give, after easy calculation,

$$I'(X, Y) = \int\int_{-\infty}^{\infty} \gamma(u, v) |\phi(u, v; X, Y)|^2 \, dudv, \qquad (3.98)$$

where

$$\phi(u, v; X, Y) = e^{ik \sin \alpha(uX_0 + vY_0)} \phi_Q(u, v; x, y)$$

$$= \iint_{u_1^2 + v_1^2 < 1} \exp\{-ik \, e(u_1, v_1; Q)\} \epsilon(u_1 - u, v_1 - v) \times \qquad (3.99)$$

$$\times e^{ik \sin \alpha(u_1 X + v_1 Y)} \, du_1 dv_1,$$

and also

$$\phi(u, v; X, Y) = \frac{k \sin \alpha}{2\pi} \iint_{\delta(Q)} E(X, Y) F(X - X_1, Y - Y_1) \times$$

$$\times e^{ik \sin \alpha(uX_1 + vY_1)} \, dX_1 dY_1, \qquad (3.100)$$

where the function $F(x, y)$ is defined by (3.95) as before.

Equation (3.98), obtained in a slightly less general form by Hopkins
(1953),† puts in evidence the parts played in image formation by the
partially coherent illumination on the one hand (through $\gamma(u, v)$) and by
the combined effects of object structure and optical system on the other
(through $\phi(u, v; X, Y)$). Equations (3.96) and (3.99), or equations (3.100)
and (3.95), express in two different ways—corresponding to the Abbe
and Rayleigh theories respectively—the manner in which object structure and ikonal function are combined in the formation of the function
$\phi(u, v; X, Y)$.

† My thanks are due to Dr. Hopkins for allowing me to consult the manuscript of
his paper in advance of publication.

The image near Q' of a self-luminous object can evidently be expressed by the equation

$$I'(X,Y) = \iint\limits_{\delta(Q)} |E(X_1,Y_1)|^2 |F(X-X_1,Y-Y_1)|^2 \, dX_1 dY_1, \quad (3.101)$$

since $E(X_1,Y_1)$ is the intensity distribution at (X_1,Y_1) in the object surface S and $|F(X-X_1,Y-Y_1)|^2 dS$ is, by (3.95), the intensity at (X,Y) on S' of the image of a surface element dS of intensity density 1 situated at (X_1,Y_1) on S. This can be fitted into the formalism of the general theory as the case $\gamma(u,v) = 1$ (all u, v) by applying Parseval's theorem to (3.101), as though the limits of integration were infinite. Using (3.100) and disregarding the finiteness of the area $\delta(Q)$ as before, we then obtain the equation

$$I'(X,Y) = \int\limits_{-\infty}^{\infty}\!\!\int |\phi(u,v; X,Y)|^2 \, dudv, \quad (3.102)$$

which is (3.98) with $\gamma(u,v)$ replaced by 1. Since there is no equivalent source Σ which can illuminate S incoherently, the self-luminous object is not physically a special case of the transilluminated one, and the formal analogy must be used with caution. From the formal point of view it is natural to refer to the self-luminous object as the case $s = \infty$.†

At the other extreme is the case $s \to 0$, where the numerical aperture of the condenser is vanishingly small compared with that of the objective. Here the general argument breaks down because the coherence patches are larger than the whole of the field surface; we have the case of *coherent illumination*. This can be axial or oblique, and it is well known that the change from one to the other can alter profoundly the appearance of fine detail in the object. From the point of view of the general theory, coherent illumination is the special case where the equivalent source is reduced to a point, axial or non-axial, and $\gamma(u,v)$ is replaced by a Dirac δ-function $\delta(u-u_0,v-v_0)$. (3.98) then becomes

$$I'(X,Y) = |\phi(u_0,v_0; X,Y)|^2, \quad (3.103)$$

where now only the equation (3.99) for $\phi(u,v; X,Y)$ is available in the general case. When the objective is such that $e(u_1,v_1; P)$ is (to within a small fraction of $\lambda/2\pi$) independent of the position of P in the working field,‡ the alternative representation (3.100) becomes available in the

---

† For a transilluminated object, $s = \sin\beta/\sin\alpha$.

‡ This condition is more stringent than ordinary isoplanatism, which does not restrict ikonal terms independent of u, v.

approximate form

$$\phi(u, v; X, Y) = \frac{k \sin \alpha}{2\pi} \int\limits_{-\infty}^{\infty}\!\!\int E(X, Y) F(X-X_1, Y-Y_1) \times$$
$$\times e^{ik \sin \alpha (uX_1 + vY_1)} \, dX_1 \, dY_1. \quad (3.104)$$

In this case we can write $e(u_1, v_1; P) = e(u_1, v_1)$, and (3.99) becomes

$$\phi(u, v; X, Y) = \int\limits_{u_1^2 + v_1^2 < 1}\!\!\int \exp\{-ik\, e(u_1, v_1)\}\epsilon(u_1 - u, v_1 - v) \times$$
$$\times e^{ik \sin \alpha (u_1 X + v_1 Y)} \, du_1 \, dv_1. \quad (3.105)$$

The complex displacement at the point P' of coordinate numbers (X, Y) in S' is now a constant multiple of $\phi(u, v; X, Y)$. In the special case $u = v = 0$ of a coherently and cophasally illuminated object, this becomes

$$\phi(0, 0; X, Y) = \int\limits_{u_1^2 + v_1^2 < 1}\!\!\int \exp\{-ik\, e(u_1, v_1)\}\epsilon(u_1, v_1) e^{ik \sin \alpha (u_1 X + v_1 Y)} \, du_1 \, dv_1.$$
$$(3.106)$$

A particular 'elementary component' or Fourier element

$$\epsilon(u_1, v_1) e^{ik \sin \alpha (u_1 X + v_1 Y)} \, du_1 \, dv_1 \quad (3.107)$$

in the spectral representation

$$E(X, Y) = \frac{k \sin \alpha}{2\pi} \int\limits_{-\infty}^{\infty}\!\!\int \epsilon(u_1, v_1) e^{ik \sin \alpha (u_1 X + v_1 Y)} \, du_1 \, dv_1 \quad (3.108)$$

of the object function therefore appears in the image with a phase-shift $-ke(u_1, v_1)$ if $u_1^2 + v_1^2 < 1$; otherwise it is suppressed. The factor

$$\exp\{-ik\, e(u_1, v_1)\}$$

which expresses the phase-shift is the 'transmission factor' of Duffieux[†] for the particular component considered. In the idealized case of an aberration-free objective, the image is the sum of those Fourier elements (3.107) of the object for which the frequencies $\nu_X = ku_1 \sin \alpha$, $\nu_Y = kv_1 \sin \alpha$ satisfy the inequality

$$\nu_X^2 + \nu_Y^2 < \frac{4\pi^2}{\lambda^2} \sin^2\alpha.$$

In terms of polar coordinates (r, θ) and (r_1, χ_1), for which $X + iY = re^{i\theta}$, $u_1 + iv_1 = r_1 e^{i\chi_1}$, the elementary components of the object take the form

$$\epsilon(r_1, \chi_1) e^{ikrr_1 \sin \alpha \cos(\chi_1 - \theta)} r_1 \, dr_1 \, d\chi_1, \quad (3.109)$$

† P. M. Duffieux, *L'intégrale de Fourier, et ses applications à l'optique*, Éditions de la revue d'optique, Paris 1946.

where $\epsilon(r_1, \chi_1)$ denotes $\epsilon(u_1, v_1)$ expressed as a function of r_1, χ_1. We call $v_1 = kr_1 \sin \alpha$ the frequency and χ_1 the azimuth of the elementary component (3.109). Because of the symmetry of the system, the ikonal $e(u_1, v_1)$ can be expressed as a function $e(r_1)$ of r_1 only. The complex displacement in the image surface is then the sum of those elementary components (3.109) in the object with frequency $v_1 < k \sin \alpha$, each component appearing in the image with a phase-shift $-ke(r_1)$ which depends on its frequency but not on its azimuth. This result is expressed by the equation

$$\phi(0, 0; X, Y) = \int\limits_{0}^{1} \exp\{-ik\,e(r_1)\} r_1 \, dr_1 \int\limits_{0}^{2\pi} \epsilon(r_1, \chi_1) e^{ik \sin \alpha\, rr_1 \cos(\theta - \chi_1)} \, d\chi_1,$$

$$(3.110)$$

obtained on changing variables in the integral on the right of (3.106).

With oblique coherent illumination, corresponding to an equivalent point source at (u_0, v_0) on M'', the frequencies $(v_X, v_Y) = k \sin \alpha(u, v)$ passed by the system are those for which

$$(u-u_0)^2 + (v-v_0)^2 < 1.$$

When $u_0^2 + v_0^2 > 1$ we have the case of coherent dark-ground illumination. Only frequencies of the object between $k \sin \alpha\{\sqrt{(u_0^2 + v_0^2)} - 1\}$ and $k \sin \alpha\{\sqrt{(u_0^2 + v_0^2)} + 1\}$ can then contribute to the image; 'smooth' areas of low optical slope therefore appear dark with bright edges. Fine detail appears strongly metamorphosed, even when the objective is aberration free, for reasons which will become clearer in § 3.74.

3.73. *Resolution of transilluminated object structure.* Provided the obliquities are not too large, oblique coherent illumination from the direction (u'', v'') results in a complex displacement density

$$E(X, Y) e^{ik \sin \alpha(u''X + v''Y)}$$

on the emitting side of the object plane S. The Fourier element $\epsilon(u, v) e^{ik \sin \alpha(uX + vY)} \, du\,dv$, corresponding in the case of axial illumination to a diffracted beam of parallel light coming off in the (u, v) direction, is replaced by an element

$$\epsilon(u, v) e^{ik \sin \alpha[(u+u'')X + (v+v'')Y]} \, du\,dv, \qquad (3.111)$$

corresponding to a similar beam coming off in the direction $(u+u'', v+v'')$. This beam will be transmitted by the objective S (assumed isoplanatic in the stricter sense $e(u, v; P) = e(u, v)$ explained above) provided

$$(u+u'')^2 + (v+v'')^2 < 1. \qquad (3.112)$$

The element (3.111) then appears, with a phase-shift $-ke(u+u'', v+v'')$, in the complex displacement function on S', which (disregarding constant multipliers) we can write as

$$\phi(u'', v''; X, Y) = \frac{k \sin \alpha}{2\pi} \int\!\!\int_{-\infty}^{\infty} \epsilon(u, v)\kappa(u+u'', v+v'') \times$$

$$\times \exp\{-ik\, e(u+u'', v+v'')\}e^{ik \sin \alpha[(u+u'')X+(v+v'')Y]}\, du\, dv, \quad (3.113)$$

where the function $\kappa(p, q) = 1$ or 0 according as $p^2+q^2 \lessgtr 1$.

In the case of an extended equivalent source of luminosity distribution $\gamma(u, v)$, connected with the coherence function

$$\Gamma_{12} = \Gamma(X_2-X_1, Y_2-Y_1)$$

on S by the equations†

$$\left.\begin{aligned}\gamma(u, v) &= \frac{1}{2\pi} \int\!\!\int_{-\infty}^{\infty} \Gamma(x, y)e^{-i(uX+vY)}\, dX\, dY \\[2mm] \Gamma(X, Y) &= \frac{1}{2\pi} \int\!\!\int_{-\infty}^{\infty} \gamma(u, v)e^{i(Xu+Yv)}\, du\, dv\end{aligned}\right\}, \quad (3.114)$$

the source element $d\sigma = du''dv''$ situated at the point of coordinate numbers (u'', v'') on the spherical surface M'' (Fig. 36) supplies oblique coherent illumination of intensity proportional to $\gamma(u'', v'')\, du''dv''$.‡ It follows that the total intensity at (X, Y) in the image on S' is proportional to

$$I'(X, Y) = \int\!\!\int_{-\infty}^{\infty} \gamma(u'', v'')|\phi(u'', v''; X, Y)|^2\, du''dv'' \quad (3.115)$$

$$= \int\!\!\int_{-\infty}^{\infty} du_1\, dv_1 \int\!\!\int_{-\infty}^{\infty} du_2\, dv_2\, t(u_1, v_1; u_2, v_2)\epsilon(u_1, v_1)e^{ik \sin \alpha(u_1X+v_1Y)} \times$$

$$\times \bar{\epsilon}(u_2, v_2)e^{-ik \sin \alpha(u_2X+v_2Y)}, \quad (3.116)$$

where the real quantity

$$t(u_1, v_1; u_2, v_2) = \int\!\!\int_{-\infty}^{\infty} \gamma(u'', v'')\kappa(u''+u_1, v''+v_1)\kappa(u''+u_2, v''+v_2) \times$$

$$\times \exp\{ik[e(u''+u_2, v''+v_2)-e(u''+u_1, v''+v_1)]\}\, du''dv'', \quad (3.117)$$

and the domains of integration in (3.116), (3.117) are only formally infinite.

† One, but not both, of $\gamma(u, v)$, $\Gamma(x, y)$ may be supposed identically zero for large values of u^2+v^2, x^2+y^2 respectively; we suppose $\gamma(u, v) = 0$ everywhere outside $u^2+v^2 = 4$. Because $E(x, y) = 0$ for $x^2+y^2 > a^2$, it is of no consequence what values $\Gamma(x, y)$ takes outside $x^2+y^2 = 4a^2$.

‡ $\gamma(u'', v'')$ is real because $\Gamma_{21} = \bar{\Gamma}_{12}$.

The relationship of $t(u_1, v_1; u_2, v_2)$ to Duffieux's transmission function $\tau(u, v)$ for coherent illumination is seen by writing (3.117) in the form

$$t(u_1, v_1; u_2, v_2) = \int\!\!\int\limits_{-\infty}^{\infty} \gamma(u'', v'') \tau(u''+u_1, v''+v_1) \bar{\tau}(u''+u_2, v''+v_2) \, du'' dv''.$$

$$(3.118)$$

Equation (3.116) can be regarded as expressing $I'(X, Y)$ as a (Hermitian) bilinear form in the Fourier elements

$$f_{u,v}(X, Y) = \epsilon(u, v) e^{ik \sin \alpha(uX + vY)} \, dudv; \qquad (3.119)$$

the 'coefficients' $t(u_1, v_1; u_2, v_2)$ of this form express the transmission properties of the isoplanatic objective **S** when used with the transillumination $\gamma(u, v)$, that is to say the effects of finite aperture, aberrations and defocusing.† We may call them the transmission cross-coefficients of **S** working with the given transillumination.

From the same point of view (essentially that of Abbe) it is possible to give a reasonable theoretical definition of resolution in terms of the Fourier elements

$$\epsilon(u, v) e^{ik \sin \alpha(uX + vY)} \, dudv, \qquad (3.120)$$

which together build up the object structure $E(X, Y)$. (See equation (3.108).) We can agree to say that one of these elements is *resolved* if it makes a non-zero contribution to $I'(X, Y)$, i.e. if the transmission cross-coefficient $t(u, v; u', v')$ does not vanish for all u', v' satisfying $u'^2 + v'^2 < 1$. The physical criterion for this is simply that some of the diffraction beams from an object of the special form

$$E(X, Y) = e^{ik \sin \alpha(uX + vY)}, \qquad (3.121)$$

uniformly transilluminated with the given partial coherence Γ_{12}, shall pass through **S**.

It now appears that, generally speaking, neither aberrations of the isoplanatic objective nor the details of the flux distribution $\gamma(u, v)$ in the equivalent source will affect resolution in the above sense;‡ provided the condenser is properly 'filled', the resolution is determined simply by the numerical apertures $\sin \alpha$, $\sin \beta$ of objective and condenser. Periodic detail in the object which is of too high a frequency is not transmitted by the system consisting of **S** together with the given transillumination; it simply disappears in the image. Aberrations of the objective cannot

---

† Non-uniform transparency of the lenses can be taken account of by giving the ikonal function $e(u, v; Q)$ complex values.

‡ 'Accidental' vanishing of $t(u_1, v_1; u_2, v_2)$ for isolated sets of values u_1, u_2, v_1, v_2 may of course occur at particular focal settings.

cause this disappearance, though they may cause the periodic detail to appear with diminished, or distorted, or even reversed contrast. From (3.117) it is evident that frequencies $\nu = k \sin \alpha \sqrt{(u^2 + v^2)}$ higher than $(1+s)k \sin \alpha$ cannot be resolved, since then $\kappa(u''+u, v''+v)$ is zero for every (u'', v'') in the circle $u''^2 + v''^2 < s^2$, and the integral (3.117) is consequently zero. Frequencies just below this value, though 'resolved'

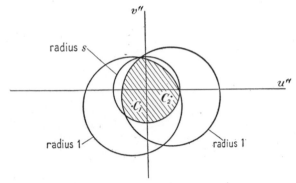

FIG. 37. Effective domain of integration in (3.117). C_1 is the point $(-u_1, -v_1)$, C_2 the point $(-u_2, -v_2)$.

according to the above definition, have small transmission cross-coefficients, because the (u'', v'')-region where $\gamma(u, v)\kappa(u''+u, v''+v) \neq 0$ is of small area and (3.117) is consequently small.

The general case is represented in Fig. 37. The product

$$\gamma(u'', v'')\kappa(u''+u_1, v''+v_1)\kappa(u''+u_2, v''+v_2)$$

can only differ from zero in the (u'', v'')-region common to three circles; the first of centre $C_1 = (-u_1, -v_1)$ and radius 1, the second of centre $C_2 = (-u_2, -v_2)$ and radius 1, the third of centre $O = (0, 0)$ and radius s.

This region, shaded in Fig. 37, represents the part of Σ from which flux $\gamma(u'', v'')$ contributes to the integral (3.117) defining the cross-coefficient $t(u_1, v_1; u_2, v_2)$. In the special case where the objective is error free and where $\gamma(u, v)$ is 1 or 0 according as $u^2 + v^2 \lessgtr s^2$, the value of $t(u_1, v_1; u_2, v_2)$ is equal to the area of the shaded region. In the case of transillumination with an annular equivalent source, the third circle in Fig. 37 is replaced by an annular region

$$s_1^2 < u''^2 + v''^2 < s_2^2. \tag{3.122}$$

The shaded area in Fig. 38 then represents the effective region of integration in the integral expression (3.117) for $t(u_1, v_1; u_2, v_2)$.

The cross-coefficients for a self-luminous object are obtained on replacing $\gamma(u'', v'')$ by 1 in (3.117). Then the effective region of integration is the area common to the first two circles in Fig. 37, and in the case $e(u, v) = 0$ of an aberration-free objective

$$t(u_1, v_1; u_2, v_2) = \int\!\!\int_{-\infty}^{\infty} \kappa(u''+u_1, v''+v_1)\kappa(u''+u_2, v''+v_2)\, du''dv''$$

$$= \begin{cases} 2\arccos(\tfrac{1}{2}r_{12}) - r_{12}\sqrt{(1-\tfrac{1}{4}r_{12}^2)} & (0 < r_{12} < 2) \\ 0 & (r_{12} \geqslant 2), \end{cases} \qquad (3.123)$$

where
$$r_{12} = C_1 C_2 = +\sqrt{\{(u_1-u_2)^2+(v_1-v_2)^2\}}. \qquad (3.124)$$

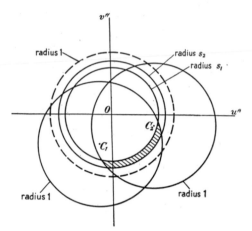

FIG. 38. Transillumination with annular equivalent source. Effective domain of integration in (3.117).

3.74. *Periodic objects.* When the object function $E(X, Y)$ is doubly periodic inside the field circle $X^2+Y^2 < a^2$ and this circle contains a large number of period-cells, the function $\epsilon(u, v)$ develops a lattice of sharp, regularly spaced peaks and is small in between these peaks. The Fourier integral representations (3.105) and (3.108), in which the function $\epsilon(u, v)$ occurs under the integral sign, then begin to resemble double Fourier series.

In such a case it is more convenient to work with double Fourier series from the start. We assume

$$E(X, Y) = \begin{cases} \sum_{m,n} a_{mn}\, e^{ik\sin\alpha(mX/p+nY/q)} & (X^2+Y^2 < a^2) \\ 0 \quad \text{elsewhere,} \end{cases} \qquad (3.125)$$

where the integers m, n run from $-\infty$ to $+\infty$ and the coefficients a_{mn} are complex. The periods of $E(X, Y)$ in X and Y are then $p\lambda/\sin\alpha$ and $q\lambda/\sin\alpha$, i.e. $p/1\cdot22$ and $q/1\cdot22$ Airy disk diameters respectively.

The condition that $E(X, Y)$ should be real for all X, Y is

$$a_{-m,-n} = \bar{a}_{m,n} \quad \text{(all } m, n\text{)}. \tag{3.126}$$

This follows easily from the vanishing of the imaginary parts of the mean values of the functions

$$E(X, Y)\frac{\cos}{\sin}\left(\frac{mX}{p}k\sin\alpha\right)\frac{\cos}{\sin}\left(\frac{nY}{q}k\sin\alpha\right).$$

Physically, a real function $E(X, Y)$ corresponds to an object which absorbs without introducing appreciable phase differences. As special cases of (3.126) we have

$$a_{m,0} = \bar{a}_{-m,0}, \qquad a_{0,n} = \bar{a}_{0,-n} \quad \text{(all } m, n\text{)}. \tag{3.127}$$

(3.96) now gives

$$\epsilon(u, v) = \frac{k\sin\alpha}{2\pi} \int\!\!\!\int_{-\infty}^{\infty} E(X, Y)e^{-ik\sin\alpha(uX+vY)}\, dX dY$$

$$= \frac{k\sin\alpha}{2\pi} \int\!\!\!\int_{X^2+Y^2<a^2} \sum_{mn} a_{mn} e^{ik\sin\alpha[(m/p-u)X+(n/q-v)Y]}\, dX dY$$

$$= a^2 k\sin\alpha \sum_{mn} a_{mn} \frac{J_1(z_{mn})}{z_{mn}}, \tag{3.128}$$

where

$$z_{mn} = ak\sin\alpha \sqrt{\left\{\left(u-\frac{m}{p}\right)^2 + \left(v-\frac{n}{q}\right)^2\right\}}. \tag{3.129}$$

Equation (3.128) puts in evidence the peaks of $\epsilon(u, v)$ at the points $u = m/p$, $v = n/q$.

Substituting from (3.128) into (3.113), we obtain

$$\phi(u'', v''; X, Y) = \frac{(ak\sin\alpha)^2}{2\pi} \sum_{mn} a_{mn} \int\!\!\!\int_{-\infty}^{\infty} \frac{J_1(z_{mn})}{z_{mn}} \kappa(u+u'', v+v'') \times$$

$$\times \exp\{-ik\, e(u+u'', v+v'')\}e^{ik\sin\alpha[(u+u'')X+(v+v'')Y]}\, dudv. \tag{3.130}$$

With a field diameter of 500 Airy disks, the value of $ak\sin\alpha$ is a little more than 1900 and we can use in (3.130) the approximation

$$a^2 k^2 \sin^2\alpha \frac{J_1(z_{mn})}{z_{mn}} = \delta\left(u-\frac{m}{p}, v-\frac{n}{q}\right), \tag{3.131}$$

where δ is a Dirac δ-function. This gives the approximate equation

$$\phi(u'',v'';X,Y) = \frac{1}{2\pi} \sum_{mn} a_{mn} \kappa\left(\frac{m}{p}+u'', \frac{n}{q}+v''\right) \times$$

$$\times \exp\left\{-ik\, e\left(\frac{m}{p}+u'', \frac{n}{q}+v''\right)\right\} e^{ik \sin \alpha[(m/p+u'')X+(n/q+v'')Y]}, \quad (3.132)$$

and on substituting in (3.115) we obtain for the normalized intensity distribution $4\pi I'(X,Y)$ in the image the approximate equation

$$4\pi I'(X,Y) = 4\pi \int\!\!\!\int_{-\infty}^{\infty} \gamma(u'',v'') |\phi(u'',v'';X,Y)|^2 \, du''dv''$$

$$= \sum_{mnm'n'} c_{mnm'n'}\, a_{mn}\, \bar{a}_{m'n'}\, e^{ik \sin \alpha[(m-m')X/p+(n-n')Y/q]}, \quad (3.133)$$

where the 'transmission cross-coefficient'

$$c_{mnm'n'} = \frac{1}{\pi} \int\!\!\!\int_{-\infty}^{\infty} \gamma(u'',v'') \kappa\left(\frac{m}{p}+u'', \frac{n}{q}+v''\right) \kappa\left(\frac{m'}{p}+u'', \frac{n'}{q}+v''\right) \times$$

$$\times \exp\left\{ik\left[e\left(\frac{m'}{p}+u'', \frac{n'}{q}+v''\right) - e\left(\frac{m}{p}+u'', \frac{n}{q}+v''\right)\right]\right\} du''dv''$$

$$= \frac{1}{\pi} t\left(\frac{m}{p}, \frac{n}{q}; \frac{m'}{p}, \frac{n'}{q}\right), \quad (3.134)$$

by (3.117). Since $\gamma(u'',v'')$ is real,

$$c_{m'n'mn} = \bar{c}_{mnm'n'}. \quad (3.135)$$

We note in passing that a substitution direct into (3.128) of the approximation (3.131), giving

$$\epsilon(u,v) = \frac{1}{k \sin \alpha} \sum_{mn} a_{mn} \delta\left(u-\frac{m}{p}, v-\frac{n}{q}\right), \quad (3.136)$$

would be equivalent to supposing that, with an object of the form (3.125), the diffraction spectrum breaks up into a discrete set of sharp parallel beams. This actually occurs if $E(X,Y)$ is taken as given by the first of equations (3.125) for all values of X and Y.

A comparison of (3.133) with the equation

$$I(X,Y) = |E(X,Y)|^2 = \sum_{mnm'n'} a_{mn} \bar{a}_{m'n'}\, e^{ik \sin \alpha[(m-m')X/p+(n-n')Y/q]} \quad (3.137)$$

for the intensity distribution on the emitting side of the plane S shows that a 'perfect' image will be obtained only if $c_{mnm'n'} = $ const. for all values of m, n, m', n' for which $a_{mn} \bar{a}_{m'n'} \neq 0$. In all other cases, some information regarding the object is lost or falsified by the imaging process. The influence on the $c_{mnm'n'}$ of the coherence conditions in the object plane may be studied by giving, in (3.134), suitable forms to $\gamma(u'', v'')$, the flux distribution in the equivalent source. The influence of the aberrations (including defocusing) is expressed in (3.134) through the ikonal function $e(u, v)$. Broadly speaking, it is the numerical apertures $\sin \alpha$, $\sin \beta$ of objective and condenser which between them determine the resolution; aberrations and change of focus of the objective determine the 'contrast' (in a generalized sense) of the resolved frequencies as they appear in the image.

More precisely, we have in the object

$$I(X, Y) = |E(X, Y)|^2 = \sum_{mnm'n'} a_{mn} \bar{a}_{m'n'} e^{ik \sin \alpha[(m-m')X/p + (n-n')Y/q]}$$

$$= \sum_{rs} A_{rs} e^{ik \sin \alpha(rX/p + sY/q)}, \tag{3.138}$$

where

$$A_{rs} = \sum_{mn} a_{mn} \bar{a}_{m-r,n-s}, \tag{3.139}$$

and in the image

$$I'(X, Y) = \sum_{mnm'n'} c_{mnm'n'} a_{mn} \bar{a}_{m'n'} e^{ik \sin \alpha[(m-m')X/p + (n-n')Y/q]}$$

$$= \sum_{rs} B_{rs} e^{ik \sin \alpha(rX/p + sY/q)}, \tag{3,140}$$

where

$$B_{rs} = \sum_{mn} c_{m,n,m-r,n-s} a_{mn} \bar{a}_{m-r,n-s}. \tag{3.141}$$

Because I and I' are real quantities, the A_{rs} and B_{rs} satisfy the relations

$$A_{-r,-s} = \bar{A}_{r,s}, \qquad B_{-r,-s} = \bar{B}_{r,s} \tag{3.142}$$

(compare (3.126)). The absolute values $|A_{rs}|$, $|B_{rs}|$ may be regarded as specifying the 'contrast' with which the periodicities $(\lambda p/r \sin \alpha, \lambda q/s \sin \alpha)$ appear in $I(X, Y)$ and $I'(X, Y)$ respectively.

In the case '$s = \infty$' of a self-luminous object, it is easily seen with the help of Fig. 37 that $c_{mnm'n'}$ depends only on $m-m'$, $n-n'$, even when the isoplanatic system S suffers from aberrations or focus error. We express this by writing

$$c_{mnm'n'} = d_{m-m',n-n'}. \tag{3.143}$$

Then (3.141) gives

$$B_{rs} = \sum_{mn} d_{rs} a_{mn} \bar{a}_{m-r,n-s} = d_{rs} A_{rs}, \tag{3.144}$$

from which it appears that the d_{rs} are transmission factors in the sense of Duffieux.

It is only in the two extreme cases of fully coherent and fully incoherent objects that transmission factors of this type exist. However, in the general case of a partially coherent object surface, the relation between the intensity distributions $I(X, Y)$ and $I'(X, Y)$ can still be expressed in terms of frequency-components by means of the transmission cross-coefficients $\dot{c}_{mnm'n'}$.

3.75. *Imaging of periodic line structures (gratings).* If $a_{mn} = 0$ for all $n \neq 0$, we can define $a_m = a_{m0}$ and write

$$E(X, Y) = \sum_m a_m e^{ik \sin \alpha . mX/p}, \qquad (3.145)$$

$$I(X, Y) = |E(X, Y)|^2 = \sum_{mm'} a_m \bar{a}_{m'} e^{ik \sin \alpha . (m-m')X/p}$$

$$= \sum_r A_r e^{ik \sin \alpha . rX/p}; \qquad (3.146)$$

$$I'(X, Y) = \sum_{mm'} c_{m0m'0} a_m \bar{a}_m e^{ik \sin \alpha . (m-m')X/p}$$

$$= \sum_r B_r e^{ik \sin \alpha . rX/p}, \qquad (3.147)$$

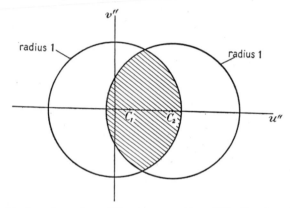

Fig. 39. Imaging of a self-luminous grating. Effective domain in the integral for the transmission coefficient $d_{m-m'} = c_{m0m'0}$. The centre of the first circle is the point $C_1 = (-m/p, 0)$, that of the second circle the point $C_2 = (-m'/p, 0)$.

where

$$A_r = \sum_m a_m \bar{a}_{m-r}, \qquad B_r = \sum_m c_{m,0,m-r,0} a_m \bar{a}_{m-r} \qquad (3.148)$$

and

$$A_{-r} = \bar{A}_r, \qquad B_{-r} = \bar{B}_r. \qquad (3.149)$$

This is the case of a periodic transmission grating with lines parallel to the Y-axis. When the object is self-luminous, we can write

$$c_{m0m'0} = d_{m-m',0} = d_{m-m'}$$

(compare (3.143)) and obtain from (3.148)

$$B_r = d_r A_r. \qquad (3.150)$$

The numbers d_r are the Duffieux transmission factors for the imaging of a self-luminous line structure. In general, they are affected by aberrations of **S** and by defocusing. When these are absent, we have from (3.123) and (3.124)

$$d_r = \frac{1}{\pi} t\left(\frac{m}{p}, 0; \frac{m-r}{p}, 0\right)$$

$$= \begin{cases} \frac{2}{\pi} \arccos\left|\frac{r}{2p}\right| - \frac{1}{\pi}\left|\frac{r}{p}\right| \sqrt{\left(1 - \frac{r^2}{4p^2}\right)} & \left(0 < \left|\frac{r}{p}\right| \leqslant 2\right), \\ 0 & \left(\left|\frac{r}{p}\right| > 2\right). \end{cases}$$

(3.151)

The factor $1/\pi$ results from the normalization adopted in (3.133), which secures that the intensities are equal at corresponding points of an object and its 'perfect' image.

3.76. *Resolution of fine gratings.* By the *normalized frequency* of the grating (3.145) is meant the quantity $\omega = |1/p|$. By a 'fine' grating we here mean one in which the normalized frequency ω is comparable with unity, i.e. in which the period $\lambda p/\sin\alpha$ is comparable with the Airy disk diameter $1 \cdot 22\lambda/\sin\alpha$ of the objective which images it. By an *amplitude grating* is meant one in which $E(X, Y)$ is everywhere real; by a *phase grating* one in which $|E(X, Y)| = 1$. The name *phase-amplitude grating* is sometimes applied to the general case, in which $E(X, Y)$ is complex.

By a *sinusoidal phase-amplitude grating* we mean one which can be represented by an equation of the form

$$E(X, Y) = a_{-1} e^{-ik\sin\alpha \cdot X/p} + a_0 + a_1 e^{ik\sin\alpha \cdot X/p}. \qquad (3.152)$$

This is the special case of (3.145) in which a_{-1}, a_0, a_1 are the only non-zero a_m. It reduces to an amplitude grating if $a_0 = \bar{a}_0, a_{-1} = \bar{a}_1$. Setting in this case $a_0 = \alpha_0, a_1 = \frac{1}{2}(\alpha_1 + i\beta_1), a_{-1} = \frac{1}{2}(\alpha_1 - i\beta_1)$, where $\alpha_0, \alpha_1, \beta_1$ are real, we obtain (3.152) in the form

$$E(X, Y) = \alpha_0 + \alpha_1 \cos(k\sin\alpha \cdot X/p) + \beta_1 \sin(k\sin\alpha \cdot X/p).$$

If we suppose the grating placed symmetrically with respect to the field-centre, this equation reduces to

$$E(X, Y) = \alpha_0 + \alpha_1 \cos(k\sin\alpha \cdot X/p). \qquad (3.153)$$

Coherent illumination. Under axial illumination a sinusoidal grating (3.152) gives three diffracted beams, all of which are passed by **S** if the normalized frequency $\omega = |1/p|$ is less than one. If $\omega > 1$ only the central beam is passed, and the grating is not resolved; in this case

$I'(X, Y)$ is constant and the image is completely featureless.† In terms of the definition of resolution made in § 3.73, we must say that all three of the Fourier elements

$$a_0, \quad a_1 e^{ik \sin \alpha . X/p}, \quad a_{-1} e^{-ik \sin \alpha . X/p} \tag{3.154}$$

of the function $E(X, Y)$ are resolved if $\omega < 1$, but only the element a_0 if $\omega > 1$.

If $1 < \omega < 2$, two of the Fourier elements‡ can be 'resolved' under suitable oblique coherent illumination (for example under that corresponding to $u_0 = (1+\omega)/2$, $v_0 = 0$) and the image then shows a sinusoidal intensity variation corresponding in period to the structure of the object. The grating is 'resolved' in the ordinary sense of the word but the relation between image and object is much less simple than the appearance of the image suggests.

The last point becomes more striking if we consider the effects of defocusing on the image in these two cases.

To represent axial or oblique coherent illumination, we set

$$\gamma(u'', v'') = \delta(u'' - u_0, v'' - v_0)$$

in (3.117), obtaining

$$c_{m0m'0} = \frac{1}{\pi} t(m\omega, 0; m'\omega, 0)$$

$$= \kappa(u_0 + m\omega, v_0)\kappa(u_0 + m'\omega, v_0) \times$$

$$\times \exp\{ik[e(u_0 + m\omega, v_0) - e(u_0 + m'\omega, v_0)]\}.$$

The factor $\kappa(u_0 + m\omega, v_0)\kappa(u_0 + m'\omega, v_0)$ is equal to 1 when the elements $a_m e^{ik \sin \alpha . mX/p}$, $a_{m'} e^{ik \sin \alpha . m'X/p}$ are both resolved and to zero otherwise. Thus, in the case $\omega < 1$, $u_0 = v_0 = 0$,

$$c_{m0m'0} = \exp\{ik[e(m\omega, 0) - e(m'\omega, 0)]\} = \exp\{ik[e(m\omega) - e(m'\omega)]\}$$

for $m, m' = -1, 0, +1$,

$$= 0 \quad \text{otherwise.} \tag{3.155}$$

Writing η_m for $\exp\{ik\, e(m\omega, 0)\}$ we obtain, after calculation,

$$I'(X, Y) = (|a_{-1}|^2 + |a_0|^2 + |a_1|^2) +$$

$$+ 2\, \Re\{(\bar{a}_0 a_{-1} \bar{\eta}_0 \eta_{-1} + a_0 \bar{a}_1 \eta_0 \bar{\eta}_1)e^{-ik \sin \alpha . X/p}\}. \tag{3.156}$$

In the case of (3.153) of an amplitude grating symmetrically placed in

---

† The complications which ensue when ω is very nearly equal to 1 need not be discussed here.

‡ a_0 and $a_1 e^{ik \sin \alpha . X/p}$ or a_0 and $a_{-1} e^{-ik \sin \alpha . X/p}$.

the field, and imaged by a symmetrical system (for which $\eta_{-1} = \eta_1$) this becomes

$$I'(X, Y)$$
$$= (\alpha_0^2 + \tfrac{1}{2}\alpha_1^2) + 2\alpha_0\,\alpha_1\,\Re(\bar{\eta}_0\,\eta_1)\cos(k\sin\alpha\,.\,X/p) + \tfrac{1}{2}\alpha_1^2\cos(2k\sin\alpha\,.\,X/p) \tag{3.157}$$

$$= \alpha_0^2 + 2\alpha_0\,\alpha_1\cos\{k[e(\omega) - e(0)]\}\cos(k\sin\alpha\,.\,X/p) +$$
$$+ \alpha_1^2\cos^2(k\sin\alpha\,.\,X/p). \tag{3.158}$$

Comparing (3.158) with the intensity distribution in the object

$$I(X, Y) = [\alpha_0 + \alpha_1\cos(k\sin\alpha\,.\,X/p)]^2$$
$$= \alpha_0^2 + 2\alpha_0\,\alpha_1\cos(k\sin\alpha\,.\,X/p) + \alpha_1^2\cos^2(k\sin\alpha\,.\,X/p), \tag{3.159}$$

we see that there is perfect imaging at those focal settings for which $e(\omega) - e(0) = m\lambda$ $(m = 0, \pm 1,...)$. At the focal settings (midway between consecutive members of the first series) for which $e(\omega) - e(0) = (m+\tfrac{1}{2})\lambda$, (3.155) gives

$$I'(X, Y) = [\alpha_0 - \alpha_1\cos(k\sin\alpha\,.\,X/p)]^2$$

and the lines in the grating appear with reversed contrast. At a third series of equidistant focal settings, those for which $e(\omega) - e(0) = (m\pm\tfrac{1}{4})\lambda$, (3.155) gives

$$I'(X, Y) = \alpha_0^2 + \alpha_1^2\cos^2(k\sin\alpha\,.\,X/p)$$
$$= (\alpha_0^2 + \tfrac{1}{2}\alpha_1^2) + \tfrac{1}{2}\alpha_1^2\cos(2k\sin\alpha\,.\,X/p)$$

and the image shows 'spurious resolution', its frequency appearing to be doubled.

Fig. 40 shows, in the particular case $\alpha_0 = \alpha_1 = \tfrac{1}{2}$, the appearance of the image at these focal settings.

The response of the image to change of focus is quite different when (as in the case $1 < \omega < 2$; $u_0 = (1+\omega)/2$, $v_0 = 0$) only two of the Fourier elements (3.154) of the grating are resolved. We then have, in place of (3.155), the equations

$$c_{m0m'0} = \exp\{ik[e(m\omega) - e(m'\omega)]\} = \eta_m\,\bar{\eta}_{m'} \quad \text{for } m, m' = -1, 0,$$
$$= 0 \quad \text{otherwise};$$

whence, by (3.147) and (3.148),

$$I'(X, Y) = \alpha_0^2 + \tfrac{1}{4}\alpha_1^2 + \alpha_0\,\alpha_1\,\Re\{\eta_{-1}\,\bar{\eta}_0\,e^{-ik\sin\alpha\,.\,X/p}\}. \tag{3.160}$$

In the case (3.153) of an amplitude grating symmetrically placed in the field, this becomes

$$I'(X, Y) = (\alpha_0^2 + \tfrac{1}{4}\alpha_1^2) + \alpha_0\,\alpha_1\cos\{k[e(0) - e(\omega) + \sin\alpha\,.\,X/p]\}. \tag{3.161}$$

Here the image appears as a fairly good representation of the object, but the contrast is reduced; it is approximately halved when $\alpha_1 \ll \alpha_0$. The most interesting feature is that focus-shift or aberrations of the isoplanatic objective cause no change in the appearance of the image structure; they merely give the image a small apparent lateral displacement when $e(\omega) - e(0)$ is not an integer multiple of λ.

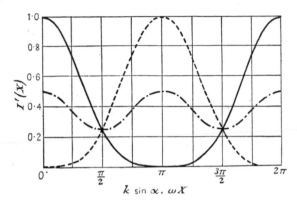

FIG. 40. Images at selected focal settings of the grating $E(X) = \frac{1}{2}[1 + \cos(k \sin \alpha . \omega X)]$ under axial illumination in the case $\omega < 1$. *After* Hopkins (1953). —— $e(\omega) - e(0) = m\lambda$; ---- $e(\omega) - e(0) = (m + \frac{1}{2})\lambda$; —·—·— $e(\omega) - e(0) = (m \pm \frac{1}{4})\lambda$.

These results have a more general application than to gratings of the form (3.151). For, if $\frac{1}{2} < \omega < 1$, any axially illuminated phase amplitude grating of the form (3.145) will 'lose' all its Fourier elements except (3.153) when imaged by **S**, and its image is therefore identical with that of a sinusoidal grating (3.152).

Similarly if $1 < \omega < 2$, any grating (3.145) gives under oblique coherent illumination $(u_0, 0)$ (with $-1 < u_0 < 1$) an image identical with that of (3.152).

We conclude that gratings of frequency $\omega > 1$ show no structure under axial illumination and gratings of frequency $\omega > 2$ show no structure under oblique coherent illumination. The frequencies $\omega = 1$ and $\omega = 2$ are therefore, in a certain sense, limits of resolution for these two types of transillumination. Further, the appearance of the image at 'best focus' of a coherently illuminated amplitude grating of frequency near to the resolution limit is independent of the aberrations of the (isoplanatic) objective. It follows that a fine coherently illuminated amplitude grating is of little or no value as a visual test object for a micro-objective.

Incoherent illumination. When the grating is self-luminous, we suppose the intensity distribution given by (3.146), namely

$$I(X,Y) = \sum_r A_r e^{ik \sin \alpha . r X/p} \quad (A_{-r} = \bar{A}_r). \qquad (3.162)$$

That in the image is then

$$I'(X,Y) = \sum_r B_r e^{ik \sin \alpha . r X/p}, \qquad (3.163)$$

where $B_{-r} = \bar{B}_r$ and, by (3.151),

$$B_r = d_r A_r = \left\{ \frac{2}{\pi} \arccos\left| \frac{r}{2p} \right| - \frac{1}{\pi} \left| \frac{r}{p} \right| \sqrt{\left(1 - \frac{r^2}{4p^2}\right)} \right\} A_r \quad (0 \leqslant |r/p| \leqslant 2),$$

$$= 0 \quad (|r/p| > 2) \qquad (3.164)$$

if **S** is free from aberrations and defocusing. In any case, $|d_r|$ is less than or equal to the right-hand side of (3.151)† and $d_{-r} = \bar{d}_r$.

It follows that frequencies $|r|\omega = |r/p| \geqslant 2$ in the self-luminous object are not resolved, and the image is featureless if $\omega \geqslant 2$. This is therefore the resolution limit for a self-luminous grating. If $1 < \omega < 2$, only terms with $r = -1, 0, 1$ contribute to the image, which is therefore identical with the image of the self-luminous sinusoidal grating

$$I'(X,Y) = A_0 + 2 \Re(A_1 e^{ik \sin \alpha . X/p}). \qquad (3.165)$$

The image reproduces the structure of this latter grating with diminished contrast, and the contrast decreases monotonically to zero as $\omega \to 2$ from below, whereas in the image of a coherently and cophasally illuminated sinusoidal grating the contrast is unimpaired up to the limit of resolution, though the finest resolvable structure is then twice as coarse.

Fig. 41 shows the intensity distribution in the image of the amplitude grating $E(X,Y) = \frac{1}{2}[1 + \cos(k \sin \alpha . \omega X)]$ by an error-free objective under incoherent illumination, when the structure is specified by the intensity distribution

$$I(X,Y) = \tfrac{3}{8} + \tfrac{1}{2} \cos(k \sin \alpha . \omega X) + \tfrac{1}{8} \cos(2k \sin \alpha . \omega X),$$

and under oblique coherent illumination, as in the case (3.161). It will be seen that when ω lies between approximately 1·3 and 2, oblique coherent illumination gives a 'correct' rendering of the structure with

---

† Because the absolute value of the integrand in (3.134) is everywhere $\leqslant 1$ if $\gamma(u'', v'') = 1$.

better contrast than could be got from a self-luminous object. If $\omega < 1$, a 'perfect' image is obtained with axial illumination.

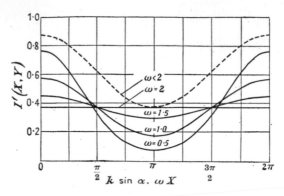

FIG. 41. Images of the amplitude grating $E(X) = \frac{1}{2}[1+\cos(k \sin \alpha \cdot \omega X)]$ at the geometrical focus of an aberration-free objective. *After* Hopkins (1953). ———— self-luminous, $\cdot\cdot\cdot\cdot\cdot\cdot$ oblique coherent illumination.

Partially coherent illumination. The discussion is less simple in the case of critical or Köhler illumination, since it is now necessary to evaluate the transmission cross-coefficients $c_{m0m'0}$. We shall not go beyond a few general remarks, supplemented by illustrative examples. In a fine grating with $\omega \geqslant \frac{1}{2}$, $c_{m0m'0}$ vanishes whenever $|m-m'| > 1$, since $\kappa(m\omega+u'', v'')\kappa(m'\omega+u'', v'')$ is then zero everywhere (or everywhere except at two isolated points). In the practically important case $s = \sin\beta/\sin\alpha < 1$, $\omega \geqslant \frac{1}{2}$, $c_{m0m'0}$ vanishes whenever $|m|$ or $|m'|$ is greater than 2, as may be seen from Fig. 42.

Suppose now that the objective **S** is free from aberrations and focus error. Then $c_{m0m'0}$ is $1/\pi$ times the area common to the dotted circle (of radius s) and the two circles (of radius 1) centred on C_m and $C_{m'}$. We can use the above results to examine the influence of condenser aperture on the image of the sinusoidal grating

$$E(X, Y) = E(X) = \tfrac{1}{2}[1+\cos(k \sin\alpha \cdot \omega X)], \qquad (3.166)$$

already used as an example in Fig. 40. The intensity distributions in the image for the values $\omega = 0\cdot5$, $1\cdot0$, and $1\cdot5$ and for selected values of s in each case, are shown in Fig. 43.

If $\omega = 2$, the structure is not resolved; since $c_{m0m'0}$ is then zero whenever $m \neq m'$, it follows from (3.148) that $B_r = 0$ for $r \neq 0$.

In the case $\omega = 0\cdot5$, it is easy to show that for $s < 0\cdot50$ the intensity distribution is the same as with axial illumination. For larger values

of s there is some decrease in contrast, but, as may be seen from the
first diagram in Fig. 43, the change is not of much practical consequence.

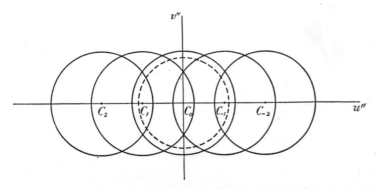

FIG. 42. Imaging of a grating under critical or Köhler illumination. C_r is the point
$u'' = -r\omega$, $v'' = 0$. The dotted circle Σ, of radius $s = \sin\beta/\sin\alpha$, has its centre at C_0.

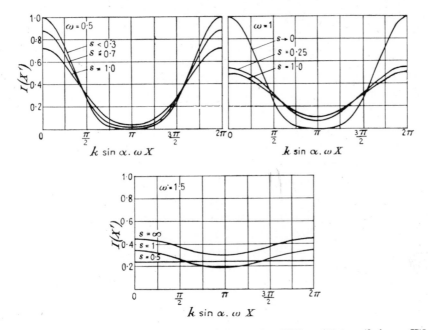

FIG. 43. Influence of coherence on image of the grating $E(X) = \frac{1}{2}[1+\cos(k\sin\alpha.\omega X)]$.
After Hopkins (1953).

For finer structures, the effect of a change in s is more marked. When
$\omega = 1$, for example, there is 'perfect' imaging with axial illumination;
but the contrast drops rapidly as s increases and at $s = 0.25$ (see Fig. 43)
it is already almost as low as with $s = 1.00$ or (see Fig. 41) with '$s = \infty$'.

When $\omega = 1 \cdot 5$ the grating is not resolved for $s \leqslant 0 \cdot 5$ (see Fig. 42); above this value resolution begins and the contrast increases until $s = 1$. A further increase in s, up to $s = 1 \cdot 5$, merely adds a constant to $I'(X)$ and thereby decreases the contrast.

In the general case, we see from Fig. 42 that when $s \leqslant 2\omega - 1$, the dotted circle can only intersect the circles (of radius 1) centred at C_{-1}, C_0, and C_1. Therefore the image of a general periodic grating (3.145) by an isoplanatic objective will, if $s \leqslant 2\omega - 1$, appear identical with that of the corresponding sinusoidal grating (3.152) at the same focal setting.

3.8. *The phase-contrast microscope*

In the usual form of the phase-contrast microscope,† Köhler illumination with an annular source or critical illumination with an annular condenser aperture is used. In both cases, the coherence properties in the object plane correspond to an equivalent source Σ of the form

$$\gamma(u'', v'') = \begin{cases} 1 & (s_1^2 < u''^2 + v''^2 < s_2^2) \\ 0 & \text{elsewhere} \end{cases} \tag{3.167}$$

lying in the distant sphere M'' centred on O (see Fig. 36).

A transmission lamina is placed in the plane Z of the Gauss image of the distant surface M'' by the micro-objective **S**. A system of coordinate numbers (agreeing to a first approximation with scale-normalized Cartesian coordinates) can be set up in the lamina, just as was done in the reference spheres M_Q and M'_Q of Fig. 36, assigning to the intersection with Z of the (u, v)-ray through Q (see Fig. 44) the coordinate numbers u, v. To each different point Q in the field corresponds, strictly speaking, a different system of coordinate numbers (u_Q, v_Q) on Z, but because Z is (in Gaussian approximation) conjugate to the surface M'', it follows that the coordinate numbers $u_Q(P_Z)$, $v_Q(P_Z)$ assigned to a given point P_Z in Z are nearly independent of the choice of Q.

The transmission lamina Z carries a 'phase-ring' filling the area

$$s_1'^2 < u^2 + v^2 < s_2'^2, \tag{3.168}$$

where u, v refer to the coordinate number system in Z obtained by taking Q at O. In the ring the transmission differs from that over the rest of Z by a complex factor $c = |c|e^{i\theta}$; that is to say by an amplitude factor $|c|$ and a phase-advance θ. Values of $|c|$ less than 1 are the most useful; they can be obtained by evaporating aluminium *in vacuo* on to the area (3.168) of the thin glass plate which carries the phase-ring. The phase-

† See Zernike (1942).

shift θ can then be adjusted by evaporation of a suitable dielectric, such as cryolite, on to the aluminized area.

The mean radius of the phase-ring often corresponds to about three-quarters of the full aperture of $\mathbf{S}$: $\frac{1}{2}(s_1' + s_2') \simeq \frac{3}{4}$. The width of the phase-ring is small compared with its mean radius, but large compared with the variations in $u_Q(T)$, $v_Q(T)$ as Q varies over the field. A commonly used value is $s_2' - s_1' = \frac{1}{8}$.

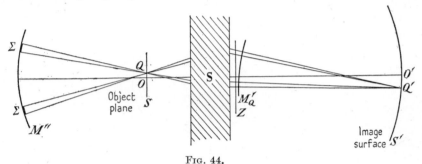

FIG. 44.

The phase-ring is made to cover, with a small margin to spare at either edge, the image of Σ in the plane Z; thus $s_1' < s_1 < s_2 < s_2'$. The margin is desirable partly because it makes the practical adjustment of the system less critical, and partly because the image of Σ by S on to Z is slightly 'spread' by aberrations and by diffraction.† The values of $s_1 - s_1'$ and $s_2' - s_2$ are small compared with $s_2 - s_1$. We denote by δ the lesser of $s_1 - s_1'$, $s_2' - s_2$.

Using the notation, assumptions and arguments of § 3.72 we now obtain, as a generalization of (3.98), (3.99), (3.100), the approximate equation

$$I'(X, Y) = \iint \gamma(u, v)|\phi_Q(u, v; X, Y)|^2 \, du \, dv \qquad (3.169)$$

for the intensity near Q' in S', where

$$\phi_Q(u, v; X, Y) = \frac{k \sin \alpha}{2\pi} \iint_{\delta(Q)} E_Q(X, Y) F(X - X_1, Y - Y_1) \times$$
$$\times e^{ik \sin \alpha (uX_1 + vY_1)} \, dX_1 \, dY_1, \qquad (3.170)$$

and

$$F(X, Y) = \frac{k \sin \alpha}{2\pi} \iint_{u_1^2 + v_1^2 < 1} R(u_1, v_1; Q) \exp\{-ik \, e(u_1, v_1; Q)\} \times$$
$$\times e^{ik \sin \alpha (Xu_1 + Yv_1)} \, du_1 \, dv_1. \qquad (3.171)$$

---

† In a high power objective, Z may actually lie inside the system $\mathbf{S}$ and the imaging of Σ on to Z is performed by the front part of the objective only. See Zernike (1942), p. 984, Fig. 14.

The function $R(u_1, v_1; Q)$, which represents the effect of the phase-ring, is defined as $|c|e^{i\theta}$ or 1 according as the point P_Z of coordinate numbers $u_Q(P_Z) = u_1$, $v_Q(P_Z) = v_1$ in Z does or does not lie in the phase-ring. The (u_Q, v_Q)-region corresponding to the phase-ring is a slight distortion of the annulus $s_1'^2 < u_Q^2 + v_Q^2 < s_2'^2$, the lateral displacement of the boundary being everywhere small compared with $s_2' - s_1'$.

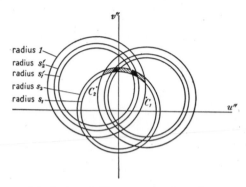

FIG. 45. Calculation of $t^*(u_1, v_1; u_2, v_2)$ in a phase-contrast microscope. C_1 is the point $(-u_1, -v_1)$; C_2 the point $(-u_2, -v_2)$.

From the last three equations it appears that the effect of the phase-ring is most conveniently expressed in the analysis as a change in the ikonal function $e(u, v; Q)$, which is now replaced by the function

$$e^*(u, v; Q) = e(u, v; Q) + \frac{1}{ik} \log R(u, v; Q).$$

The new ikonal function is complex-valued whenever $|R(u, v; Q)| \neq 1$.

Suppose now that $|c| < 1$ and that the ikonal function $e(u, v; Q)$ is effectively independent of Q, i.e. that we can write

$$e(u, v; Q) = e(u, v) \qquad (3.172)$$

with an error which is small compared with $\lambda/2\pi$ for all points Q in the working field.

Suppose also that the object structure causes only small changes of phase and amplitude in the waves which pass through it; more precisely, that

$$E(X, Y) = \begin{cases} 1 + \eta(X, Y) & (X^2 + Y^2 < a^2) \\ 0 & \text{elsewhere}, \end{cases} \qquad (3.173)$$

where the complex function $\eta(X, Y)$ is small compared with λ. Then it is a permissible approximation, for phase-rings which cover the image of Σ in the manner described above, to replace $R(u_1, v_1; Q)$ by the function

$$T(u_1, v_1) = \begin{cases} c & (s_1'^2 < u_1^2 + v_1^2 < s_2'^2) \\ 1 & \text{otherwise,} \end{cases} \qquad (3.174)$$

and to replace $R(u_1, v_1; Q)\exp\{-ik\,e(u_1, v_1; Q)\}$ in (3.171) by

$$\exp\{-ik\,e_c^*(u_1, v_1)\},$$

where

$$e_c^*(u, v) = e(u, v) + \frac{1}{ik}\log T(u, v). \qquad (3.175)$$

When $c = 1$, $e_c^*(u, v)$ reduces to $e(u, v)$ and the system becomes an ordinary microscope with annular illumination. In the presence of the phase-ring, the equation (3.116) for the intensity distribution $I'(X, Y)$ in the image is replaced by

$$I'(X, Y) = \int\!\!\int_{-\infty}^{\infty} du_1\,dv_1 \int\!\!\int_{-\infty}^{\infty} du_2\,dv_2\, t_c^*(u_1, v_1; u_2, v_2)\epsilon(u_1, v_1)e^{ik\sin\alpha(u_1 X + v_1 Y)}\times$$

$$\times\,\bar{\epsilon}(u_2, v_2)e^{-ik\sin\alpha(u_2 X + v_2 Y)}, \quad (3.176)$$

where

$$t_c^*(u_1, v_1; u_2, v_2) = \int\!\!\int_{-\infty}^{\infty} \gamma(u'', v'')\kappa(u'' + u_1, v'' + v_1)\kappa(u'' + u_2, v'' + v_2)\times$$

$$\times\exp\{ik[e_c^*(u'' + u_2, v'' + v_2) - \bar{e}_c^*(u'' + u_1, v'' + v_1)]\}\,du''dv''. \quad (3.177)$$

The domains of integration in (3.176) and (3.177) are only formally infinite; the effective domain of integration in (3.177) is shown as a shaded area in Fig. 45, from which it is clear that $t_c^* = 0$ whenever either $\sqrt{(u_1^2 + v_1^2)}$ or $\sqrt{(u_2^2 + v_2^2)}$ exceeds $1 + s_2$.

When $E(X, Y)$ has the form (3.173), its spectral function

$$\epsilon(u, v) = \frac{k\sin\alpha}{2\pi}\int\!\!\int_{-\infty}^{\infty} E(X, Y)e^{-ik\sin\alpha(uX + vY)}\,dXdY$$

$$= a^2 k\sin\alpha\frac{J_1(z)}{z} + H(u, v), \qquad (3.178)$$

where $z = ak\sin\alpha\sqrt{(u^2 + v^2)}$ and

$$H(u, v) = \frac{k\sin\alpha}{2\pi}\int\!\!\int_{-\infty}^{\infty} \eta(X, Y)e^{-ik\sin\alpha(uX + vY)}\,dXdY. \qquad (3.179)$$

Suppose now that $H(u, v)$ only differs appreciably from zero when $\sqrt{(u^2 + v^2)} > \frac{1}{4}$, say.† The physical meaning of this condition is that the

---

† A smaller number than $\frac{1}{4}$ can be used if the phase ring is sufficiently narrow.

object contains fine detail but no appreciable amount of coarse detail. Then, in the spectral representation

$$E(X, Y) = \frac{k \sin \alpha}{2\pi} \int\limits_{-\infty}^{\infty}\!\!\int \epsilon(u, v) e^{ik \sin \alpha(uX+vY)} \, du \, dv \qquad (3.180)$$

(valid as an approximation in the region $u^2+v^2 < 1$) of $E(X, Y)$ as a sum of Fourier elements

$$f_{u,v}(X, Y) = \epsilon(u, v) e^{ik \sin \alpha(uX+vY)} \, du \, dv$$

$$= a^2 k \sin \alpha \frac{J_1(z)}{z} e^{ik \sin \alpha(uX+vY)} \, du \, dv \; +$$

$$+ H(u, v) e^{ik \sin \alpha(uX+vY)} \, du \, dv \qquad (3.181)$$

$$= f_{u,v}^{(1)}(X, Y) + f_{u,v}^{(\eta)}(X, Y), \qquad (3.182)$$

say, only the first term can be appreciable for $\sqrt{(u^2+v^2)} < \frac{1}{4}$ and only the second term for $\sqrt{(u^2+v^2)} > \min(s_1-s_1', s_2'-s_2) = \delta$. Consequently, in the representation (3.176) of $I'(X, Y)$ as a bilinear form in the Fourier elements (3.182), the general 'term'

$$t_c^*(u_1, v_1; u_2, v_2) f_{u_1,v_1}(X, Y) \bar{f}_{u_2,v_2}(X, Y) \qquad (3.183)$$

is zero (to a sufficient approximation) except in the four cases

(i) $\sqrt{(u_1^2+v_1^2)} < \delta, \quad \sqrt{(u_2^2+v_2^2)} < \delta,$

(ii) $\sqrt{(u_1^2+v_1^2)} < \delta, \quad \sqrt{(u_2^2+v_2^2)} > \frac{1}{4},$

(iii) $\sqrt{(u_1^2+v_1^2)} > \frac{1}{4}, \quad \sqrt{(u_2^2+v_2^2)} < \delta,$

(iv) $\sqrt{(u_1^2+v_1^2)} > \frac{1}{4}, \quad \sqrt{(u_2^2+v_2^2)} > \frac{1}{4}.$

From Fig. 45 and (3.177) we obtain, provided $s_2'-s_1'$ is not too large, the approximate equations

$$t_c^*(u_1, v_1; u_2, v_2) = |c|^2 t_1^*(u_1, v_1; u_2, v_2) \quad \text{in case (i)},$$

$$= c t_1^*(u_1, v_1; u_2, v_2) \quad \text{in case (ii)},$$

$$= \bar{c} t_1^*(u_1, v_1; u_2, v_2) \quad \text{in case (iii)},$$

$$= t_1^*(u_1, v_1; u_2, v_2) \quad \text{in case (iv)}.$$

$$(3.184)$$

For, since $|c| < 1$, the contributions to the integral in (3.177) from the regions shown cross-hatched in Fig. 45 are small compared with that from the whole of the shaded region.†

† Any values of u_1, v_1, u_2, v_2 for which $t_1^*(u_1, v_1; u_2, v_2)$ is 'accidentally' very small are exceptions to this statement, but not to (3.185).

Combining these results we obtain the approximate equation

$$t_c^*(u_1, v_1; u_2, v_2) f_{u_1,v_1}(X,Y) \bar{f}_{u_2,v_2}(X,Y)$$
$$= t_1^*(u_1, v_1; u_2, v_2) g_{u_1,v_1}(X,Y) \bar{g}_{u_2,v_2}(X,Y), \quad (3.185)$$

where

$$g_{u,v}(X,Y) = ca^2 k \sin \alpha \frac{J_1(z)}{z} e^{ik \sin \alpha(uX+vY)} \, du \, dv +$$
$$+ H(u,v) e^{ik \sin \alpha(uX+vY)} \, du \, dv. \quad (3.186)$$

But $g_{u,v}(X,Y)$ is simply the Fourier element of the object function

$$E_c(X,Y) = \begin{cases} c + \eta(X,Y) & (X^2 + Y^2 < a^2) \\ 0 & \text{elsewhere,} \end{cases} \quad (3.187)$$

with the spectral function

$$\epsilon_c(u,v) = ca^2 k \sin \alpha \frac{J_1(z)}{z} + H(u,v). \quad (3.188)$$

It follows that the intensity distribution

$$I_c'(X,Y) = \iint du_1 \, dv_1 \iint du_2 \, dv_2 \, t_c^*(u_1, v_1; u_2, v_2) f_{u_1,v_1}(X,Y) \bar{f}_{u_2,v_2}(X,Y)$$
$$= \iint du_1 \, dv_1 \iint du_2 \, dv_2 \, t_1^*(u_1, v_1; u_2, v_2) g_{u_1,v_1}(X,Y) \bar{g}_{u_2,v_2}(X,Y)$$

in the phase-contrast image of the object (3.173), supposed free from coarse detail, agrees (after suitable renormalization) with that in the image of the object

$$\frac{1}{c} E_c(X,Y) = \begin{cases} 1 + \frac{1}{c} \eta(X,Y) & (X^2 + Y^2 < a^2) \\ 0 & \text{elsewhere} \end{cases} \quad (3.189)$$

by the same system, with the same illumination but with the phase ring removed. When coarse detail is present, or when $\eta(X,Y)$ is no longer everywhere small compared with the wavelength, the relations between object and image become more complicated. In the first case, fine detail is metamorphosed in much the same way as above, while the coarsest detail is reproduced very nearly as if the phase ring were absent.

In the case (corresponding to a transparent object) where

$$E(X,Y) = \begin{cases} e^{ik \phi(X,Y)} & (X^2 + Y^2 < a^2) \\ 0 & \text{elsewhere} \end{cases} \quad (3.190)$$

and the real function $\phi(X,Y)$ is small compared with $\lambda/2\pi$, we can write, to a sufficient approximation,

$$E(X,Y) = \begin{cases} 1 + ik \phi(X,Y) & (X^2 + Y^2 < a^2) \\ 0 & \text{elsewhere.} \end{cases} \quad (3.191)$$

A 'phase object' of this kind is difficult to observe with an ordinary microscope; the intensity distribution in its image at focus is practically uniform, and the appearances inside and outside focus bear no simple relation to the value distribution of the function $\phi(X, Y)$. But if suitable annular illumination and a phase-ring with $c = |c|e^{i\frac{1}{2}\pi}$ are used, the fine detail in the image of the phase object (3.191) appears similar to that in the image of the 'amplitude object'

$$E(X, Y) = \begin{cases} 1 + \dfrac{1}{|c|} k\phi(X, Y) & (X^2 + Y^2 < a^2) \\ 0 & \text{elsewhere} \end{cases} \tag{3.192}$$

under the same illumination but without the phase-ring. Observation of the fine structure of a transparent object is therefore made possible *at focus*, where the image most resembles the object. By choosing $|c|$ small ($|c| = 0.35$ is a practicable value) the contrast in the image is enhanced and smaller variations in optical thickness become observable.

Phase contrast can also be of value in the microscopy of amplitude objects, such as stained specimens. For, when $\eta(X, Y)$ is purely real and small compared with unity, a real value of $c < 1$ in the phase-ring (then more properly described as an amplitude ring) increases the contrast of fine detail in the image. When coarse detail is absent, (3.189) shows that the effects of the phase-ring on the image is the same as would result from an increase of object contrast by a factor $1/c$.

REFERENCES

A. Boivin, *J.O.S.A.* **42**, 1952, 60.

H. H. Hopkins, *Proc. Roy. Soc.* A, **208**, 1951 *a*, 263.

—— *Sci. J. Roy. Coll. Sci.* **20**, 1951 *b*, 1.

—— *Proc. Roy. Soc.* A, **217**, 1953, 408.

—— and P. M. Barham, *Proc. Phys. Soc.* **63**, 1950, 72.

E. H. Linfoot, *M.N.* **111**, 1951, 75.

—— and E. Wolf, *J.O.S.A.* **39**, 752, 1949.

—— —— *M.N.* **112**, 1953 *a*, 452.

—— —— *Proc. Phys. Soc.* B, **66**, 1953 *b*, 145.

E. von Lommel, *Abh. der Bayerischen Akad. der Wiss.* **53**, 1885, 233.

A. Maréchal, *Rev. Opt.* **27**, 1948, 73.

K. Nienhuis, Thesis, Groningen 1948.

—— and B. R. A. Nijboer, *Physica*, **14**, 1949, 590.

B. R. A. Nijboer, Thesis, Groningen 1942.

F. Richter, *Z. f. Instrumentenkunde*, **45**, 1925, 1.

G. C. Steward, *Phil. Trans. Roy. Soc.* A, **225**, 1925, 131.

H. Struve, *Mém. de l'Acad. de St. Pétersbourg* (7) 34, No. 5, 1886, 1.

H. Dennis Taylor, *M.N.* **54**, 1894, 67.

P. A. Wayman, Thesis, Cambridge 1952.

E. Wolf, *Proc. Roy. Soc.* A, **204**, 1951 *a*, 533.

—— *Reports on Progress in Physics XIV*, 1951 *b*, 95.

—— *J.O.S.A.* **42**, 1952, 547.

F. Zernike, *Physica*, **9**, 1942, 974.

—— and B. R. A. Nijboer, contribution to *Théorie des Images Optiques*, Paris 1949, 227.

THE FOUCAULT TEST

1. Introduction

ALTHOUGH more than ninety years have passed since Léon Foucault published the first account of his knife-edge test, it is still by far the most widely used method of testing astronomical mirrors and other high-quality optical systems of large aperture during the process of optical figuring. The test is too well known to need a description here; it is only necessary to note that it is of unsurpassed simplicity and delicacy when the stigmatism of a pencil is the property to be tested. For then the interpretation of the test is so easy as to be in a sense intuitive; the shadow contrasts, interpreted as if they arose from the illumination of a nearly flat disk by light coming in at grazing incidence from the side opposite to the knife-edge, depict to the eye the deviations of the wave surface from a sphere centred where the knife-edge meets the axis. And its sensitiveness is such that errors in the wave-front far too small to cause any observable change in the image at best focus can be clearly seen and accurately located.

In his original description of the test Foucault (1859) gave a purely ray-theoretic explanation of its properties. Such an explanation serves well enough when large errors are present. Certain unexplained effects are seen, but they can be disregarded without impairing the practical usefulness of the test. As the errors are reduced, however, these effects become more disturbing, and one of them—a brilliant line of light round the rim of the disk—often causes trouble to the inexperienced mirror-maker through being taken (as on ray theory it must be taken) to indicate the presence of a steep, narrow-turned edge. Dark fringes appear on the brightly lit areas of the disk seen under the test, and if the knife-edge is kept at a fixed setting there is no satisfactory way of deciding whether or not these indicate a local reversal of the error-slope, such as might occur from rapid zonal error on the wave-front. Fortunately, their characteristic behaviour as the knife edge is moved from side to side makes it easy to distinguish these diffraction fringes, which evanesce and reform in different positions as the knife-edge is moved, from 'true knife-edge shadows', which change their form and intensity much more slowly. The usual practice is to advance the knife-edge laterally until no diffraction fringes remain on the zone under examination. It is far from evident, however, that the shape of the zone profile is thereby correctly inferred from its variations in brightness when the errors are comparable with the wavelength of light.[†]

An adequate diffraction theory of the Foucault test is therefore desirable on practical as well as on theoretical grounds. Moreover, it is a necessary basis for any estimate of the theoretical limit to the sensitiveness of the test.

The first approach to such a theory was made by Rayleigh (1917). Using a simplified two-dimensional model, he explained, qualitatively at least, the bright rim shown by an error-free mirror under the test and the rather similar bright line which appears at a step-discontinuity on the mirror surface.

Zernike (1934), in a remarkable paper[‡] on the knife-edge test and the phase-contrast test, developed in 1934 a theory covering errors of arbitrary form, but under the restriction that the optical retardations should be small compared with the wavelength of light. Gascoigne (1945), taking the Zernike theory as his starting-point, obtained expressions for the knife-edge intensities, valid for errors of arbitrary form and amount, in terms of definite integrals (Hilbert transforms) of a very simple type. He applied these to a discussion of the fringes which appear on the 'bright slopes' when turned edge or zonal error amount to several wavelengths. Though derived, like Zernike's for the simplified two-dimensional model,[§] his formulae yield results of great practical value connecting the depths of errors of certain commonly occurring types with the number of fringes observed.

In the present chapter the three-dimensional diffraction theory of the Foucault test is developed in a form which allows the prediction of the appearance under test of a mirror possessing smooth errors of figure of arbitrary shape, and is applied to discuss some questions of importance to the practical optician.

2. General theory of the Foucault test

2.1. *Notation and basic approximations*

All the cases where an aberration-free pencil is being tested can be covered by supposing that the wave-fronts originate at the surface of a spherical mirror which is being tested at its centre of curvature. The wave leaving the surface of the mirror at the point (x, y) is described

[†] We shall return to this point in § 6 below.

[‡] Equations (18) and (20) of this paper are rendered incorrect by an error in sign in equation (14).

[§] The second part of Zernike's paper, in which he discusses the phase-contrast test, is three dimensional.

by an electric wave displacement

$$E(x, y)e^{(2\pi i/\lambda)ct},$$

the real part of which measures the electric intensity at (x, y) at the time t. Here λ denotes the wavelength, c the velocity of light. To express the fact that a wave surface of constant intensity and phase is leaving the surface of a circular mirror M of radius 1, we set

$$E(x, y) = 1 \quad (x^2 + y^2 \leqslant 1)$$
$$= 0 \quad (x^2 + y^2 > 1). \tag{2.1}$$

Of course, such a discontinuous distribution of electric displacement values cannot be strictly realized.

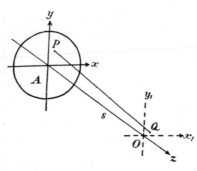

FIG. 46.

The more general case where the pencil under test is not fully stigmatic can be covered by supposing that spherical wave-fronts, originating from a pinhole near its approximate centre of curvature, are reflected from the surface of a nearly spherical mirror M. The results of the knife-edge test are then interpreted in terms of errors of figure of the mirror M. We suppose that these errors of figure may amount to several reflection fringes,† but that the error slopes on the mirror, besides being free from discontinuities, are not so steep as to spread out the visible image to more than a moderate multiple, say 5 or 10, of the size of the Airy disk. Then it makes no appreciable difference if we suppose that the wave is leaving a true spherical surface M_0, lying everywhere within a few wave-lengths of the surface M, and that at the point (x, y, z) on M_0 the complex displacement is

$$E(x, y) = |E(x, y)| \exp\left\{ -\frac{2\pi i}{\lambda} \phi(x, y) \right\}. \tag{2.2}$$

$|E(x, y)|$ is then the amplitude at the point (x, y) on M_0 and $-\phi(x, y)$ the phase there; the variation in the retardation function $\phi(x, y)$ expresses the distortion of the wave-fronts. The approximation here consists in the assumption that the amplitude is unchanged in passing from the point (x, y) on M to the point (x, y) on M_0.

† Since errors of figure on the mirror are transferred with a factor 2 to the reflected wave-fronts, it is convenient to express them in terms of 'reflection fringes', a term borrowed from interferometry; a reflection fringe is half a wavelength.

The fact that a circular mirror of diameter 2 is illuminated with uniform intensity may be expressed by setting

$$|E(x, y)| = 1 \quad (x^2 + y^2 \leqslant 1),$$
$$= 0 \quad (x^2 + y^2 < 1); \tag{2.3}$$

that is, by defining $E(x, y)$ as zero over the part of M_0 outside the circle C which corresponds to the boundary of the mirror M. $\mathrm{Exp}\left\{-\dfrac{2\pi i}{\lambda}\phi(x, y)\right\}$ is the phase function which describes the errors of M.

After leaving the mirror, the light comes to a more or less imperfect focus in the neighbourhood of O, the centre of curvature of M_0. See Fig. 46. By an application of Huyghens's principle† the wave displacement is calculated in the 'intermediate image surface', namely the sphere S, centred at A, which passes through the focal point O. The knife-edge will later lie in the tangent plane to this sphere. It is supposed throughout that the pencil under test is of small angular aperture; that is to say, the focal distance $AO = s$ is supposed large compared with the diameter of M. Then the distance between a point $Q = (x_1, y_1)$ near O in the surface S and an arbitrary point $P = (x, y)$ on the part of M_0 enclosed by C is approximately given by the equation‡

$$PQ = s - \frac{xx_1 + yy_1}{s}. \tag{2.4}$$

The contribution to the wave displacement at Q from the element $dx\,dy$ of area situated at P on M_0 is thus a constant multiple of

$$E(x, y)e^{(2\pi i/\lambda)ct}\exp\left\{\frac{2\pi i}{\lambda}\frac{xx_1 + yy_1}{s}\right\}dx\,dy,$$

† A discussion based directly on Maxwell's equations meets with formidable mathematical difficulties; see Poincaré (1892, 1897).

‡ The position of P is given by its x, y space coordinates; its z-coordinate is a first-order small quantity, since $s \gg 1$. The position of Q in the surface S is similarly defined by the space coordinates x_1, y_1 (see Fig. 1). The object of the device, due to Michelson (1890) of the spherical intermediate image surface S is to secure that (2.4) shall remain correct to within a small fraction of a wavelength over an area of the intermediate image surface which is large compared with the Airy disk of M. In fact, it is easy to show that if Q lies in the surface S,

$$\frac{PQ}{s} = 1 - \frac{xx_1 + yy_1}{s^2} + O\left(\frac{r^2r_1^2}{s^4}\right),$$

while if Q lies in the *plane* throughout O normal to the axis, then

$$\frac{PQ}{s} = 1 - \frac{xx_1 + yy_1}{s^2} + \frac{1}{2}\frac{r_1^2}{s^2} + O\left(\frac{r^2r_1^2 + r_1^4}{s^4}\right),$$

where $r^2 = x^2 + y^2$, $r_1^2 = x_1^2 + y_1^2$.

the fractional variation in the amplitude factor $1/PQ$ as P ranges over M_0 and the fractional error committed in writing $dxdy$ in place of the element of area on M_0 being both small enough to be disregarded.† The total wave displacement at Q is therefore

$$\frac{1}{2\pi} \iint_M E(x,y) \exp\left\{\frac{2\pi i}{\lambda} \frac{xx_1+yy_1}{s}\right\} dxdy$$

times a constant multiple of $\exp\{(2\pi i/\lambda)ct\}$. It is convenient to omit factors of this form and to use the term 'complex displacements' for the expressions which remain when they are removed. Thus a complex displacement is indeterminate to the extent of a constant normalizing factor.

On writing
$$\frac{2\pi x_1}{\lambda s} = u, \qquad \frac{2\pi y_1}{\lambda s} = v \tag{2.5}$$

and dropping a constant factor, we obtain for the complex displacement at Q the expression

$$W(u,v) = \frac{1}{2\pi} \iint_{x^2+y^2\leqslant 1} E(x,y)e^{iux+ivy} \, dxdy$$

$$= \frac{1}{2\pi} \int_{-\infty}^{\infty} \int_{-\infty}^{\infty} E(x,y)e^{iux+ivy} \, dxdy, \tag{2.6}$$

since $E(x,y)$ is defined as zero for $x^2+y^2 > 1$.

It is easy to verify that, in the case (2.1) of a true mirror, (2.6) reduces to the well-known expression

$$J_1\{\sqrt{(u^2+v^2)}\}/\sqrt{(u^2+v^2)};$$

the intensity in the surface S is then measured by the quantity

$$|W(u,v)|^2 = \frac{J_1^2\{\sqrt{(u^2+v^2)}\}}{u^2+v^2}. \tag{2.7}$$

This agrees with the usual formula for the Airy disk and rings in the *plane* through O perpendicular to the axis, which will be called the (x_1,y_1)-plane. As is well known, it follows from (2.7) that when λs is small‡ nearly all the light crosses S in a small region surrounding the point O.

---

† For a mirror working at f/10, the latter is equivalent to a variation in the intensity of illumination of less than ¼ per cent.

‡ Its value is 0·0004 for a mirror working at f/10 and for $\lambda = 2\times10^{-5}$.

2.2. *Analytical representation of the test*

To carry out the knife-edge test, the part of the (x_1, y_1)-plane defined by $x_1 \leqslant 0$ is covered by an opaque screen. Immediately behind O, a viewing system L receives the light and images M_0 on to the final image surface M_0' (see Fig. 47). L may be the observer's eye-lens and M_0' his retina, but for testing a mirror of long focal ratio a viewing telescope immediately behind the knife-edge is desirable; L then consists of this

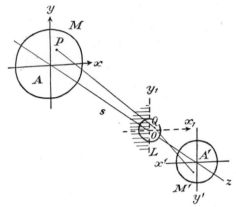

Fig. 47.

telescope together with the observer's eye- or camera-lens. In any case, the effect of L is to give equality of optical path between pairs of conjugate points P, P' on M_0, M_0'. In particular the optical path-lengths $(PQ...P'$ and $PO...P')$ are equal for every position of Q. It follows that the optical path difference

$$(Q...P')-(O...P') = -PQ+PO = \frac{xx_1+yy_1}{s} \tag{2.8}$$

if it be supposed, as it may for sufficiently large s, that the approximation (2.4) is usable throughout the part of the intermediate image surface S from which light is passed by L.† A system of coordinate numbers (x', y') in the surface M_0' is defined by assigning to the image P' of the point $P = (x, y, z)$ in M_0 the coordinate numbers $x' = x$, $y' = y$. Thus the intensity at P' is the same thing as the 'intensity seen under the test' at P, and the path difference (2.8) can be written $(x'x_1+y'y_1)/s$.

† It can be shown that the errors of L do not affect the general run of the intensity distribution in the final image surface; they merely result in a loss of sharpness comparable (though not identical) with that which would be observed in the image of a self-luminous object lying in the surface of M. But as an adequate discussion of this point would lead too far afield, the problem is here idealized by supposing that the system L is error-free.

The complex displacement $D(x', y')$ at the point (x', y') of M_0' is then obtained by integrating (2.6), multiplied by

$$\exp\left\{-\frac{2\pi i}{\lambda}\frac{x'x_1+y'y_1}{s}\right\} = \exp(-iux'-ivy')$$

over that part Γ of the intermediate image surface S from which light is passed by the knife-edge and received by the lens system L. In saying this we make the usual assumption, which cannot be strictly true, that the effect of a screen is merely to stop those parts of the wave which impinge upon it, without influencing the neighbouring parts. The error involved is small provided that the Airy disk is large compared with the wavelength λ, i.e. provided that the angular aperture of the pencil under test is small. Then

$$D(x', y') = \frac{1}{2\pi}\int\!\!\int_\Gamma e^{-iux'-ivy'}\,W(u, v)\sec\left(\frac{\lambda}{2\pi}\sqrt{(u^2+v^2)}\right)dudv; \quad (2.9)$$

the factor $\sec\{(\lambda/2\pi)\sqrt{(u^2+v^2)}\}$ allows for the fact that the element of area in the surface S is not $dx_1\,dy_1 = (\lambda s/2\pi)^2\,dudv$ but this quantity multiplied by the secant of the angle between the (x_1, y_1)-plane and the tangent plane to S at the point (u, v). The constant factor $(\lambda s/2\pi)^2$ is omitted in accordance with our convention.

To replace the factor $\sec\{(\lambda/2\pi)\sqrt{(u^2+v^2)}\}$ by 1 is equivalent to introducing a small variation in the amplitude of the complex displacement $W(u, v)$, which in the case of a 12-inch circular mirror M working at f/10 and a viewing telescope of 1-inch aperture amounts to less than 1 part in 100,000 at the edge of Γ. In this case R, the value of $\sqrt{(u^2+v^2)}$ corresponding to the semicircular edge of Γ, is approximately 1300 (inch)$^{-1}$. The effect of dropping the factor $\sec\{(\lambda/2\pi)\sqrt{(u^2+v^2)}\}$ is therefore negligible and (2.9) can be replaced by the equation

$$D(x', y') = \frac{1}{2\pi}\int\!\!\int_{u\geqslant 0,\,u^2+v^2\leqslant R^2} e^{-iux'-ivy'}\,W(u, v)\,dudv. \quad (2.10)$$

The next step is to replace R by ∞ in (2.10); this corresponds to disregarding the effects of the finite aperture of the viewing system. Now it is not true that the replacing of R by ∞ in (2.10) causes only a small change in the value of $D(x', y')$ over the whole mirror, since (as may be shown without great difficulty) the effect of the change is to make $D(x', y')$ tend in general to infinity as the point (x', y') approaches the boundary circle C' corresponding to the edge of the mirror. But if this circle be covered by a narrow annulus, then, provided R is sufficiently large, the change in $D(x', y')$ on replacing R by ∞ is small throughout the remainder of the surface M'_0.† It follows that, except in the immediate neighbourhood of C', the value of $D(x', y')$ is given with sufficient accuracy for the purposes of visual knife-edge testing by the equation

$$D(x', y') = \frac{1}{2\pi} \int_0^\infty du \int_{-\infty}^\infty e^{-iux'-ivy'} W(u, v) \, dv, \qquad (2.11)$$

provided that the test is carried out with a viewing system of sufficiently large aperture. It remains to examine whether the apertures ordinarily used in practice are sufficiently large in this sense. This can be done by fitting an iris diaphragm to the front of the viewing telescope. In an actual experiment by the writer the mirror, of 5 cm. diameter and 275 cm. radius of curvature, was illuminated by an artificial star (pinhole) of diameter 0·006 mm.,‡ placed close to its centre of curvature. The aperture of the iris could be varied from 3 to 16 mm.; its plane was 2 cm. behind that of the knife-edge. An aperture of 3 mm. in the plane of the knife-edge would correspond to the value $R = 43$, one of 16 mm. to the value $R = 230$. The magnification of the viewing telescope was 6.

The experiment was tried both with the true mirror and with small errors introduced into the pencil under test by placing pieces of annealed plate glass in front of the mirror. These errors appeared under the knife-edge test as flutings on the apparent surface of the mirror. They increased the overall size of the visible image at best focus to about three times its value for the true mirror. Several different settings of the knife-edge were used in each trial.

When the effect of varying the aperture of the iris was examined, it was found that, over the whole range of variation, no change could be detected in the appearance of the interior of the disk or of the halo. The only visible changes, as the iris was closed down, were a softening in the outline of the brilliant outer rim of the disk, a decrease in its maximum intensity, and the appearance of a fine dark fringe, just inside the outer rim and separating it from the interior of the disk. At minimum aperture, traces of a second dark fringe could be detected inside the first.

† An analytical proof of this result will not be included here. Its truth follows from the fact that if, in the surface M_0, the wave function $E(x, y)$ is given the value

$$\frac{1}{2\pi} \int_0^\infty du \int_{-\infty}^\infty e^{-ixu-ivy} W(u, v) \, dv$$

and the knife-edge removed, then the complex displacement in M'_0 is again given by (2.10).

‡ i.e. about one-tenth of the diameter, 134λ, of the Airy disk.

In the case of the true mirror a change in the appearance of the rim could first be distinctly seen when the iris aperture was reduced to about 6 mm. (90 Airy disks); this corresponds to the value $R = 95$ and to an exit-pupil diameter of 1 mm. In the case of a pencil with small errors, the aperture usually needed to be reduced a little below this value before the effect could be seen with certainty.

With a mirror of shorter focal ratio, the same aperture of the viewing telescope would correspond to a larger value of R and to an exit pupil of the same size. We conclude that, except in the immediate vicinity of the edge contour C', the intensity $I(x', y')$ in the final image surface is given, with accuracy more than sufficient for the purposes of visual knife-edge testing, by the equation

$$I(x', y') = 4\pi^2 |D(x', y')|^2, \qquad (2.12)$$

where
$$D(x', y) = \frac{1}{2\pi} \int\limits_{0}^{\infty} du \int\limits_{-\infty}^{\infty} e^{-iux' - ivy'} W(u, v) \, dv. \qquad (2.13)$$

2.3. The Reduction Theorem

We suppose that $E(x, y)$ is a differentiable function of x and y at all points (x, y) inside C. Outside C it is differentiable since its value is everywhere zero. On substituting from (2.6) into (2.13) and inverting the order of integration, we obtain

$$D(x', y') = \frac{1}{4\pi^2} \int\limits_{0}^{\infty} e^{-iux'} du \int\limits_{-\infty}^{\infty} e^{ixu} dx \int\limits_{-\infty}^{\infty} e^{-ivy'} dv \int\limits_{-\infty}^{\infty} e^{ivy} E(x, y) \, dy.$$

By Fourier's integral formula, the inner repeated integral

$$\int\limits_{-\infty}^{\infty} e^{-ivy'} dv \int\limits_{-\infty}^{\infty} e^{ivy} E(x, y) \, dy = 2\pi E(x, y'),$$

except at points (x, y') for which $x^2 + y'^2 = 1$. Thus

$$2\pi D(x', y') = \int\limits_{0}^{\infty} e^{-iux'} du \int\limits_{-\infty}^{\infty} e^{ixu} E(x, y') \, dx. \qquad (2.14)$$

It follows from (2.14) that the intensity seen under test at the point P on the mirror depends only on the values of $E(x, y)$ along the horizontal line through P, and is correctly given by applying two-dimensional diffraction theory along this line. This result is sometimes referred to as the Reduction Theorem.

In (2.14)

$$\int_0^\infty e^{-iux'}\,du \int_{-\infty}^\infty e^{ixu}E(x,y')\,dx = \lim_{U\to\infty} \int_0^U e^{-iux} \int_{-B}^B e^{ixu}E(x,y')\,dx,$$

provided B is chosen greater than 1. The expression under the limit sign

$$\int_0^U e^{-iux'}\,du \int_{-B}^B e^{ixu}E(x,y')\,dx = \int_{-B}^B E(x,y')\,dx \int_0^U e^{-iu(x-x')}\,du$$

$$= -i \int_{-B}^B \frac{E(x,y')}{x'-x}(1-e^{-iU(x'-x)})\,dx$$

$$= i \int_{-B-x'}^{B-x'} \frac{E(x'+t,y')}{t}(1-e^{iUt})\,dt$$

$$= i \int_{-2B}^{2B} \frac{E(x'+t,y')}{t}(1-e^{iUt})\,dt,$$

since $E(x,y) = 0$ whenever $|x| > 1$,

$$= i \int_0^{2B} [E(x'+t,y')-E(x'-t,y')](1-\cos Ut)\frac{dt}{t} +$$

$$+ \int_0^{2B} [E(x'+t,y')+E(x'-t,y')]\frac{\sin Ut}{t}\,dt. \quad (2.15)$$

Now let $U \to \infty$. By an argument familiar in the classical convergence theory of Fourier series, the second term tends to the limit $\pi E(x',y')$ at all points (x',y') at which $E(x,y)$ is a differentiable function of x, that is to say, at all points (x',y') not on C'.

In the first term of (2.15)

$$\frac{E(x'+t,y')-E(x'-t,y')}{t} = 2\frac{\partial}{\partial x'}E(x',y')+O(t)$$

as $t \to 0$. It follows by an application of the Riemann–Lebesgue theorem that

$$\int_0^{2B} \frac{E(x'+t,y')-E(x'-t,y')}{t}\cos Ut\,dt \to 0$$

as $U \to \infty$. Therefore

$$2\pi D(x', y') = \pi E(x', y') + i \int_0^{2B} [E(x'+t, y') - E(x'-t, y')] \frac{dt}{t}$$

$$= \pi E(x', y') + i \int_0^\infty [E(x'+t, y') - E(x'-t, y')] \frac{dt}{t}, \quad (2.16)$$

provided (x', y') does not lie on C'. But

$$\int_\epsilon^\infty [E(x'+t, y') - E(x'-t, y')] \frac{dt}{t} = \left(\int_{-\infty}^{x'-\epsilon} + \int_{x'+\epsilon}^\infty \right) \frac{E(t, y')}{t - x'} \, dt$$

for every $\epsilon > 0$; making $\epsilon \to 0$, we obtain from (2.16)

$$2\pi D(x', y') = \pi E(x', y') + i \int_{-\infty}^\infty \frac{E(t, y')}{t - x'} \, dt, \quad (2.17)$$

for all (x', y') not on C', the integral being interpreted as a Cauchy principal value when (x', y') is inside C'.

This equation, together with (2.12), gives the intensity distribution seen under the knife-edge test on a mirror whose wave-form is described by the arbitrary function $E(x, y)$, subject only to the conditions:

(1) the diameter of the mirror subtends only a small angle at the focal point;

(2) the errors of figure of the mirror, though they may amount to many wavelengths, are small compared with the focal distance s;

(3) the errors of slope on the mirror surface are small and, except at points on the boundary C, the function $E(x, y)$ is a continuous function of (x, y), differentiable with respect to x and y.

It will be seen from the proof of (2.17) that its validity is not confined to the circular mirrors of uniform reflecting power which are discussed in the present chapter. The equation is valid, in the same sense as above, for mirrors of arbitrary edge contour, including central piercings or irregularly shaped obstructions, and of variable reflecting power, whenever the maximum angular diameter of the pencil is small and the circumstances are such as to justify disregarding the effect of the finite aperture of the viewing system.

2.4. *Two special cases*

Equation (2.17) reduces the problem of computing the knife-edge intensities to the carrying out of a pair of single integrations at each point (x', y'). In the general case of an arbitrarily given wave function $E(x, y)$, these integrations must of course be carried out by numerical methods. There are some physically important special cases, however, in which they can be evaluated in terms of known functions. The simplest such case, that of a true mirror tested with the knife-edge centrally set, is obtained on setting

$$E(x, y) = 1 \quad (x^2 + y^2 \leqslant 1),$$
$$= 0 \quad (x^2 + y^2 > 1),$$

as in (2.1). (2.17) then yields at once the formulae

$$2\pi D_0(x', y') = \pi - i \log \left| \frac{x' + \sqrt{(1 - y'^2)}}{x' - \sqrt{(1 - y'^2)}} \right| \quad (x'^2 + y'^2 < 1)$$

$$= -i \log \left| \frac{x' + \sqrt{(1 - y'^2)}}{x' - \sqrt{(1 - y'^2)}} \right| \quad (y'^2 \leqslant 1 < x'^2 + y'^2)$$

$$= 0 \quad (1 < y'^2); \tag{2.18}$$

$$I_0(x', y') = \pi^2 + \log^2 \left| \frac{x' + \sqrt{(1 - y'^2)}}{x' - \sqrt{(1 - y'^2)}} \right| \quad (x'^2 + y'^2 < 1)$$

$$= \log^2 \left| \frac{x' + \sqrt{(1 - y'^2)}}{x' - \sqrt{(1 - y'^2)}} \right| \quad (y'^2 \leqslant 1 < x'^2 + y'^2)$$

$$= 0 \quad (1 < y'^2), \tag{2.19}$$

which predict the intensities on the mirror disk and in the halo. The halo is therefore confined to the horizontal band $-1 < y' < 1$ of the surface M_0'. Along a thin strip $y' = $ constant lying in the band, the intensity function can be written

$$I_0 = \pi^2 + \log^2 \left| \frac{1 + X}{1 - X} \right| \quad (|X| < 1)$$

$$= \log^2 \left| \frac{1 + X}{1 - X} \right| \quad (|X| > 1),$$

where $X = x'/\sqrt{(1 - y'^2)}$ runs between -1 and 1 in that part of the strip which lies inside C'. It follows that the isophotal lines are ellipses with the vertical diameter BB' as a common axis (see Fig. 48) and, since

$$\int_{-1}^{1} \log^2 \left| \frac{1 + X}{1 - X} \right| dX = \tfrac{2}{3}\pi^2, \qquad \int_{-\infty}^{\infty} \log^2 \left| \frac{1 + X}{1 - X} \right| dX = 2\pi^2,$$

that the halo contains one-third of the total illumination.

Along the vertical diameter BB' in Fig. 48 the intensity remains constant; there is therefore no logarithmic infinity at the ends of this diameter. Taken together with the run of the isophotal lines in the interior of the disk, this leads one to expect that in practice the brilliance of the outer rim will not be uniform, but will decrease from a maximum at A, A' to a minimum at B, B'. A practical test confirms this expectation. The effect becomes much more conspicuous when the knife-edge is advanced beyond the central position.†

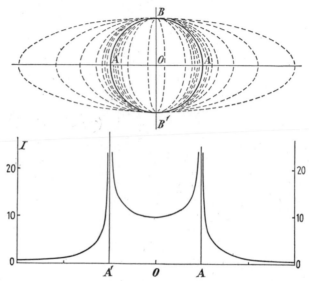

FIG. 48. *Above*: Isophotal lines for a true mirror under the Foucault test, with knife-edge central. *Below*: Intensity distribution along horizontal diameter.

By applying Babinet's principle, the intensity distribution for a true mirror with a pierced central hole can at once be derived from (2.18). The result, for a mirror of inner and outer radii a and b respectively, is

$$I(x',y') = \pi^2\left[\epsilon\left(\frac{r'}{b}\right) - \epsilon\left(\frac{r'}{a}\right)\right] +$$
$$+ \left[\epsilon\left(\frac{y'}{b}\right)\log\left|\frac{x'+\sqrt{(b^2-y'^2)}}{x'-\sqrt{(b^2-y'^2)}}\right| - \epsilon\left(\frac{y'}{b}\right)\log\left|\frac{x'+\sqrt{(a^2-y'^2)}}{x'-\sqrt{(a^2-y'^2)}}\right|\right]^2, \quad (2.20)$$

where $\epsilon(t)$ is defined as 1 or 0 according as $|t| \leqslant 1$ or $|t| > 1$, and $r' = \sqrt{(x'^2+y'^2)}$. The intensity along the horizontal diameter is shown in Fig. 49. It is of some interest that its value falls to zero at the centre of the hole when the knife-edge is centrally set. Very striking is the bright appearance of the hole and its accompanying band-halo when

† A photograph showing the effect in this case will be found in an interesting paper on edge-diffraction effects by S. Banerji, *Phil. Mag.* **37**, 144, pl. 3, fig. 9.

the knife-edge is advanced beyond the central position; this can be predicted by applying Babinet's principle to (2.21) below.

To calculate the effects of small displacements of the knife-edge on the intensities, we may express them as 'induced errors' of figure on the mirror. Thus, to determine the effect of advancing c, $E(x, y)$ is replaced

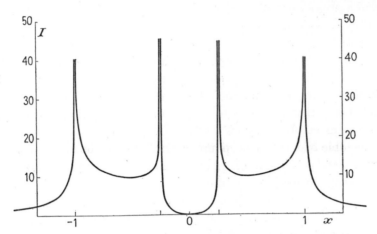

Fig. 49. Pierced mirror tested with knife-edge central. Intensity along horizontal diameter.

on the right of (2.17) by $e^{ic'x}E(x, y)$ and $D(x', y')$ on its left by $e^{ic'x'}D(x', y')$, where $c' = 2\pi c/\lambda s$. The resulting equation

$$2\pi D(x', y') = \pi E(x', y') + i \int_{-\sqrt{(1-y'^2)}}^{\sqrt{(1-y'^2)}} \frac{E(t, y')}{t-x'} e^{ic'(t-x')} \, dt$$

$$= \pi E(x', y') + i \int_{x'-\sqrt{(1-y'^2)}}^{x'+\sqrt{(1-y'^2)}} E(x'+u, y') \frac{e^{ic'u}}{u} \, du \quad (2.21)$$

gives the new value of $D(x', y')$. The effect of a change δs in the focal setting can be calculated in a similar way by writing $e^{i\alpha(x^2+y^2)}E(x, y)$ for $E(x, y)$ and $e^{i\alpha(x'^2+y'^2)}D(x', y')$ for $D(x', y')$ in (2.17), where $\alpha = (\pi/\lambda s^2)\,\delta s$.

2.5. The knife-edge test with a slit source

A practical difficulty in the knife-edge testing of unsilvered glass mirrors is that when, in order to obtain something near to maximum sensitivity, a very fine pinhole is used as light source, it is difficult to obtain enough light through the pinhole to make the Foucault shadows comfortably visible, even in a darkened room. The question is not merely one of convenience, since when the level of illumination is too low the discriminating power of the eye is reduced, and with it the practical sensitiveness of the test.

The shortage of light can be overcome in a very simple way by substituting a fine slit for the pinhole and testing with the knife-edge set as accurately parallel as possible to the image of the slit. However, it is not obvious *a priori* what effect this change has on the properties of the test; it is only clear that they will be unaffected to the degree of approximation represented by ray theory.

Equation (2.17) makes it possible to investigate this question in more detail and to show that the relative intensities seen under the test are unaltered by the substitution of a very narrow slit for the pinhole, provided only that the slit is too short for the aberrations of the system to vary appreciably along its length.

In the case of a slit of negligible width, each point of the slit can be regarded as a point source. If each point of the primary light source were sharply focused on to the plane of the slit by a wide-aperture condenser system of negligible aberrations, the different points of the slit could be treated as independent sources. In such a case, the observed intensity under the test would simply be the sum of the intensity contributions from the different point sources. If we suppose that the length of the slit is not great enough for off-axis aberrations of the system to make an appreciable contribution to the apparent errors of the surface under test, the intensity distributions contributed by any two points of the slit differ only by a constant factor. Therefore the intensity function $I(x', y')$ is still given by (2.17) and (2.12).

However, in a practical case the aperture of the condenser system is often comparable with that of the system under test and it is not true that all points of the primary source are sharply focused on to the plane of the slit by the condenser. Each luminous particle w of the primary source contributes a wave displacement

$$E_w(x, y) = A_w(x, y)E(x, y) \qquad (2.22)$$

on the surface M_0, where $E(x, y) = \exp\{-(2\pi i/\lambda)\phi(x, y)\}$ inside C and zero outside C, as before, while $A_w(x, y)$ expresses the characteristics of the wave emitted by the w-particle when, after passing through the condenser system and the slit, it arrives at the point x, y on the nearly spherical mirror M. Because the width of the slit is negligible, $A_w(x, y)$ does not vary appreciably with x and we may write, to a sufficient approximation,

$$E_w(x, y) = A_w(x, y)E(x, y). \qquad (2.23)$$

$|E_w(x,y)|^2$ measures the intensity of the wave at this point, so that if the mirror is to appear uniformly lit in the absence of the knife-edge

$$\sum_w |E_w(x,y)|^2$$

must be constant over its surface. By a suitable choice of units we can write this condition in the form

$$\sum_w |A_w(y)|^2 = 1 \quad \text{on } M_0. \tag{2.24}$$

The complex displacement contribution from the w-particle in the final image surface is then obtained on replacing $E(x,y)$ by $A_w(y)E(x,y)$ in the previous analysis; it is given by the equation

$$2\pi D_w(x',y') = \pi A_w(y')E(x',y') + i \int_{-\infty}^{\infty} A_w(y') \frac{E(t,y')}{t-x'} \, dt$$

$$= A_w(y') \cdot 2\pi D(x',y'),$$

where $D(x',y')$ is given by (2.17). Since the waves from the different w-particles are mutually incoherent, the total intensity seen on M_0 under the test is now $4\pi^2$ times

$$\sum_w |D_w(x',y')|^2 = \sum_w |A_w(y')|^2 |D(x',y')|^2$$

$$= |D(x',y')|^2,$$

by (2.24). That is, the intensities seen on the mirror are still given (2.17) and (2.12). The same is true of the intensities in the halo, since these differ from zero only in the y-range where (2.24) holds.

In most practical cases, the use of a slit in place of a pinhole allows 50 or 100 times as much light to be passed without making the slit too long, and the test can be carried out with ease and comfort in a partially darkened room. Fine scratches ruled in a silver film deposited on a thin glass plate make excellent slits for the purpose; they are used with the silvered face towards the system under test.

3. The true mirror under the Foucault test

To determine the appearance of a true circular mirror, tested with the knife-edge in the focal plane† but displaced laterally a distance c from the central setting, one must write in (2.17)

$$E(x,y) = e^{ic'x} \quad (x^2+y^2 \leqslant 1),$$
$$= 0 \quad (x^2+y^2 > 1),$$

† i.e. at the longitudinal setting which produces left-to-right symmetry in the intensities seen under the test.

where $c' = 2\pi c/\lambda s$, and multiply $D(x', y')$ on the left by the phase factor $e^{ic'x'}$. It follows that the complex displacement is given for $|y'| \leqslant 1$ by the equations

$$2\pi e^{ic'x'} D(x', y') = \frac{\pi}{0} e^{ic'x'} + i \int_{-\sqrt{(1-y'^2)}}^{\sqrt{(1-y'^2)}} \frac{e^{ic't}}{t-x'} dt,$$

i.e.

$$2\pi D(x', y') = \frac{\pi}{0} - i \int_{x'-\sqrt{(1-y'^2)}}^{x'+\sqrt{(1-y'^2)}} e^{-ic'u} \frac{du}{u}, \qquad (3.1)$$

according as $x'^2 + y'^2 \lessgtr 1$, while for $|y'| > 1$, $D(x', y') = 0$.

When $c' = 0$, this reduces to (2.18) above; when $c' \neq 0$, the integral can be evaluated in terms of the functions

$$\text{Si}(x) = \int_0^x \frac{\sin t}{t} dt, \qquad \text{Ci}(x) = - \int_x^\infty \frac{\cos t}{t} dt \qquad (3.2)$$

to give the formulae

$$2\pi D(x', y') = \frac{\pi}{0} - \text{Si}\{c'[x' + \sqrt{(1-y'^2)}]\} + \text{Si}\{c'[x' - \sqrt{(1-y'^2)}]\} -$$

$$- i\,\text{Ci}\{|c'[x' + \sqrt{(1-y'^2)}]|\} + i\,\text{Ci}\{|c'[x' - \sqrt{(1-y'^2)}]|\}, \quad (3.3)$$

$$I(x', y') = \left[\frac{\pi}{0} - \text{Si}\{c'[x' + \sqrt{(1-y'^2)}]\} + \text{Si}\{c'[x' - \sqrt{(1-y'^2)}]\}\right]^2 +$$

$$+ [\text{Ci}\{|c'[x' + \sqrt{(1-y'^2)}]|\} - \text{Ci}\{|c'[x' - \sqrt{(1-y'^2)}]|\}]^2. \quad (3.4)$$

Some of the consequences of these formulae are of physical interest. When $x'^2 + y'^2 > 1$, i.e. when the point (x', y') is outside the boundary curve C', (3.4) shows that the intensity in the halo is an even function of c', as well as of x' and y'. It is a familiar fact that, as the knife-edge is moved across the Airy disk, the halo brightens to a maximum and then fades out as the mirror disk darkens. The conclusion may therefore be drawn that the halo is brightest when the knife-edge is central.

Of more practical interest are the changes in the brightness of the disk as the knife-edge is advanced. Benerji (1918) drew attention to the large fluctuations in the observed brightness on the surface of a rectangular mirror which occur as the knife-edge is advanced, and explained them by an application of Rayleigh's theory. Later writers on the practical side of the test are almost unanimous in asserting that, as the knife-edge is advanced, a true mirror with circular boundary darkens evenly all over, and published photographs of the test often show a nearly uniform illumination.† The above discussion shows that, as the knife-edge cuts into the image, undulatory fluctuations of intensity should be seen on the surface of the mirror, and formula (3.4) predicts their appearance when the test is carried out with a pinhole whose diameter is small compared with that of the Airy disk.

Fig. 50 a shows the changes in intensity distribution which take place along the horizontal diameter as the knife-edge advances up to the central position, Fig. 50 b those as the knife-edge advances beyond it. It will be seen that, far from darkening evenly all over, the mirror actually brightens in the centre when $c' = -\pi$, i.e. when about one-tenth of the horizontal diameter of the Airy disk is occulted. Fig. 51 a shows the appearance of the disk at this setting. As the knife-edge is advanced, the central intensity maximum flattens out and at $c' = -1$ the disk appears fairly uniformly illuminated (see Fig. 51 b). Its appearance when the knife-edge is advanced to the central position is shown in Fig. 51 c; the darkening of the central part is then easily perceptible to the eye. The changes described above can be observed without any difficulty on using an f/55 spherical mirror, a pinhole of diameter 0·006 mm. and a viewing telescope of aperture 2·5 cm. and magnification 6, placed 2 cm. behind the plane of the knife-edge. It is perhaps relevant that when the eye judges the disk to be half lit, the knife-edge is not central but near to the setting of Fig. 51 b, while when the knife-edge is centrally set (by observing the halo intensity or with the help of a microscope) the disk appears considerably less than half lit and the darkening of its centre is easily recognized. In point of fact, as was shown above, the disk contains only one-third as much illumination at this setting as with the knife-edge withdrawn, the remaining one-sixth being sent into the halo.

4. Foucault properties of the astigmatic circular mirror

We first establish the following properties, well known to experimental opticians, of an astigmatic circular mirror under the Foucault test:

(1) there is a unique focal setting at which the illumination seen on the mirror retains its left-to-right symmetry as the knife-edge is advanced across the image;

(2) the presence of astigmatism is inferred from any vertical asymmetry in the appearance of the mirror at this focal setting, which we shall call the preferred setting;

(3) astigmatism shows itself most strongly when the mirror is oriented with its astigmatic principal directions at angles of 45° with the direction

† See, for example, Couder (1937).

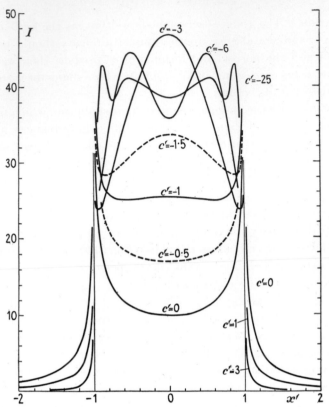

FIG. 50 *a*. True mirror with knife-edge non-central; intensities along horizontal diameter.

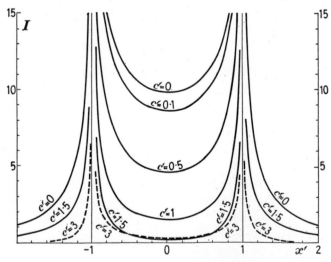

FIG. 50 *b*. True mirror with knife-edge non-central; intensities along horizontal diameter.

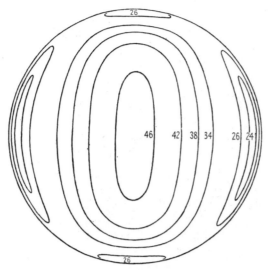

FIG. 51 a. True mirror with knife-edge non-central ($c' = -\pi$).

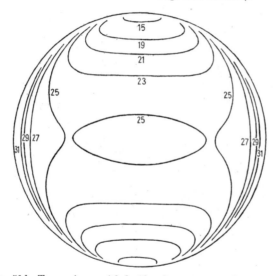

FIG. 51 b. True mirror with knife-edge non-central ($c' = -1$).

of the knife-edge. If one of these directions is parallel to the knife-edge, the appearance of the mirror under test is the same as that of a true mirror and the astigmatism accordingly escapes detection.

To derive these properties from the general theory, we apply (2.17) to a mirror whose wave function

$$E(x, y) = e^{i(ax^2+2hxy+by^2)} \quad (x^2+y^2 \leqslant 1),$$
$$= 0 \qquad\qquad (x^2+y^2 > 1). \qquad (4.1)$$

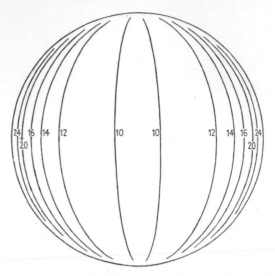

FIG. 51c. True mirror with knife-edge central ($c' = 0$).

If the plane of the knife-edge is at mean focus, the coefficients a, b satisfy the condition $a+b = 0$, but as this is not the focal setting used in practice (unless the mirror has its astigmatic axes equally inclined to the direction of the knife-edge) we discard the condition and allow for variations in the knife-edge setting by writing

$$E(x,y) = e^{i[(ax^2+2hxy+by^2)+\alpha(x^2+y^2)+c'x]} \quad (x^2+y^2 \leqslant 1),$$
$$= 0 \quad (x^2+y^2 > 1) \tag{4.2}$$

on the right of (2.17) and replacing $D(x',y')$ by $e^{i\alpha(x'^2+y'^2)+ic'x'}D(x',y')$ on the left. The parameter α then specifies the focal setting of the knife-edge, while $c' = 2\pi c/\lambda s$ gives its lateral distance c from the central position. Choosing $\alpha = -\frac{1}{2}(a+b)$ would correspond to setting the knife-edge at mean focus.

Applying (2.17) in this way, we obtain for the complex displacement $D(x',y')$ the equation

$$2\pi D(x',y') = e^{i(ax'^2+2hx'y'+by'^2-c'x')} \times$$

$$\times \left[\frac{\pi}{0} + i \int_{-\sqrt{(1-y'^2)}}^{\sqrt{(1-y'^2)}} e^{i[(a+\alpha)(t^2-x'^2)+2h(t-x')y'+c'(t-x')]} \frac{dt}{t-x'} \right]$$

$$(y'^2 \leqslant 1, \ x'^2+y'^2 \lessgtr 1),$$
$$= 0 \quad (y'^2 > 1). \tag{4.3}$$

When $\alpha = -a$, the square bracket is changed into its complex conjugate on writing $-x'$ for x' and hence

$$I(-x', y') = I(x', y');$$

when $\alpha \neq -a$ this relation no longer holds. Thus there is a unique focal setting at which the mirror shows a laterally symmetrical appearance for all values of c'. This preferred setting is the one used in practice and it is, broadly speaking, the focal setting at which the errors on the mirror are most plainly seen.

At the preferred focal setting we have, for $y'^2 \leqslant 1$, $x'^2 + y'^2 < 1$ and for $y'^2 \leqslant 1$, $x'^2 + y'^2 > 1$ respectively,

$$2\pi D(x', y') = e^{i(ax'^2 + 2hx'y' + by'^2 + c'x')}\left[\frac{\pi}{0} + i \int_{-\sqrt{(1-y'^2)}}^{\sqrt{(1-y'^2)}} e^{i(2hy' + c')(t-x')} \frac{dt}{t-x'}\right]$$

$$= e^{i(ax'^2 + 2hx'y' + by'^2 + c'x')}\left[\frac{\pi}{0} - i \int_{x' - \sqrt{(1-y'^2)}}^{x' + \sqrt{(1-y'^2)}} e^{-i(2hy' + c')u} \frac{du}{u}\right], \qquad (4.4)$$

which gives

$$I(x', y') = \left[\frac{\pi}{0} - \text{Si}[(2hy' + c')\{x' + \sqrt{(1-y'^2)}\}] + \right.$$
$$\left. + \text{Si}[(2hy' + c')\{x' - \sqrt{(1-y'^2)}\}]\right]^2 +$$
$$+ [\text{Ci}[|(2hy' + c')\{x' + \sqrt{(1-y'^2)}\}|] - $$
$$- \text{Ci}[|(2hy' + c')\{x' - \sqrt{(1-y'^2)}\}|]]^2, \qquad (4.5)$$

the second term on the right being understood, when $2hy' + c' = 0$, to stand for its limiting value

$$\left(\log\left|\frac{x' + \sqrt{(1-y'^2)}}{x' - \sqrt{(1-y'^2)}}\right|\right)^2.$$

Properties (1) and (2) have now been established. To prove property (3), we observe that of the coefficients a, h, b in (4.1) only h appears in (4.5). This means that a mirror for which

$$E(x, y) = e^{2ihxy} \qquad (x^2 + y^2 \leqslant 1),$$
$$= 0 \qquad (x^2 + y^2 > 1) \qquad (4.6)$$

and one of the figure (4.1) show the same intensities when each is tested at the preferred focal setting. The strength with which a given astigmatism shows itself under the test therefore corresponds to the size of the coefficient h in (4.1), and property (3) follows by a well-known result in coordinate geometry. For a mirror oriented so as to give h its maximum value, mean focus and preferred focus coincide, $E(x, y)$ is of the form (4.6) at the preferred focal setting, and $2h$ is 2π times the maximum optical path-difference at mean focus, measured in fringes. We suppose for the rest of the present section that the mirror is so oriented and that $E(x, y)$ has this form.

As already remarked, the mirror darkens symmetrically from left to right, but not from top to bottom, as the knife-edge is advanced. Its appearance when the knife-edge cuts the axis ($c' = 0$) is shown for an astigmatism of approximately $\frac{1}{20}$ fringe ($E(x, y) = e^{0 \cdot 3ixy}$) in Fig. 52 and for one of one fringe ($E(x, y) = e^{2\pi ixy}$) in Fig. 53. In the former case the vertical asymmetry is already very marked; in the latter the intensity distribution is beginning to approach that predicted by ray theory, namely a dark upper semicircle and a fully lit lower semicircle. It is easy to verify from (4.5) that when the astigmatism amounts to a large number of fringes the value of $I(x', y')$ is nearly $4\pi^2$ below the line $y' = -c'/2h$ and nearly zero above this line, while close to the line itself narrow dark fringes appear in the bright area. Thus equation (4.5) provides a simple means of predicting the observed phenomena, for large as well as for small amounts of astigmatism, when the test is carried out with a pinhole whose dimensions are small compared with those of the Airy disk.

5. Circular mirror with arbitrary errors. Special cases

5.1. *Small errors tested with knife-edge centrally set*

To apply (2.17) to the discussion of arbitrary smooth errors on a circular mirror, we write

$$E(x, y) = \sum_{m,n \geqslant 0} a_{mn} x^m y^n \quad (x^2 + y^2 \leqslant 1),$$

$$= 0 \quad (x^2 + y^2 > 1). \tag{5.1}$$

Then, if $-1 \leqslant y' \leqslant 1$,

$$\int_{-\infty}^{\infty} \frac{E(t, y')}{x' - t} \, dt = \int_{-\sqrt{(1-y'^2)}}^{\sqrt{(1-y'^2)}} \frac{E(t, y')}{x' - t} \, dt$$

$$= \sum_{m,n \geqslant 0} a_{mn} y'^n \int_{-Y}^{Y} \frac{t^m \, dt}{x' - t},$$

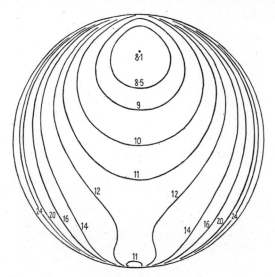

FIG. 52. $\frac{1}{20}$ fringe of astigmatism, tested with knife-edge centrally set.
Isophotal lines.

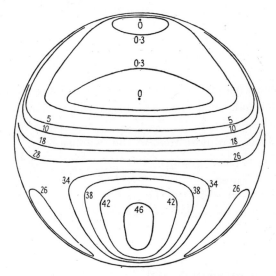

FIG. 53. One fringe of astigmatism, tested with knife-edge centrally set.
Isophotal lines.

where Y stands for $\sqrt{(1-y'^2)}$. Here

$$\int_{-Y}^{Y} \frac{t^m \, dt}{x'-t} = \int_{x'-Y}^{x'+Y} (x'-u)^m \frac{du}{u}$$

$$= \sum_{0 \leqslant r \leqslant m} (-1)^r \binom{m}{r} x'^{m-r} \int_{x'-Y}^{x'+Y} u^{r-1} \, du$$

$$= x'^m \log\left|\frac{x'+\sqrt{(1-y'^2)}}{x'-\sqrt{(1-y'^2)}}\right| +$$

$$+ \sum_{1 \leqslant r \leqslant m} (-1)^r \binom{m}{r} x'^{m-r} \frac{(x'+Y)^r - (x'-Y)^r}{r}.$$

Thus, in the strip $-1 \leqslant y' \leqslant 1$,

$$2\pi D(x',y') = \pi E(x',y') - i \sum_{m,n \geqslant 0} a_{mn} x'^m y'^n \log\left|\frac{x'+\sqrt{(1-y'^2)}}{x'-\sqrt{(1-y'^2)}}\right| -$$

$$- i \sum_{\substack{1 \leqslant r \leqslant m \\ n \geqslant 0}} a_{mn} x'^{m-r} y'^n (-1)^r \binom{m}{r} \frac{(x'+Y)^r - (x'-Y)^r}{r}$$

$$= 2\pi D_0(x',y') E(x',y') -$$

$$- i \sum_{\substack{1 \leqslant r \leqslant m \\ n \geqslant 0}} a_{mn} x'^{m-r} y'^n (-1)^r \binom{m}{r} \frac{(x'+Y)^r - (x'-Y)^r}{r},$$

$$(5.2)$$

where $D_0(x',y')$ is the value (2.18) of $D(x',y')$ for a true mirror. Outside the strip, $D(x',y') = 0$ by (2.17).

(5.2), together with (2.12), gives the intensities seen under test on the disk and in the halo of a circular mirror whose error coefficients are defined by the equation (5.1).

As a special case, suppose that in the expansion

$$-\phi(x,y) = \sum_{m,n \geqslant 0} \alpha_{mn} x^m y^n$$

of the error function $-\phi(x,y)$ the squares of the quantities $(2\pi/\lambda)\alpha_{mn}$ are small enough to be neglected. Then on the mirror

$$E(x,y) = \exp\left\{-\frac{2\pi i}{\lambda} \phi(x,y)\right\} = 1 - \frac{2\pi i}{\lambda} \phi(x,y), \qquad (5.3)$$

to a sufficient approximation, and the a_{mn} satisfy the equations†

$$a_{00} = 1 + \frac{2\pi i}{\lambda} \alpha_{00}, \qquad a_{mn} = \frac{2\pi i}{\lambda} \alpha_{mn} \quad (m^2 + n^2 > 0). \qquad (5.4)$$

† It makes no physical difference if we suppose that $\alpha_{00} = 0$.

The equations (5.2) and (2.12) then give

$$I(x', y') = |2\pi D(x', y')|^2$$

$$= \left| \left(\underset{0}{\pi} - i \log \left| \frac{x'+Y}{x'-Y} \right| \right) \left(1 - \frac{2\pi i}{\lambda} \phi(x', y') + \right. \right.$$

$$\left. \left. + \frac{2\pi}{\lambda} \sum_{1 \leqslant r \leqslant m} \alpha_{mn} x'^{m-r} y'^n (-1)^r \binom{m}{r} \frac{(x'+Y)^r - (x'-Y)^r}{r} \right) \right|^2$$

$$= \left(\underset{0}{\pi} - \frac{2\pi}{\lambda} \phi(x', y') \log \left| \frac{x'+Y}{x'-Y} \right| + \frac{2\pi}{\lambda} \sum \right)^2 +$$

$$+ \left(\log \left| \frac{x'+Y}{x'-Y} \right| - \underset{0}{\pi} \frac{2\pi}{\lambda} \sum \right)^2$$

$$= \underset{0}{\pi^2} + \log^2 \left| \frac{x'+Y}{x'-Y} \right| + \underset{0}{2\pi} \frac{2\pi}{\lambda} \sum,$$

on discarding terms in $(2\pi\alpha_{mn}/\lambda)^2$,

$$= I_0(x', y') + \underset{0}{\frac{4\pi^2/\lambda}{}} \sum_{\substack{1 \leqslant m \leqslant r \\ n \geqslant 0}} \alpha_{mn} x'^{m-r} y'^n (-1)^r \binom{m}{r} \frac{(x'+Y)^r - (x'-Y)^r}{r}, \tag{5.5}$$

where I_0 is the value (2.19) of the intensity for a true mirror and where the upper or lower alternatives are to be taken according as $x'^2 + y'^2 \lessgtr 1$. It follows that *small errors on the mirror do not appreciably affect the halo*, a result which it is easy to derive directly from (2.17) and (5.3).

The further specialization

$$a_{00} = 1; \qquad a_{20} = a_{02} = i(\alpha + \beta);$$

$$a_{40} = \tfrac{1}{2} a_{22} = a_{04} = -i\alpha; \qquad \text{all other } a_{mn} = 0, \tag{5.6}$$

where α and β are small enough for their squares to be neglected, corresponds to the wave function

$$E(x, y) = 1 + i\alpha(r^2 - r^4) + i\beta r^2. \tag{5.7}$$

(5.2) and (5.5) now reduce to the equations

$$2\pi D(x', y') = 2\pi D_0(x', y') E(x', y') -$$

$$- \tfrac{2}{3}\alpha x' \sqrt{(1 - y'^2)}(2 - 3x'^2 - 5y'^2) - 2\beta x' \sqrt{(1 - y'^2)}, \tag{5.8}$$

$$I(x', y') = I_0(x', y') -$$

$$- \underset{0}{\frac{2\pi}{}} [\tfrac{2}{3}\alpha x' \sqrt{(1 - y'^2)}(2 - 3x'^2 - 5y'^2) + 2\beta x' \sqrt{(1 - y'^2)}], \tag{5.9}$$

which therefore give the intensity seen on a mirror possessing a small amount of primary spherical aberration, tested with the knife-edge centrally set near mean focus.

5.2. *Effects of varying the knife-edge setting*

In deriving formulae which shall predict the effects of varying the knife-edge setting, we treat lateral displacements of the knife-edge in a different way from variations in its focal setting. The difference in treatment corresponds to the circumstance that an optician using the Foucault test does in practice use these two adjustments of the knife-edge in different ways. Having chosen a focal setting which shows up as prominently as possible the error on which he is working, he tests by moving the knife-edge laterally to and fro and noting the changes in the appearance of the shadows.

If the errors on the mirror are small, the different focal settings which can be usefully employed are all covered, in the manner explained in § 2.4, by multiplying $E(x,y)$ by a factor $e^{i\alpha(x^2+y^2)}$ in which $\alpha = (\pi/\lambda s^2)\,\delta s$ is small. In the formulae (5.3) $\phi(x,y)$ is replaced by $\phi(x,y)-(\delta s/2s^2)(x^2+y^2)$ and in (5.5) $\delta s/2s^2$ is added to α_{20} and α_{02}.

The situation is different with regard to the factor $e^{ic'x}$ which expresses the effect of a lateral shift of the knife-edge, since c' cannot be supposed small even in testing a true mirror, while values of c' up to 5 or 6 may be used in the observation of a fairly narrow zone only $\frac{1}{10}$ fringe in depth.

We therefore take the equation

$$2\pi D(x',y') = \overset{\pi}{\underset{0}{}} E(x',y') + i \int\limits_{-\sqrt{(1-y'^2)}}^{\sqrt{(1-y'^2)}} e^{ic'(t-x')}\frac{E(t,y)}{t-x'}\,dt, \qquad (5.10)$$

obtained on writing $e^{ic'x}E(x,y)$ for $E(x,y)$ and $e^{ic'x'}D(x',y')$ for $D(x',y')$ in (2.17), set

$$E(x,y) = \sum_{m,n\geqslant 0} a_{mn}x^m y^n \quad (x^2+y^2 \leqslant 1),$$

$$= 0 \qquad\qquad\qquad (x^2+y^2 > 1), \qquad (5.11)$$

as before, and (supposing the errors of the mirror small compared with $\lambda/2\pi$) write

$$E(x,y) = 1 - \frac{2\pi i}{\lambda}\left[\phi(x,y) - \frac{\delta s}{2s^2}(x^2+y^2)\right] \qquad (5.12)$$

to express the effects of an increase δs in the focal distance s of the knife-edge. (5.10) then becomes

$$2\pi D(x',y') = \overset{\pi}{\underset{0}{}} E(x',y') - i \int\limits_{x'-Y}^{x'+Y} E(x'-u,y')e^{ic'u}\frac{du}{u}$$

$$= \overset{\pi}{\underset{0}{}} E(x',y') - i \sum_{m,n\geqslant 0} a_{mn}y'^n \sum_{0\leqslant r\leqslant m}(-1)^r\binom{m}{r}x'^{m-r}I_{r-1},$$

where
$$I_{r-1} = \int_{x'-Y}^{x'+Y} u^{r-1} e^{-ic'u}\, du \quad (r \geqslant 0)$$

and Y is written for $\sqrt{(1-y'^2)}$, as before.

Here
$$I_{-1} = \mathrm{Ci}\{|c'(x'+Y)|\} - \mathrm{Ci}\{|c'(x'-Y)|\} - i\,\mathrm{Si}\{c'(x'+Y)\} + i\,\mathrm{Si}\{c'(x'-Y)\},$$
as in § 3, while for $r > 0$,
$$I_{r-1} = \sum_{s=1}^{r} (-1)^{s-1}\left(\frac{i}{c'}\right)^s \frac{(r-1)!}{(r-s)!}\left[(x'+Y)^{r-s}e^{-ic'(x'+Y)} - (x'-Y)^{r-s}e^{-ic'(x'-Y)}\right].$$

When $c' = 0$, these expressions are to be interpreted as their limiting values; for example, I_{-1} becomes $\log\left|\dfrac{x'-Y}{x'+Y}\right|$. For general c', we have

$$2\pi D(x',y') = \overset{\pi}{\underset{0}{}} E(x',y') - i\sum_{m,n\geqslant 0} a_{mn} x'^m y'^n I_{-1} -$$
$$-ie^{-ic'x'} \sum_{\substack{\geqslant 0 \\ 1\leqslant s\leqslant r\leqslant m}} a_{mn} x'^{m-r} y'^n (-1)^{r+s-1}\binom{m}{r}\left(\frac{i}{c'}\right)^s \frac{(r-1)!}{(r-s)!} M(r-s)$$
$$= 2\pi D_0(x',y')E(x',y') -$$
$$-ie^{-ic'x'} \sum_{\substack{n\geqslant 0 \\ 1\leqslant s\leqslant r\leqslant m}} a_{mn} x'^{m-r} y'^n (-1)^{r-s+1}\binom{m}{r}\left(\frac{i}{c'}\right)^s \frac{(r-1)!}{(r-s)!} M(r-s),$$
$$\tag{5.13}$$

where
$$2\pi D_0(x',y') = \overset{\pi}{\underset{0}{}} - iI_{-1}$$
$$= \overset{\pi}{\underset{0}{}} - i\,\mathrm{Ci}[\,|c'\{x'+\sqrt{(1-y'^2)}\}|\,] + i\,\mathrm{Ci}[\,|c'\{x'-\sqrt{(1-y'^2)}\}|\,] -$$
$$- \mathrm{Si}[c'\{x'+\sqrt{(1-y'^2)}\}] + \mathrm{Si}[c'\{x'-\sqrt{(1-y'^2)}\}]$$

is the value (3.3) of $2\pi D(x',y')$ for a true mirror (that is, one with $E(x,y) = 1$ or 0) at the same lateral setting of the knife-edge and
$$M(r-s) = \{x'+\sqrt{(1-y'^2)}\}^{r-s}e^{-ic'\sqrt{(1-y'^2)}} - \{x'-\sqrt{(1-y'^2)}\}^{r-s}e^{ic'\sqrt{(1-y'^2)}}.$$

Writing for shortness
$$\frac{\sin\{c'\sqrt{(1-y'^2)}\}}{c'\sqrt{(1-y'^2)}} = S, \qquad \cos\{c'\sqrt{(1-y'^2)}\} = C,$$
we find
$$M(0) = -2ic'YS,$$
$$M(1) = x'M(0) + 2YC,$$
$$M(2) = (x'^2 + Y^2)M(0) + 4x'YC, \tag{5.14}$$
$$M(3) = (x'^3 + 3x'Y^2)M(0) + 2(3x'^2 + Y^2)YC.$$

As a special case, suppose that in (5.13) all the a_{mn} are zero except $a_{00}, a_{20}, a_{02}, a_{40}, a_{22}, a_{04}$. Then

$$2\pi D(x', y') = 2\pi D_0(x', y') E(x', y') - ie^{-ic'x'} \sum, \qquad (5.15)$$

where

$$\sum = \sum_{1 \leqslant s \leqslant r \leqslant m} a_{mn} x'^{m-r} y'^n (-1)^{r-s+1} \binom{m}{r} \left(\frac{i}{c'}\right)^s \frac{(r-1)!}{(r-s)!} M(r-s)$$

$$= (a_{20} + a_{22} y'^2) \left[-2x'YS + \frac{2iY}{c'} (C-S) \right] +$$

$$+ a_{40} \left[-2x'YS(x'^2 + Y^2) + \frac{2iY}{c'} (C-S) \left(x'^2 + \frac{2x'}{c'} i - \frac{6}{c'^2} + Y^2 \right) - \right.$$

$$\left. - \frac{2iY}{c'} 2SY^2 \right]. \qquad (5.16)$$

The intensity distribution for a mirror possessing a small amount of primary spherical aberration, tested with the knife-edge near mean focus but not necessarily central, is now obtained on giving the six coefficients $a_{00}, a_{20}, a_{02}, a_{40}, a_{22}, a_{04}$ the values (5.6).

5.3. *Two special cases*

The general formula (5.16) can be used to estimate the theoretical sensitiveness of the Foucault test for errors of different types. Only the two simplest cases will be considered here, namely the determination of the focus of an aberration-free pencil and the detection of primary spherical aberration, and except in the last paragraph it will be supposed that the knife-edge intersects the axis of the system, so that the cases are covered by (5.9). In practice, the lateral adjustment of the knife-edge would of course be varied.

In the first case, the effect of an error δs of excess in the determination of the focal distance is an apparent error $(x^2 + y^2) \delta s / 16F^2$ on the surface of the mirror on which, as in § 2, the errors may be supposed to be located. Here r^2 stands for $x^2 + y^2$, F denotes the aperture ratio of the pencil, or of this mirror, and $d(r) = r^2 \delta s / 8F^2$ measures the variation in optical path distance from points on a wave-front just leaving this mirror to the axial point of the knife-edge. At the edge ($r = 1$) of the pencil, the variation reaches its greatest value $\delta s / 8F^2$. Thus the maximum variation will be $\frac{1}{20}\lambda$ if $\delta s = \frac{2}{5}\lambda F^2$, $d(r) = \frac{1}{20}\lambda r^2$. In an f/5 pencil this corresponds to a focusing error $\delta s = 0.0002$ inch.

For such small path differences $d(r)$, the approximation

$$\exp\left\{\frac{2\pi i}{\lambda} d(r)\right\} = 1 + \frac{2\pi i}{\lambda} d(r) = 1 + \frac{\pi i}{10} r^2 \qquad (5.17)$$

can be used without introducing more than a few per cent. of variation in the amplitude of the wave leaving the mirror. The expression for the intensity I_1 is then obtained on taking $\alpha = 0$, $\beta = \frac{1}{10}\pi$ in (5.9). On the disk its value is

$$I_1 = I_0 - \tfrac{2}{5}\pi^2 x' \sqrt{(1-y'^2)}. \tag{5.18}$$

Fig. 54 shows the isophotal lines in this case and Fig. 55 the intensity distribution along the horizontal diameter as calculated from (5.18) and also as calculated from the more exact formulae (5.2), (5.3), and (2.12). The error of approximation in (5.3) was reduced by using for the more exact calculation the retardation function $d(r) = \frac{1}{20}\lambda(r^2-\frac{1}{2})$. From Fig. 54 we may conclude that an error of focusing amounting to only $\frac{1}{20}$ fringe should be easily visible under the test.

In the second case, namely primary spherical aberration, the retardation function at mean focus has the form $d(r) = Ar^2(1-r^2)$. To obtain a maximum variation of optical path distance of $\frac{1}{20}\lambda$, we take $A = \frac{1}{5}\lambda$ and obtain, to a sufficient approximation,

$$\exp\left\{\frac{2\pi i}{\lambda}\,d(r)\right\} = 1 + \frac{2\pi i}{\lambda}\,d(r) = 1 + \frac{2\pi i}{5}\,r^2(1-r^2). \tag{5.19}$$

The intensity I_2 is then obtained from (5.9) on setting $\alpha = \frac{2}{5}\pi$, $\beta = 0$, and its value on the disk is

$$I_2 = I_0 - \frac{8\pi^2}{15}\,x'\sqrt{(1-y'^2)}(2-3x'^2-5y'^2). \tag{5.20}$$

Fig. 56 shows the isophotal lines in this case and Fig. 57 the intensity distribution along the horizontal diameter as calculated from (5.20) and from the more exact formulae (5.2), (5.3), and (2.12). The retardation function was taken as $\frac{1}{5}\lambda(r^2-r^4-\frac{1}{6})$ for the more exact calculation.

Figs. 58 and 59 show the isophotes for $\frac{1}{10}$ and $\frac{1}{4}$ of a fringe of primary spherical aberration; a more accurate approximation than (5.3) to the wave function $E(x,y)$ had of course to be used for the computation of Fig. 59.

On comparing Figs. 56, 58, and 59 we see how, as the amount of the error increases, the Foucault shadows move towards the form predicted by ray theory and shown in Fig. 60, until with $\frac{1}{4}$ fringe of error the resemblance is already fairly close. The principal remaining differences, attributable to the effects of diffraction, are the pronounced brightening of the mirror near the rim on both sides and the asymmetry of the isophotal line ($I(x,y) = \pi^2$ in Fig. 59) which corresponds to the 'crest of the hill' in the grazing light interpretation of the test. According to ray theory, this line would be the circle $x^2+y^2 = \frac{1}{2}$, of radius 0·707, and

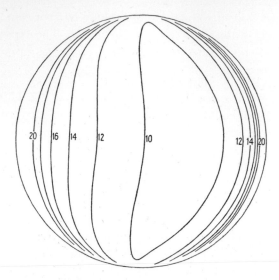

FIG. 54. Disk intensities under knife-edge test of a true mirror with $\frac{1}{20}$ fringe focus error: $d(r) = \frac{1}{20}\lambda r^2$.

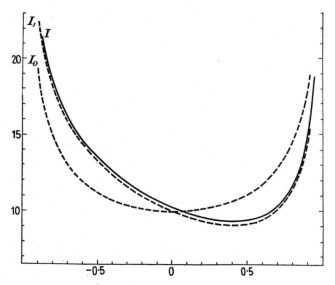

FIG. 55. Intensities along horizontal diameter of a mirror with $\frac{1}{20}$ fringe of focus error, tested with knife-edge centrally set. $I =$ intensity calculated from (5.2), (5.3); $I_1 =$ intensity calculated from the approximate formula (5.18); $I_0 =$ intensity for a true mirror.

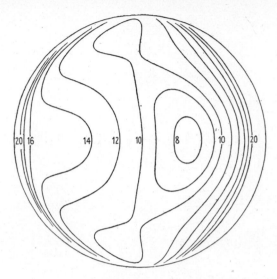

FIG. 56. Disk intensities under knife-edge test of a mirror with $\frac{1}{20}$ fringe primary spherical aberration: $d(r) = \frac{1}{5}\lambda r^2(1-r^2)$.

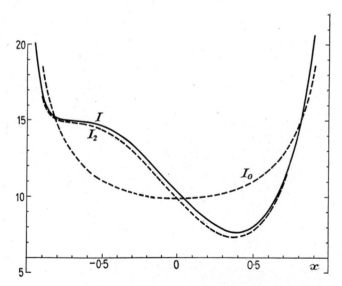

FIG. 57. Intensities along horizontal diameter of a mirror with $\frac{1}{10}$ fringe of primary spherical aberration, tested with knife-edge at mean focus. I = intensity calculated from (5.2), (5.3); I_2 = intensity calculated from the approximate formula (5.20); I_0 = intensity for a true mirror.

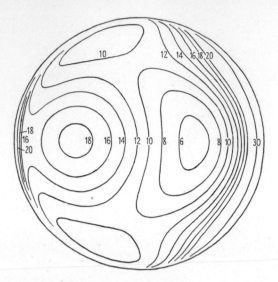

FIG. 58. Disk intensities under knife-edge test of a true mirror with $\frac{1}{10}$ fringe of primary spherical aberration: $d(r) = \frac{2}{5}\lambda r^2(1-r^2)$.

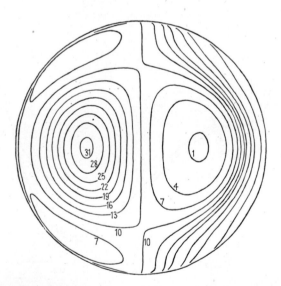

FIG. 59. Disk intensities under knife-edge test of a true mirror with $\frac{1}{4}$ fringe of primary spherical aberration: $d(r) = \lambda r^2(1-r^2)$.

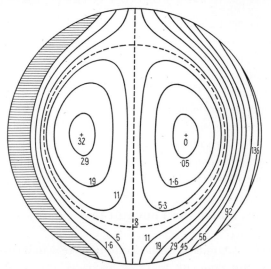

FIG. 60. Foucault shadows predicted by ray theory on a mirror with primary spherical aberration, tested with knife-edge centrally set at mean focus $[d(r) = Ar^2(1-r^2)]$ and with a slit-source of width equal to 0·20 times the diameter of the geometrical confusion disk at this setting.

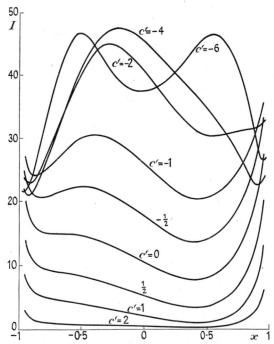

FIG. 61. Disk intensities along horizontal diameter of a mirror with $\frac{1}{20}$ fringe of primary spherical aberration, tested with knife-edge at different lateral settings in the plane of mean focus.

the elliptical distortion combined with displacement to the left which it shows in Fig. 59 would be interpreted as showing the presence of small amounts of astigmatism and of coma on the mirror surface.

From Figs. 56 and 57, we conclude that the Foucault test should be capable of detecting $\frac{1}{20}$ fringe of primary spherical aberration without difficulty even if the knife-edge is restricted to be central. From Fig. 61, which shows the intensity distributions along the horizontal diameter for a number of different lateral settings of the knife-edge, it appears that, in the present special case at least, no great increase in limiting sensitiveness is to be expected when the artificial restriction to central settings is removed.

6. Zonal errors under the Foucault test

6.1. *Introductory*

Although the explanation of the knife-edge test in terms of ray theory, originally given by Foucault in 1859, leaves certain rather conspicuous appearances unexplained, it has served ever since as the basis of the interpretation of the test by optical workers. In the practical use of the test the unexplained appearances, such as the brilliant line of light seen round the rim of a nearly true mirror, or the dark fringes which form on the bright slopes of a zonal error several wave-lengths deep, are ordinarily set aside as 'due to diffraction' and ignored as far as possible, while the interpretation of the knife-edge shadows is made in a semi-intuitive manner by means of the 'grazing light' fiction.

This device consists in replacing the mirror surface in imagination by a flat disk on which parallel light falls, at nearly grazing incidence, from the side opposite to the knife-edge. The Foucault shadows are interpreted as relief-shadows and the bas-relief figure thus 'seen' on the disk is taken to represent the error figure of the mirror. Provided that the error slopes are sufficiently small, the error figure inferred in this way agrees in shape with that which would be obtained by a photometric analysis of the Foucault shadows on the basis of ray theory. This does not mean, however, that it necessarily agrees in shape with the error figure actually present on the mirror, and the relationship between the inferred and the actual errors remains a matter for investigation.

In the present section we apply (2.21) to make such an investigation in the case of a weak, narrow zone on the surface of an otherwise nearly true mirror. This case is a favourable one for discussion, since it is one in which the conclusions are not much affected by the simplifying assumption that the pinhole size is negligible, and is not unlike cases actually met with in the zonal figuring of large astronomical mirrors.

6.2. *Effect on the knife-edge shadows of a small change in figure*

By (2.21), the intensity seen under the test, at the point (x, y) on M_0, with the knife-edge in the plane through the centre of curvature of M_0, but displaced laterally through a distance c from the central setting, is

$$I_1(x, y; c') = |2\pi D_1(x, y; c')|^2, \qquad (6.1)$$

where, for $-1 \leqslant y \leqslant 1$,

$$2\pi D_1(x, y; c') = \pi E_1(x, y) + i \int_{-Y}^{Y} \frac{E_1(t, y)}{t - x} e^{ic'(t - x)} \, dt; \qquad (6.2)$$

here $Y = \sqrt{(1 - y^2)}$, $c' = (2\pi/\lambda s)c$ and

$$E_1(x, y) = e^{-2\pi i \phi(x, y)} \quad (x^2 + y^2 \leqslant 1),$$
$$= 0 \qquad (x^2 + y^2 > 1) \qquad (6.3)$$

is the wave function which represents the complex displacement, in the surface M_0, corresponding to the unchanged figure of the mirror M. The integral in (6.2) is a Cauchy principal value when $-1 < x < 1$. When $|y| > 1$, the value of $D_1(x, y; c')$ is zero.

A change in the figure of the mirror can be expressed by adding to $-\phi(x, y)$ a deviation contribution $\psi(x, y)$, to give the new wave function

$$E(x, y) = E_1(x, y) e^{2\pi i \psi(x, y)}$$
$$= E_1(x, y)\{1 + 2\pi i \eta(x, y)\}, \qquad (6.4)$$

where

$$\eta(x, y) = \frac{1}{2\pi i}(e^{2\pi i \psi(x, y)} - 1). \qquad (6.5)$$

We suppose that $\psi(x, y)$ possesses continuous partial differential coefficients everywhere, that $\psi(x, y) \ll 1$ and that $\psi^2(x, y)$ can be neglected. Then $\eta(x, y)$ possesses continuous partial differential coefficients and, to the same order of approximation, $\eta(x, y) = \psi(x, y)$, $\eta(x, y)$ is real and $\eta^2(x, y)$ can be neglected.

We suppose further that the integral

$$T(x, y) = \int_{-Y}^{Y} \left| \frac{\eta(t, y) - \eta(x, y)}{t - x} \right| dt \qquad (6.6)$$

is, when $x^2 + y^2 < 1$, so small that its square can be neglected. This means, broadly speaking, that the changes in profile are not too violent.

The intensity seen under the test, with the knife-edge at the same setting as before, is now

$$I(x, y; c') = |2\pi D(x, y; c')|^2, \qquad (6.7)$$

where

$$2\pi D(x,y;c') = \pi E(x,y) + i \int_{-Y}^{Y} \frac{E(t,y)}{t-x} e^{ic'(t-x)}\, dt$$

$$= 2\pi D_1(x,y;c') + \pi 2\pi i \eta(x,y) E_1(x,y) -$$

$$-2\pi \int_{-Y}^{Y} \frac{\eta(t,y) E_1(t,y)}{t-x} e^{ic'(t-x)}\, dt, \quad (6.8)$$

by (6.4). Therefore

$$|2\pi D(x,y;c')|^2 = |2\pi D_1(x,y;c')|^2 + \left| 2\pi D_1(x,y;c') 2\pi i \eta(x,y) - \right.$$

$$\left. -2\pi \int_{-Y}^{Y} \frac{\eta(t,y) - \eta(x,y)}{t-x} E_1(t,y) e^{ic'(t-x)}\, dt \right|^2 + 2\,\Re\left\{ 2\pi \overline{D_1(x,y;c')} \times \right.$$

$$\times \left[\pi 2\pi i \eta(x,y) E_1(x,y) - 2\pi \int_{-Y}^{Y} \frac{\eta(t,y) E_1(x,y)}{t-x} e^{ic'(t-x)}\, dt \right] \right\}.$$

Since

$$\left| \int_{-Y}^{Y} \frac{\eta(t,y) - \eta(x,y)}{t-x} E_1(t,y) e^{ic'(t-x)}\, dt \right| \leqslant T(x,y),$$

the second term on the right can be neglected provided that x is not too close to the edge of the mirror† and we obtain the approximate formula

$$I(x,y;c') - I_1(x,y;c')$$

$$= 2\,\Re\left\{ 2\pi \overline{D_1(x,y;c')} \left[2i\pi^2 \eta(x,y) E_1(x,y) - \right. \right.$$

$$\left. \left. -2\pi \int_{-Y}^{Y} \frac{\eta(t,y) E_1(t,y)}{t-x} e^{ic'(t-x)}\, dt \right] \right\} \quad (6.9)$$

for the changes in the intensities of the knife-edge shadows which result when an arbitrary small change of $\eta(x,y)$ fringes is made in the figure of the mirror.

The effect of introducing small errors on a previously true mirror is obtained as a special case on setting $\phi(x,y) = 0$. In this case

$$E_1(x,y) = 1, \qquad 2\pi D_1(x,y) = \pi + i \int_{-Y}^{Y} \frac{e^{ic'(t-x)}}{t-x}\, dt \qquad (6.10)$$

† $D_1(x,y;c')$ becomes large near $x = \pm Y$.

for $x^2+y^2 < 1$ and after some easy manipulation (6.9) gives, for these values of x and y,

$$\frac{1}{4\pi^2}[I(x,y;c')-I_0(x,y;c')]$$

$$= C(x,y)\left[\pi\eta(x,y) - \int_{-Y}^{Y} \frac{\eta(t,y)}{t-x}\sin c'(t-x)\,dt\right] -$$

$$-[1-S(x,y)]\int_{-Y}^{Y} \frac{\eta(t,y)}{t-x}\cos c'(t-x)\,dt, \quad (6.11)$$

where

$$C(x,y) = \frac{1}{\pi}\int_{-Y}^{Y} \frac{\cos c'(u-x)}{u-x}\,du = \frac{1}{\pi}[\mathrm{Ci}\{|c'(Y+x)|\} - \mathrm{Ci}\{|c'(Y-x)|\}],$$

$$S(x,y) = \frac{1}{\pi}\int_{-Y}^{Y} \frac{\sin c'(u-x)}{u-x}\,du = \frac{1}{\pi}[\mathrm{Si}\{c'(Y+x)\} + \mathrm{Si}\{c'(Y-x)\}],$$

$$(6.12)$$

while $$I_0(x,y;c') = \pi^2\{[C(x,y)]^2 + [1-S(x,y)]^2\} \quad (6.13)$$

represents the intensities seen on the surface of a true mirror at the same knife-edge setting. The condition (6.6) is always satisfied if the slopes of the 'error surface' $z = \eta(x,y)$ are everywhere small enough for their squares to be neglected; that is, it is satisfied by small, slow errors of arbitrary form.

6.3. *Local zonal errors*

To discuss the appearance of a narrow local zone under the test, we suppose that $\psi(x,y)$ is radially symmetrical and that it vanishes outside the zone of width 2δ and mean radius r.

During the removal of zonal error from surfaces of nearly perfect revolution symmetry, attention is usually concentrated on the 'main diameter' of the surface (that is, the diameter running at right angles to the direction of the knife-edge) and the form of the zonal error is inferred from the intensities seen along this diameter. These intensities are obtained on setting $y = 0$ in (6.9). In the case of a local zone, where $\eta(x,0)$ is zero everywhere outside the ranges $-r-\delta \leqslant x \leqslant -r+\delta$ and

$r-\delta \leqslant x \leqslant r+\delta$, they satisfy the relation

$$I(x, 0; c')-I_1(x, 0; c')$$

$$= 2\,\Re\left\{2\pi\,\overline{D_1(x, 0; c')}\left[2i\pi^2\eta(x, 0)E_1(x, 0)-\right.\right.$$

$$\left.\left.-2\pi\left(\int_{-r-\delta}^{-r+\delta} + \int_{r-\delta}^{r+\delta}\right)\frac{\eta(t, 0)E_1(t, 0)}{t-x}\,e^{ic'(t-x)}\,dt\right]\right\}, \quad (6.14)$$

provided that x is not too close to the ends of the diameter.

If $E_1(x, 0)$ and $D_1(x, 0; c')$ are nearly constant as x varies on or near the zone, (6.14) can be replaced there by the approximate equation

$$I(x, 0; c')-I_1(x, 0; c')$$

$$= 4\pi^2\,\Re\left\{\overline{D_1(x, 0; c')}\left[2\pi i\eta(x, 0)E_1(\rho, 0)-\right.\right.$$

$$\left.\left.-2\left(E_1(-r, 0)\int_{-r-\delta}^{-r+\delta} + E_1(r, 0)\int_{r-\delta}^{r+\delta}\right)\frac{\eta(t, 0)}{t-x}\,e^{ic'(t-x)}\,dt\right]\right\}, \quad (6.15)$$

where $\rho = \pm r$ according as $x > 0$ or $x < 0$.

In particular, (6.15) can be used when $\delta \ll 1$ and $E_1(x, 0)$ varies only slowly over the whole range $-1 < x < 1$; that is to say, in the case of a narrow local zone on a nearly true mirror. In this case, the distance (approximately $10\,c'$-units) through which the knife-edge must be moved laterally to change the appearance of the main part of the mirror from 'fully lit' to 'fully dark' is small compared with the horizontal resolving power of each of the two segments

$$-r-\delta \leqslant t \leqslant -r+\delta \quad \text{and} \quad r-\delta \leqslant t \leqslant r+\delta$$

cut off by the zone on the main diameter, and the value of $e^{ic'(t-x)}$ is accordingly nearly constant over these two t-ranges for the relevant values of c' and of x. To make the notion of proximity more definite, we agree to say that x is 'on or near' the zone when it satisfies one of the two conditions

$$|x-r| \leqslant 6\delta, \quad\quad\quad\quad\quad (6.16)$$

$$|x+r| \leqslant 6\delta. \quad\quad\quad\quad\quad (6.17)$$

For such values of x,

$$\int_{-1}^{1} \frac{\eta(t,0)}{t-x} E_1(t,0)e^{ic'(t-x)}\, dt$$

$$= E_1(r,0)e^{ic'(r-x)} \int_{r-\delta}^{r+\delta} \frac{\eta(t,0)}{t-x}\, dt +$$

$$+ E_1(-r,0)e^{ic'(r+x)} \int_{-r-\delta}^{-r+\delta} \frac{\eta(t,0)}{t-x}\, dt, \quad (6.18)$$

approximately. When x satisfies (6.16), the second term on the right of (6.18) is small in comparison with the first; when x satisfies (6.17), the first is small in comparison with the second. In either case (6.18) can be replaced by the equation

$$\int_{-1}^{1} \frac{\eta(t,0)E_1(t,0)}{t-x} e^{ic'(t-x)}\, dt = E_1(\rho,0) \int_{-1}^{1} \frac{\zeta(\tau)}{\tau-\xi}\, d\tau,$$

where†

$$\rho = r\,\mathrm{sgn}\,x, \qquad \xi = \frac{x-\rho}{\delta}, \qquad \tau = \frac{t-\rho}{\delta}$$

and the function

$$\zeta(\tau) = \eta(t,0)$$

expresses the zone profile in terms of the new variable τ, which runs from -1 to $+1$ on a zonal segment of width 2δ.

(6.15) then gives, for points x on or near the zone,

$$\frac{1}{4\pi^2}\{I(x,0;c')-I_1(x,0;c')\}$$

$$= \Re\left\{\overline{D_1(\rho,0;c')}E_1(\rho,0)\left[2\pi i\zeta(\xi)-2\int_{-1}^{1} \frac{\zeta(\tau)}{\tau-\xi}\, d\tau\right]\right\}$$

$$= -\zeta(\xi)\Im\{2\pi\overline{D_1(\rho,0;c')}E_1(\rho,0)\}-$$

$$-\int_{-1}^{1} \frac{\zeta(\tau)}{\tau-\xi}\, d\tau\, \Re\{2\overline{D_1(\rho,0;c')}E_1(\rho,0)\}. \quad (6.19)$$

---

† $\mathrm{sgn}\,x$ is defined as 1, 0, -1 according as $x >$, $=$, < 0.

In the special case of a narrow local zone on an otherwise true mirror, (6.19) becomes, in virtue of (6.10),

$$\frac{1}{4\pi^2}\{I(x,0;c')-I_1(x,0;c')\}$$

$$= -[\text{Ci}\{|c'(1+\rho)|\}-\text{Ci}\{|c'(1-\rho)|\}]\zeta(\xi)-$$

$$-\left(1-\frac{1}{\pi}[\text{Si}\{c'(1+\rho)\}+\text{Si}\{c'(1-\rho)\}]\right)\int_{-1}^{1}\frac{\zeta(\tau)}{\tau-\xi}\,d\tau, \quad (6.20)$$

a result which can also be derived from (6.11). When the knife-edge is centrally set $(c'=0)$, (6.20) takes the simpler form

$$\frac{1}{4\pi^2}\{I(x,0;0)-I_1(x,0;0)\} = -\text{sgn}\,x\log\frac{1+r}{1-r}\zeta(\xi)-\int_{-1}^{1}\frac{\zeta(\tau)}{\tau-\xi}\,d\tau. \quad (6.21)$$

In the more general case where small, slow irregular errors may also be present on the mirror, we write

$$E_1(x,y) = e^{-2\pi i\phi(x,y)} = 1+2\pi i\eta_1(x,y)$$

and suppose $\phi(x,y)$ so small that its square can be neglected. Then $\eta_1(x,y) = -\phi(x,y)$ to the same order of approximation, and an application of (6.8), with

$$2\pi D_0(x,0;c') = \pi+i\int_{-1}^{1}\frac{e^{ic'(t-x)}}{t-x}\,dt \quad (6.22)$$

in place of $2\pi D_1$ and with D_1 in place of D, gives, by an argument very similar to that used above,

$$\frac{1}{4\pi^2}\{I(x,0;c')-I_1(x,0;c')\}$$

$$= \zeta(\xi)\int_{-1}^{1}\frac{\cos c'(t-\rho)}{t-\rho}\,dt-\int_{-1}^{1}\frac{\zeta(\tau)}{\tau-\xi}\,d\tau\left[1-\frac{1}{\pi}\int_{-1}^{1}\frac{\sin c'(t-\rho)}{t-\rho}\,dt\right]. \quad (6.23)$$

It follows that (6.20) and its particular case (6.21) remain valid approximations when, in addition to the narrow zonal error described by $\zeta(\tau)$, small irregular slow errors are present on the mirror surface.

6.4. *Interpretation of the test*

Along the main diameter $y=0$, the inferred error-slope of the mirror on and near a weak, narrow zone is proportional to $I(x,0;c')-I_1(x,0;c')$. It varies somewhat as the lateral setting of the knife-edge is varied, although the variations in the shape of the inferred error profile are not large enough to attract notice in the ordinary use of the test.

When $c' = 0$, i.e. when the knife-edge is central, the inferred error profile $P(x)$ or $\zeta^*(\xi)$ on the mirror is given, apart from an appropriate scale factor† and an arbitrary additive constant, by the equation

$$P(x) = -\frac{1}{4\pi^2} \int^x \{I(x,0;0) - I_1(x,0;0)\}\, dx, \qquad (6.24)$$

and (6.21) therefore yields, on and near the zone, the approximate formula

$$\zeta^*(\xi) = P(x) = \operatorname{sgn} x \log\frac{1+r}{1-r} \int^\xi \zeta(u)\, du + \int^\xi \left(\int_{-1}^1 \frac{\zeta(\tau)}{\tau-u}\, d\tau \right) du$$

$$= \operatorname{sgn} x \log\frac{1+r}{1-r} \int^\xi \zeta(u)\, du + \int_{-1}^1 \zeta(\tau) \log\frac{1}{|\tau-\xi|}\, d\tau. \qquad (6.25)$$

(6.25) expresses the distortion which the zone profile undergoes when 'seen' under the Foucault test with the knife-edge centrally set. That is to say, it describes the 'intrinsic error' of the test when applied to a weak, narrow zone of mean radius r on an otherwise nearly true mirror.

The corresponding formula when the knife-edge is non-central is obtained by substituting from (6.20) into (6.24); it is

$$\zeta^*(\xi) = [\operatorname{Ci}\{|c'(1+\rho)|\} - \operatorname{Ci}\{|c'(1-\rho)|\}] \int^\xi \zeta(u)\, du +$$

$$+ \left(1 - \frac{1}{\pi}[\operatorname{Si}\{c'(1+\rho)\} + \operatorname{Si}\{c'(1-\rho)\}] \right) \int_{-1}^1 \zeta(\tau) \log\frac{1}{|\tau-\xi|}\, d\tau. \qquad (6.26)$$

Equations (6.25) and (6.26) allow some general conclusions to be drawn about the relation between the inferred profile of a weak, narrow zone and its actual profile. (6.26) can be written

$$\zeta^*(\xi) = A \int_{-1}^1 \zeta(\tau) \log\frac{1}{|\tau-\xi|}\, d\tau + B \int^\xi \zeta(u)\, du, \qquad (6.27)$$

† An unknown scale factor is necessarily involved, since the intensities seen under the test with a very small pinhole are determined by the depths of the errors measured in wavelengths and not by the angular amounts of the error-slopes. Two mirrors of different sizes but of the same shape, for example two paraboloids of different sizes but of the same focal ratio, therefore show different shadow intensities under the test.

where the coefficients

$$A = 1 - \frac{1}{\pi}[\mathrm{Si}\{c'(1+\rho)\} + \mathrm{Si}\{c'(1-\rho)\}],$$

$$B = \mathrm{Ci}\{|c'(1+\rho)|\} - \mathrm{Ci}\{|c'(1-\rho)|\}$$

depend on $\rho = r\,\mathrm{sgn}\,x$ and on c', but not on δ. It follows that the apparent distortion imposed by the test on the zone profile is independent of the zone width; two narrow zones of the same mean radius but of different widths will possess the same inferred profile $\zeta^*(\xi)$ if they possess the same actual profile.

By (6.27), $\zeta^*(\xi)$ is a linear combination of the two functions

$$\zeta^{(1)}(\xi) = \int\limits_{-1}^{1} \zeta(\tau)\log\frac{1}{|\tau-\xi|}\,d\tau \tag{6.28}$$

and

$$\zeta^{(2)}(\xi) = \int\limits^{\xi} \zeta(u)\,du. \tag{6.29}$$

The first of these is a Faltung or 'smear' of $\zeta(\tau)$ by means of the function $\log(1/|\tau|)$. Rapid changes in the slope of the zone-profile are smoothed and rounded off by the smearing process, which also 'spreads' the zone, so that $\zeta^{(1)}(\tau)$ does not vanish everywhere outside the interval $-1 < \tau < 1$, as $\zeta(\tau)$ does, but tails off gradually. Fig. 62 illustrates this in the particular case

$$\zeta(\tau) = (1-\tau^2)^2 \quad (-1 < \tau < 1),$$

$$= 0 \quad\quad (\tau^2 \geqslant 1). \tag{6.30}$$

When the zone has a symmetrical profile, i.e. when $\zeta(\tau)$ is an even function of τ, $\zeta^{(1)}(\tau)$ is likewise an even function and the 'smeared' zone is symmetrical. However, the inferred profile (6.27) is not symmetrical because of the effect of the term in $\zeta^{(2)}(\xi)$. The function $\zeta^{(2)}(\xi)$ is constant outside the interval $-1 < \xi < 1$, but its value is not in general the same on both sides of the interval. In the case of a high or low zone, where $\zeta(\tau)$ is of constant sign in $(-1, 1)$, the smeared function $\zeta^{(1)}(\xi)$ is monotonic in each of the ξ-ranges outside this interval; therefore the inferred profile

$$\zeta^*(\xi) = A\zeta^{(1)}(\xi) + B\zeta^{(2)}(\xi)$$

is likewise monotonic in $(-\infty, -1)$ and in $(1, \infty)$, whatever may be the values of A and B. That is to say at no setting of the knife-edge do maxima or minima of the inferred zone-profile ever lie outside the actual zone. But their positions within the actual zone vary when the ratio B/A varies; that is, they depend on the lateral setting of the knife-edge and on the situation of the zone on the mirror disk.

The curves in Fig. 63 show the values of B/A as c' varies, for zones of mean radius 0·25, 0·5, 0·65, 0·80 respectively; the values of c' which are of most practical importance are, by Figs. 5 a and 5 b, those between -2 and $+1$. In this range of values of c', B/A may be approximated

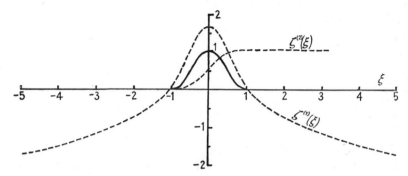

FIG. 62. The functions $\zeta(\xi)$ (solid curve), $\zeta^{(1)}(\xi)$ and $\zeta^{(2)}(\xi)$ in the case (6.30).

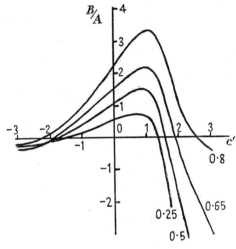

FIG. 63.

to with sufficient accuracy for practical purposes by the expression $(c'+2)\alpha(\rho)$, where

$$\alpha(\rho) = 0·25, \ 0·5, \ 0·7, \ 1·1,$$

for zones of mean radius 0·25, 0·5, 0·65, 0·80 respectively. In Fig. 64 are shown the inferred zone profile, calculated from (6.27), corresponding to the actual profile (6.30) in the cases $c' = -1$, $c' = 0$. The value $c' = -1$ corresponds to an approximately 'half-lit' mirror disk and the value $c' = 0$ to a centrally set knife-edge; in the latter case, as was shown in § 2.4, the disk contains only one-third as much light as with the knife-edge withdrawn. It will be seen from Fig. 64 that the inferred zone spreads well beyond the boundaries of the actual zone and that its crest is displaced outward by an amount which increases as c' increases from -1 to 0. The displacement, though not very noticeable on the inferred profile, amounts to an appreciable fraction of the actual zonal width when $c' = 0$.

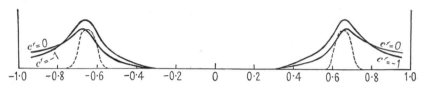

FIG. 64. Inferred error profile (6.27) in the case (6.30). The dotted curves show the shape of the actual error profile.

The zone 'seen' under the test in practice is a composite impression built up from the inferred profiles for the values of c' which make the zone show up most prominently on the mirror disk, and these values may be taken to lie between -2 and $+1$ when the mirror is nearly true. A ring-polisher made to suit the inferred zone should therefore be found to work rather too much on the outer slopes of the zone and, because it is too broad, should produce a somewhat different effect from that intended. To reduce the zone with greater efficiency, the ring-polisher should be designed to work almost entirely on the central part of the apparent zone and should be set slightly inside the inferred crest-radius.

The well-known difficulty, in correcting mirrors by local polishing with the help of the Foucault test, of preventing the polisher from trespassing outside the limits of the local error under treatment is usually regarded as a difficulty in the manual control of the polisher. According to the present analysis, it may be attributed, in part at least, to the errors inherent in the usual method of interpreting the Foucault shadows.

It remains to consider how far these conclusions, established only for sufficiently narrow zones of very small height or depth, may be expected to remain valid as useful approximations when applied to zones of the widths and depths commonly met with in practice. Some idea of this may be formed from Figs. 65 a, b and Figs. 66 a, b. To draw these figures computations of the intensities in four selected special cases were made from the basic formula (6.2), which for practical purposes can be regarded as exact, and the corresponding inferred profiles were computed from (6.24). There is of course a certain arbitrariness in the use of (6.24) to define the inferred error profile when the intensity-changes are no longer small.†

The four cases selected are high zones of mean radius 0·65, width 0·20, profile shape $\zeta(\tau)$ given by (6.30) and heights $\frac{1}{20}$ fringe and $\frac{1}{4}$ fringe respectively, tested with the knife-edge at the lateral settings $c' = -1$ and $c' = 0$.

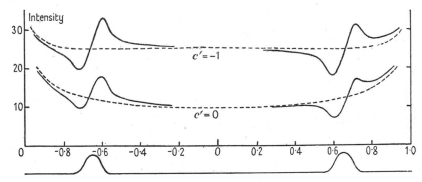

FIG. 65 a. Foucault intensities, at two different lateral settings of the knife-edge, for a local zone $\frac{1}{20}$ fringe high. The dotted curves show the intensities for a true mirror. The error profile is shown below the graph.

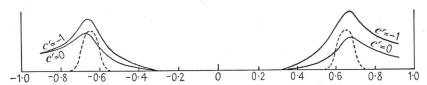

FIG. 65 b. Inferred error profiles corresponding to Fig. 65 a. The dotted curves show the shape of the actual error profile.

Figs. 65 a, b show the results for a zone of height $\frac{1}{20}$ fringe. It will be seen that in this case the inferred profile derived from the approximate formula (6.27) agrees sufficiently well in shape with that derived by computation from the accurate formula (6.2).

The results for a zone of height $\frac{1}{4}$ fringe are shown in Figs. 66 a, b. Here the inequality between the apparent strengths of the zone on the left- and on the right-hand zonal segments is considerable, and the agreement between (6.27) and the accurate formula is not very close. This is hardly surprising, since the condition that the depth of the zone

† If we define $P(x)$ as a constant multiple of $\int^{x} \{\log I - \log I_1\}\, dx$ when $I - I_1$ is no longer small (in consonance with Fechner's law) and take the error-slope as proportional to $\log(I/I_1)$ the inferred error profiles are somewhat altered but the crest of a high zone keeps the same position as before.

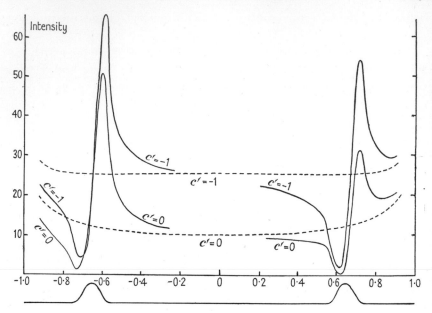

FIG. 66 a. Foucault intensities, at two different lateral settings of the knife-edge, for a local zone ¼ fringe high. The dotted curves show the intensities for a true mirror. The error profile is shown below the graph.

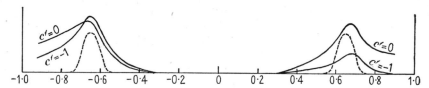

FIG. 66 b. Inferred error profiles corresponding to Fig. 66 a. The dotted curves show the shape of the actual error profile.

should be small compared with $\lambda/2\pi$ is far from being satisfied. Even in this case, however, it appears from Fig. 66 a that the general conclusions drawn above retain sufficient validity to be useful to the practical mirror-maker.

REFERENCES

S. BANERJI, *Ap. J.* **48**, 1918, 50.

—— *Phil. Mag.* **37**, 1919, 114.

A. COUDER, *Rev. Opt.* **16**, 1937, 17.

L. FOUCAULT, *Ann. Obs. Imp. Paris*, **5**, 1859, 197.

S. C. B. GASCOIGNE, *M.N.* **104**, 1945, 326.

E. H. LINFOOT, *Proc. Roy. Soc.* A, **186**, 1946, 72.

—— *M.N.* **105**, 1945, 193.

E. H. Linfoot, *Proc. Roy. Soc.* A, **193**, 1948, 248.

—— *M.N.* **108**, 1948, 428.

A. A. Michelson, *Phil. Mag.* **30**, 1890, 1.

H. Poincaré, *Acta Math.* **16**, 1892, 297.

—— ibid. **20**, 1897, 313.

Rayleigh, *Phil. Mag.* (6), **33**, 1917, 161.

F. Zernike, *Physica*, **1**, 1934, 689.

THE SCHMIDT CAMERA

1. Introduction and general discussion

THE increasing use of photography brought considerable changes in the demands which have to be met by optical systems intended for astronomical research. Instead of striving for the sharpest possible images over a very small field, the design of a photographic telescope aims at high definition over the whole of a photographic plate. For in visual work, the object under examination can always be brought to the centre of the field of view, whereas a photographic plate records the images impartially over its whole area, which is examined piecemeal after the plate has been developed.

The simple Newtonian telescope illustrates the point. We recall that a simple spherical mirror will not form a sharp image of a star situated on its axis, because the parallel rays meeting the outer zones of the mirror are brought to a shorter focus than those reflected from the parts near its pole A (see Fig. 67); the image suffers from spherical aberration. If the mirror is replaced by a paraboloid touching the original spherical surface at its centre and passing through its edge, the spherical aberration is eliminated and the rays are brought to a sharp focus. The change in form of the surface is easily found. On taking Cartesian coordinates t, y in a plane through the axis of the mirror, with origin at the pole A of the mirror surface, the surface profile of a spherical mirror of radius of curvature $2f$ is given by the equation

$$(t-2f)^2+y^2 = (2f)^2,$$

i.e.
$$4ft = y^2+t^2,$$

which on solving for t in terms of y yields the power series

$$t = \frac{y^2}{4f}+\frac{y^4}{64f^3}+\cdots. \tag{1.1}$$

The numerical value of the term in y^4 is very small; in the case of an f/5 mirror of 20 inches aperture, it amounts at the edge of the mirror to $1/6400$ inch, or about 8 wavelengths of light. The term in y^6 is in this case less than $1/800$ of the term in y^4 and we can safely neglect it, together with all higher terms. Thus the term in y^4 gives the distance, measured horizontally, between the surface of the sphere of paraxial focal length f and that of the paraboloid of focal length f which touches it at its centre A.

A more relevant comparison is with the paraboloid

$$t = y^2/4f' \tag{1.2}$$

which touches the sphere at its centre and passes through its edge $y = y_0$. This is, except for a slight displacement parallel to the t-axis, the paraboloid into which the sphere can be 'figured' by optical polishing with the removal of the least possible depth of glass. Subtraction of (1.1) from

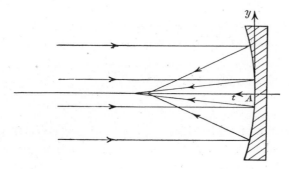

FIG. 67. Spherical mirror imaging parallel light.

(1.2) gives for the horizontal difference ξ at height y between these two surfaces the equation

$$\xi = y^2\left(\frac{1}{4f'} - \frac{1}{4f}\right) - \frac{y^4}{64f^3} \tag{1.3}$$

$$= (y^2 y_0^2 - y^4)/64f^3, \tag{1.4}$$

on making use of the fact that $\xi = 0$ when $y = y_0$ in order to eliminate f'. Now the greatest value of $y^2 y_0^2 - y^4 = y^2(y_0^2 - y^2)$ as y runs from 0 to y_0 is assumed when $y = \frac{1}{2}\sqrt{2}\, y_0 = 0.707 y_0$, and is $\frac{1}{4} y_0^4$. Hence the 'figuring depth' ξ in the above example is greatest on the zone of radius 7 inches and its value there is about 2 wavelengths. It is of no practical consequence whether the figuring-depth is measured horizontally, as here, or normally to the mirror surface, since the discrepancy nowhere exceeds one-hundredth of a wavelength.

A useful alternative formulation of the same results is made possible by the notion of a wave surface or wave-front; that is to say, a surface orthogonal to all the rays belonging to a single pencil. In the case of a paraboloid imaging a star on its axis, the wave surfaces are plane before meeting the mirror, since each is orthogonal to the rays of a parallel beam. After reflection the wave surfaces are spheres, since they are orthogonal to rays which meet in a point. The effect of 'figuring' the mirror is to deform slightly the wave surfaces which leave it; removal of a layer of glass δ wavelengths thick from a part of the mirror surface will retard the wave surface leaving this part by an amount $2\delta \cos i$, where i is the angle of incidence of the rays on this part. In many practical cases, including the one given above, δ amounts only to a few wavelengths and $\cos i$ differs from unity by less than 1 per cent. over the whole of the wave-front. We can then say to a sufficient approximation that a figuring depth δ on the mirror corresponds to a retardation 2δ in the reflected wave-fronts.

Since the figuring (1.4) will convert the wave-fronts reflected from the mirror into spherical shells, it follows that without this figuring the reflected wave-fronts are distorted from the spherical form in accordance with the retardation function

$$\xi^* = -(y^2 y_0^2 - y^4)/32f^3. \tag{1.5}$$

Here the parameter y identifies the zones of any wave-front by means of the points where the rays through them meet the mirror surface and y_0 corresponds to the edge-zone.

When a field of stars is photographed at the prime focus of a simple paraboloid, the images close to the axis are good, but those farther out appear as asymmetrical, comet-shaped smudges; the system suffers from off-axis coma. For this reason, the optical system of the simple Newtonian telescope is not well suited to astronomical photography. The classical Cassegrain system suffers from the same drawback; its off-axis coma is the same as that of a Newtonian of the same focal ratio and is only smaller in practice because the focal ratio is longer. The first systematic attempt to design coma-free reflecting telescopes appears to have been made by K. Schwarzschild (1905), who published designs of a coma-free two-mirror telescope with a useful field of about 3° at an aperture ratio of f/3. Both mirrors are 'figured', i.e. aspheric. The figurings are of course different from that on a paraboloid.

Two-mirror systems are the simplest type of telescope which can be coma-free, and it is rather remarkable that Schwarzschild's designs did not attract more attention. Only two examples appear to have been put into use; one, of 24-inch aperture, at the University of Indiana and the other, of 12-inch aperture, at Brown University, U.S.A.

An important step forward, and one of an entirely novel kind, was made by Bernhard Schmidt in 1930 when he introduced the new type of optical system which bears his name. Schmidt was a remarkable and interesting personality. He was born in 1879 on Nargen Island in Esthonia, and R. Schorr (1936) in his biographical note on Schmidt records that he attempted as a boy to make a concave mirror by grinding together the lower parts of bottles with sea-sand from the beaches of Nargen. Later, he studied engineering in Götenburg and Mittweide and about 1900 began to make telescope mirrors of outstanding quality for amateur astronomers. In 1905 he executed with extraordinary accuracy and in the short space of three months an f/2·26 paraboloid of 40 cm. aperture for the Potsdam Astrophysical Observatory. Schmidt carried out his optical work with the simplest means, using relatively thin glass

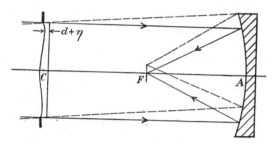

FIG. 68. The Schmidt camera. (The deformation of the aspheric plate surface is exaggerated about 100 times.)

tools for fine grinding and polishing and working all surfaces by hand— with his left hand, indeed, for he had lost his right arm in an accident in early youth. When making a Cassegrain system, he would usually leave the primary mirror spherical and remove the spherical aberration by figuring the convex secondary mirror.

In addition to being an outstanding optician and a first-class engineer, Schmidt was an enthusiastic astronomical observer and during the latter part of his life he worked in the Bergedorf Observatory near Hamburg. He showed much ingenuity in the construction of mountings and drives for his telescopes; two of his novel mountings were installed at Bergedorf and one at Breslau Observatory.

Schmidt's crowning achievement, however, was the invention and construction of his 'lichtstarkes, comafreies Spiegelsystem', now known as the Schmidt camera (Schmidt 1932). It consists of a spherical mirror together with a nearly plane-parallel figured plate situated at the centre of curvature of the mirror, as shown in Fig. 68. The mirror is larger than the plate, in order to receive the off-axis pencils. The field surface is curved, and is concentric with the mirror. The object of the plate is to 'pre-correct' the wave-fronts in the parallel pencils entering the system so that they may be spherical after reflection by the mirror, and so converge to a sharp focus. Consider first the axial pencil. By equation

(1.3) above, the amount of pre-correction required at the zone of para-meter y is a retardation

$$2\xi = 2y^2\left(\frac{1}{4f'} - \frac{1}{4f}\right) + \frac{y^4}{32f^3}, \tag{1.6}$$

approximately. For 2ξ is, to a good approximation, the amount by which the reflected wave-fronts are pushed forward, on the y-zone, in advance of the desired spherical form. Since the optical path distance through a plate of thickness d and refractive index n is nd for rays entering normally, it follows that the retardation (1.6) will be obtained if one surface of the plate is figured to the profile

$$\eta = \frac{2\xi}{n-1} = \frac{y^2}{n-1}\left(\frac{1}{2f'} - \frac{1}{2f}\right) + \frac{y^4}{32(n-1)f^3}; \tag{1.7}$$

here η denotes the depth of the 'figuring-layer' on the plate surface, that is, the least thickness of glass which, laid on to a plane surface, would produce the required asphericity; y is the parameter of the plate zone, i.e. the distance from the axis at which the rays through this plate zone meet the mirror surface. Because the rays, after passage through the plate, are still very nearly parallel to the axis of the system, it is per-missible in the present approximation to take the parameter y as equal to the radius of the plate zone. Then the Cartesian equation of the aspheric plate profile can be written in the form

$$\eta = (y^4 - ay_0^2 y^2)/32(n-1)f^3, \tag{1.8}$$

where y_0 denotes the radius of the edge-zone of the plate and the constant

$$a = \frac{32f^3}{y_0^2}\left(\frac{1}{2f} - \frac{1}{2f'}\right) \tag{1.9}$$

can be varied at will by varying the value of f', which, it will be remem-bered, is merely the focal length of the chosen reference-paraboloid. The *strength* of an aspheric plate is defined as $(n-1)$ times the coefficient of y^4 in its surface profile; thus it is independent of a and is $1/32f^3$ in the case of the Schmidt camera.

From Fig. 68 it will be seen that, in order to determine the image errors at an angular distance ϕ from the centre of the field, it is sufficient to calculate the effect on the axial image of tilting the plate, together with the aperture stop, through an angle ϕ about an axis through C parallel to the plane surface of the plate. Taking Cartesian coordinates x, y in the plane of the aperture stop, with origin at its centre C, suppose that the plate is tilted through an angle ϕ about the axis Cy. The plate thickness $T(x,y) = d+\eta$ is very nearly constant and the slopes $\partial T/\partial x$

and $\partial T/\partial y$ of its aspheric surface in the x and y directions are very small, so that their squares can be neglected.

Now consider a ray, initially parallel to the axis of the system and passing through the point x, y of the aspheric plate surface. The angular deviations which this ray receives from the untilted plate amounts to

$$(n-1)\frac{\partial T}{\partial x}, \qquad (n-1)\frac{\partial T}{\partial y}$$

radians in the x and y directions respectively. These deviations produce an error-free axial image, and it is the changes which they undergo when the plate is tilted which give rise to the off-axis aberrations. Two main factors operate to produce these changes. In the first place, the tilted plate is traversed obliquely by the rays, and this increases the angular deviations associated with each point of the plate surface. The new values are given, when $\sin^4\phi$ is neglected, by the expressions

$$(n-1)\frac{\partial T}{\partial x}\left(1+\frac{n+1}{2n}\sin^2\phi\right), \qquad (n-1)\frac{\partial T}{\partial y}\left(1+\frac{1}{2n}\sin^2\phi\right). \qquad (1.10)$$

(A proof of this statement, and of (1.11), (1.12) below, will be derived as a by-product of the more rigorous treatment in § 2.) In the second place, owing to the tilt of the plate, a point (x, y) of the aspheric surface now transmits light to the point of the mirror surface which formerly received it from, approximately, the point $(x\cos\phi, y)$. This causes a further change, of amount

$$(n-1)x\frac{\partial^2 T}{\partial x^2}(1-\cos\phi), \qquad (n-1)x\frac{\partial^2 T}{\partial x\partial y}(1-\cos\phi) \qquad (1.11)$$

in the angular deviations. We therefore obtain for the leading terms in the components of angular aberration in the ray through the point (x, y) of the entry pupil the expressions

$$(n-1)\sin^2\phi\left(\frac{n+1}{2n}\frac{\partial T}{\partial x}+\tfrac{1}{2}x\frac{\partial^2 T}{\partial x^2}\right), \qquad (n-1)\sin^2\phi\left(\frac{1}{2n}\frac{\partial T}{\partial y}+\tfrac{1}{2}x\frac{\partial^2 T}{\partial x\partial y}\right),$$
$$(1.12)$$

where
$$T = T(x, y) = d+\eta\{\sqrt{(x^2+y^2)}\}$$
$$= d+\frac{1}{32(n-1)f^3}\{(x^2+y^2)^2-ay_0^2(x^2+y^2)\} \qquad (1.13)$$

is the plate thickness at the point (x, y).

This analysis, due to Carathéodory (1940), shows that the off-axis errors of the Schmidt camera are very small and are of a symmetrical character. Their symmetry (or rather, that of their leading terms) follows at once from (1.12) and (1.13). To estimate their size in a practical case, consider an f/3·5 Schmidt camera working over a 6° diameter field. The greatest aberrations are at the edge of the field and are provided by the points $(\pm x_0, 0)$ on the boundary of the aperture; by (1.12), (1.13) they are

$$\pm\sin^2 3°\left[\frac{n+1}{2n}\tfrac{1}{8}(1-\tfrac{1}{2}a)+\tfrac{1}{16}(3-\tfrac{1}{2}a)\right]y_0^3/f^3,\ 0,$$

where y_0/f is equal to $\tfrac{1}{7}$ in an f/3·5 system. If $n = 1·5$ and if we set $a = \tfrac{3}{2}$ so as to minimize the axial colour-spread of the system, as explained below, this expression has the values

$$\pm 1/750,000,\ 0;$$

that is, the deviations amount to $\pm 4/15$ second of arc. In an f/3·5 camera, therefore, the off-axis image spreads run up to approximately half a second of arc at the edge of a 6° diameter field.

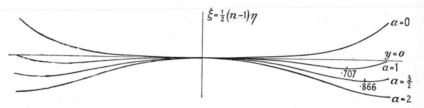

FIG. 69. Aspheric plate profiles corresponding to different values of the parameter a.

In the discussion given earlier of the 'figuring' of a sphere into a paraboloid, the parameter value $a = 1$ was singled out as reducing the overall figuring-depth to its least possible value. Such a value of a would not be adopted by the practical mirror-maker; he would use a value near to 2. For it is easier to control the figure of a mirror near its centre than near its edge, and parabolization with $a = 2$ can be effected by polishing away glass on the inner parts of the mirror, leaving the edge zones almost untouched (see Fig. 69).

In choosing the value of the parameter a for Schmidt plates, ease of construction is no longer the chief consideration. The colour-error of the plate is large enough to attract attention in some systems; in such cases the value of a is chosen so as to minimize this colour-error. With a low-dispersion crown glass plate, the angular colour-split over the spectral range $F–C$ may be taken as $\tfrac{1}{60}$ of the greatest angular deviation imposed by the plate. By (1.8), this deviation

$$(n-1)\frac{d\eta}{dy} = (y^3 - \tfrac{1}{2}ay_0^2\,y)/8f^3.$$

The greatest value of $|y^3 - \frac{1}{2}ay_0^2 y|$ in the range $0 \leqslant y \leqslant y_0$ is taken either at its stationary point $y = y_0\sqrt{(a/6)}$ or at $y = y_0$. At the former its value is $2y_0^3(a/6)^{\frac{3}{2}}$; at the latter $(1 - \frac{1}{2}a)y_0^3$. If $a = \frac{3}{2}$ these are both equal to $\frac{1}{4}y_0^3$. Hence the angular colour-spread $(F\text{–}C)$ of the plate is least when $a = \frac{3}{2}$ and its value is then

$$\frac{1}{60}\frac{1}{8f^3}\frac{1}{4}y_0^3 = \frac{1}{15{,}360F^3} \text{ radian,}$$

where $F = f/2y_0$ is the focal ratio of the camera.

For example, in an f/3·5 Schmidt camera with $a = \frac{3}{2}$, the angular colour-spread $(F\text{–}C)$ of the plate is

$$\frac{1}{15{,}360}\left(\frac{2}{7}\right)^3 \text{ radian} = \frac{1}{3} \text{ second of arc,}$$

approximately, and the diameter of the colour-confusion circles in C-light when the plate is correctly figured in F-light, is approximately $\frac{2}{3}$ second of arc at all points of the field. The colour-confusion circles in h-light are also about $\frac{2}{3}$ second of arc in diameter, i.e. the system is overcorrected in h-light to about the same degree as it is undercorrected in C-light.

The first Schmidt camera, constructed and put into use by its inventor at Bergedorf in 1930, was an f/1·75 system with a corrector plate of 36 cm. aperture. The mirror was 44 cm. in diameter. Photographs, taken on curved film, gave perfectly round stellar images over a field 16° in diameter. Later, Schmidt made a second camera, of 60 cm. aperture and 3 metres focal length, together with a paraboloid mirror of the same aperture and focal length, and mounted them as a double reflector in an English mounting at the Bergedorf Observatory. The drive was a novel one of his own devising: it employed a lever arm 2·4 m. long, the end of which rested freely against a rotating worm wheel. Schmidt was engaged in the adjustment of this instrument during his last days; he died in 1935.

The central obstruction of the Schmidt camera by its own field surface restricts the field-size at a given aperture ratio. If the permissible linear obstruction ratio is c, the maximum angular field diameter which can be obtained at a focal ratio F is $60°c/F$, approximately. Thus the angular field-size of an f/3·5 camera must not be greater than 6° if the obstruction ratio is not to exceed $\frac{1}{3}$. Schmidt's first camera, working at f/1·75 over a 15° field, had an obstruction ratio a little less than 0·4. The Schmidt optical system does not satisfy the exact sine condition, but the variation in $h/\sin\theta$—about one part in 250,000 at an aperture of f/1·75—is so small that the symmetry of the photographic images is not visibly affected.

2. The monochromatic aberrations of the Schmidt camera

Fig. 70 shows the optical system of the ordinary Schmidt camera. For the present we suppose that the aspheric surface of the corrector plate faces the spherical mirror and passes through its centre of curvature C. (x, y, z) are rectangular Cartesian coordinates with C as origin

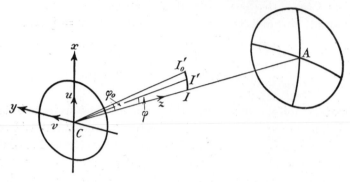

FIG. 70.

and with CA as z-axis. We take the aperture stop of the system to be the circle $x^2 + y^2 = H^2$ in the plane $z = 0$, i.e. in the tangent plane to the aspheric surface. In an actual system of focal ratio f/2·5 or longer, the aspheric surface lies everywhere within a few thousandths of an inch of this plane.

The Cartesian equation of the aspheric surface can be written

$$z = T(x, y) - T(0, 0) = a_1 h^2 + a_2 h^4 + a_3 h^6 + ..., \qquad (2.1)$$

where $h^2 = x^2 + y^2$ and $T(x, y)$ denotes the thickness of the plate at the point (x, y). The values of the coefficients a_1, a_2, a_3,... are discussed in the next section, and it is shown there that, if the terms in h^6, h^8,... are small enough for their sum to be neglected,

$$T(x, y) = T(0, 0) + \frac{1}{n-1} \frac{1}{32 f^3} (h^4 - 2h_0^2 h^2) + O\left(\frac{H^6}{32 f^5}\right), \qquad (2.2)$$

where n is the refractive index of the plate, h_0 the radius of its neutral zone, and f the focal length of the system.

A notation better adapted to the discussion of the off-axis errors is obtained on setting

$$\mu = H/R, \qquad (2.3)$$

where R is the radius of curvature of the mirror.

Since f is very nearly equal to $\frac{1}{2}R$, the quantity 2μ is very nearly equal to the numerical aperture of the system and

$$\mu = \frac{1}{4F} \text{ nearly}, \tag{2.4}$$

where F is the focal ratio; the error in these approximate equalities is less than one part in 300 in the case of an f/3 system.

We introduce the dimensionless variables u, v, and r by means of the equations

$$x = \mu Ru, \qquad y = \mu Rv, \qquad h = \mu Rr; \tag{2.5}$$

thus $r^2 = u^2 + v^2$ and the aperture stop is defined by the inequality $u^2 + v^2 \leqslant 1$. In order to keep the formulae as simple as possible, we suppose for the time being that $R = 1$; this is equivalent to taking the radius of curvature of the mirror as unit of length. Equation (2.2) now becomes

$$T(x, y) - T(0, 0) = \frac{1}{n-1} \frac{1}{4} \mu^4 (r^4 - 2r_0^2 r^2) + O(\mu^6). \tag{2.6}$$

In an f/3 camera $\mu^2 = \frac{1}{144}$ nearly, while $r \leqslant 1$ always and r_0 lies between 0·7 and 1 in a practical case. Therefore the error-term in this equation amounts to only a few per cent. of the maximum size of the leading term.

Let d_0 be the least thickness of the plate. Then the plate is equivalent to a plane-parallel plate of thickness d_0, together with a 'figuring layer', of which the thickness is $T(0,0) - d_0$ at the centre of the plate and decreases to zero at its neutral zone. Let the thickness of the figuring layer at the point (x, y) be denoted by

$$U(x, y) = T(x, y) - d_0. \tag{2.7}$$

Then it follows from (2.6) that

$$U(x, y) = O(\mu^4) \tag{2.8}$$

at all points (x, y) of the aperture.

First suppose the system to consist of the mirror and the figuring layer only. The effect on the images of adding in the remainder of the plate-thickness will be considered later; it is evidently zero when the aspheric side of the plate is towards the mirror. As before, let c be the central obstruction ratio of the system by its spherical field surface. Then if $2\phi_0$ is the angular diameter of the field,

$$\sin \phi_0 = cH/f = 2c\mu$$

approximately. In cases (such as the 24–36-inch f/3·5 Burrell telescope and the 48–72-inch f/2·5 Palomar Schmidt telescope) where the mirror diameter is $\frac{3}{2}$ times the clear aperture, we have, to within 1 per cent.,

$$c = \tfrac{1}{4}, \qquad \sin \phi_0 = \tfrac{1}{2}\mu.$$

In an f/3·5 system this gives $\sin \phi_0 = \frac{1}{28}$ and the unvignetted field has a diameter of just over 4 degrees; in an f/2·5 system the unvignetted field is 6 degrees in diameter. In all the large Schmidt telescopes so far built, the value of c lies between $\frac{1}{4}$ and $\frac{1}{2}$.

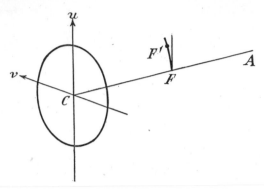

FIG. 71a.

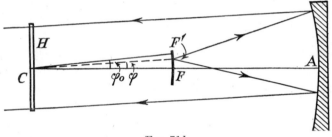

FIG. 71b.

A parallel pencil entering the camera at an angle ϕ with the axis forms an image on the photographic plate if $0 \leqslant \phi \leqslant \phi_0$. The new variable V, defined by the equation

$$\sin \phi = 2c\mu V, \tag{2.9}$$

runs from 0 at the centre of the field to approximately 1 at its edge.

The new variables have the property that u, v, r, V all range from -1 to 1 or from 0 to 1, while μ^2 is usually less than 0·01. The numerical order of magnitude of the different terms in our expressions is therefore indicated by the powers of μ which they contain.

Consider a pencil of rays, and their orthogonal surfaces the associated wave-fronts, issuing from a point F' in the field surface such that $FCF' = \phi$ and F' lies in the plane uCz. See Figs. 71a, 71b. If the system had no off-axis aberrations, these wave-fronts would emerge from it as plane surfaces; their actual deviations from flatness indicate the aberrations of the system.

These deviations arise in the following way. In the first place, the retardation imposed by a plane-parallel plate upon plane waves meeting it at an angle ϕ is greater when $\phi \neq 0$ than when $\phi = 0$. The increase, by Fig. 72, is

$$nPQ - [PM + (n-1)d],$$

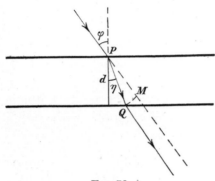

FIG. 72.

where d is the thickness of the plate and n its refractive index. Since

$$PQ = d \sec \eta, \qquad PM = PQ \cos(\phi - \eta), \qquad \sin \eta = \frac{1}{n} \sin \phi,$$

it follows that

$$nPQ - [PM + (n-1)d] = nd(\sec \eta - 1) - d(\cos \phi + \sin \phi \tan \eta - 1).$$

Here
$$\sin \phi \tan \eta = \frac{1}{n} \sin^2\phi \sec \eta = \frac{1}{n} \sin^2\phi + O(\sin^4\phi).$$

Therefore

$$nPQ - [PM + (n-1)d] = \frac{1}{2n} d \sin^2\phi - d\left(\frac{1}{n} \sin^2\phi - \tfrac{1}{2} \sin^2\phi\right) + O(d \sin^4\phi)$$

$$= \frac{n-1}{2n} d \sin^2\phi + O(d \sin^4\phi). \tag{2.10}$$

Now suppose that the wave-fronts are nearly plane, with angular deviations $O(\mu^3)$ from flatness, the plate nearly plane-parallel, with thickness $O(\mu^4)$ and surface-slope deviations $O(\mu^3)$, and the angle of incidence $\phi = O(\mu)$. This change in the hypotheses introduces an inaccuracy $O(\mu^8)$ in the retardations and (2.10) can therefore be replaced by the expression

$$\frac{n-1}{2n} d \sin^2\phi + O(\mu^8). \tag{2.11}$$

By (2.6), (2.7) the new hypotheses are applicable to any element δS of the aspheric surface of the figuring layer surrounding the point $(x, y, U(x, y) - U(0, 0))$. It follows that the retardation imposed by the figuring layer on that part of the oblique, near-flat wave-front which crosses its aspheric surface in the element δS exceeds the retardation imposed upon a wave-front arriving square on by an amount

$$\sin^2\!\phi\,\frac{n-1}{2n}\,U(x,y)+O(\mu^8) = 4\mu^2c^2V^2\frac{n-1}{2n}\,U(x,y)+O(\mu^8), \quad (2.12)$$

by (2.9).

A further contribution to the change in retardation of the wave-fronts arises from 'foreshortening', in the following way. Consider that ray γ traced out from F (see Fig. 71 a) which, after reflection at the spherical mirror, meets the plane $z = 0$ of the aperture stop in the point $(x, y, 0)$ and, consequently, the aspheric surface in a point

$$(x+O(\mu^7),\ y+O(\mu^7),\ O(\mu^4)).$$

If the pencil issuing from F be rotated bodily through an angle ϕ about the axis Cv, it becomes a pencil issuing from F'; let γ' be the ray of the new pencil which corresponds to γ. After reflection in the sphere, γ' meets the plane of the aperture stop in a point of coordinates

$$(x\sec\phi+O(\mu^3)O(x\sin\phi), y+O(\mu^3)O(x\sin\phi), 0)$$

$$= (x\sec\phi+O(\mu^5), y+O(\mu^5), 0)$$

and meets the aspheric surface in a point whose coordinates differ from these values by $O(\mu^4)O(\sin\phi) = O(\mu^5)$. This causes a change

$$(n-1)U(x\sec\phi+O(\mu^5), y+O(\mu^5))-(n-1)U(x+O(\mu^5), y+O(\mu^5))$$

$$= (n-1)(\sec\phi-1)x\frac{\partial U(x,y)}{\partial x}+O(\mu^8)$$

$$= 4c^2\mu^2V^2(n-1)\tfrac{1}{2}x\frac{\partial U}{\partial x}+O(\mu^8) \quad (2.13)$$

in the retardation of the emerging wave-front by the plate.

The cross terms between the two effects (2.12) and (2.13) being $O(\mu^8)$, their resultant is

$$4(n-1)c^2\mu^2V^2\!\left(\frac{1}{2n}+\frac{1}{2}x\frac{\partial}{\partial x}\right)U(x,y)+O(\mu^8). \quad (2.14)$$

Since the rays from the axial focal point F become a parallel beam after passing through the aspheric surface, (2.14) gives the deviations from flatness of the wave-fronts corresponding to the pencil from F' after passing out through the figuring layer of thickness $O(\mu^8)$. If we assume (what is true in a practical case) that the overall thickness of the Schmidt plate is at most $O(\mu^2)$, then the deviation from flatness of a wave-front after passing through the whole plate differs by $O(\mu^8)$ from its deviation, at the corresponding point of its surface, after passing (into air) through the figuring layer only; it is therefore still given by (2.14).

This means that the 'aberration function' of the Schmidt camera working backwards can be written

$$\mu^6\Phi(x, y, V) = 4(n-1)c^2\mu^2V^2\left(\frac{1}{2n}+\frac{1}{2}x\frac{\partial}{\partial x}\right)U(x,y)+O(\mu^8). \quad (2.15)$$

If the plate is turned round, with its aspheric face away from the mirror, and placed so that its plane face is $1/n$ times the axial-plate thickness inside C, then with a plate thickness $O(\mu^2)$ the effect on the error function is $O(\mu^8)$. For, in the on-axis pencil, the only effect is on the zonal aberration of the plane-parallel part of the plate in the nearly parallel pencil coming from the mirror; this contributes a wave distortion $O(\mu^{14})$. In the off-axis pencils, there is also a contribution

$$O(\mu^3)O(\mu^2)O(\mu^4/\mu) = O(\mu^8)$$

due to lateral shift of the wave-fronts impinging on the aspheric surface. Thus (2.15) gives the aberration function in this case also.

The mathematical form of the function

$$\mu^6\Phi(x, y, V) = 4\mu^2(n-1)c^2V^2\left(\frac{1}{2n}+\frac{1}{2}x\frac{\partial}{\partial x}\right)U(x,y)+O(\mu^8) \quad (2.16)$$

$$= \tfrac{1}{2}\mu^6c^2V^2\left(\frac{1}{n}+u\frac{\partial}{\partial u}\right)(r^4-2r_0^2r^2)+O(\mu^8) \quad (2.17)$$

embodies a description of the optical aberrations of the system when working backwards. The quantities

$$\left(\mu^6\frac{\partial\Phi}{\partial x},\ \mu^6\frac{\partial\Phi}{\partial y}\right) = \left(\mu^5\frac{\partial\Phi}{\partial u},\ \mu^5\frac{\partial\Phi}{\partial v}\right) \quad (2.18)$$

measure, in radians, the radial and tangential aberration displacements corresponding to the point (u, v) of the aperture stop $u^2+v^2 \leqslant 1$, at any given angular distance $\phi = \arcsin(2c\mu V)$ from the centre of the field in the u-direction. So far as leading terms are concerned, these displacements are the same whether we consider rays traced out from a single focal point or rays traced in from a single parallel pencil. It follows that (2.17) also describes the optical aberrations of the Schmidt camera working normally with object at infinity, and is valid with the corrector plate either way round, provided that the thickness of this plate is $O(\mu^2)$.

Since (2.17) is valid with the system working either forwards or backwards, it follows that the curves $\Phi(x, y, V) = $ constant give the fringes seen on the plate when the camera is tested, on and off axis, by autostigmatism on an interferometer.

From (2.16) and (2.18), the angular displacement components in the field surface are

$$4(n-1)\mu^2 c^2 V^2 \left(\frac{n+1}{2n} \frac{\partial}{\partial x} + \frac{1}{2} x \frac{\partial^2}{\partial x^2}, \ \frac{1}{2n} \frac{\partial}{\partial y} + \frac{1}{2} x \frac{\partial^2}{\partial x \partial y} \right) U(x,y) + O(\mu^7)\dagger$$

$$\tag{2.19}$$

$$= (n-1)\sin^2\phi \left(\frac{n+1}{2n} \frac{\partial}{\partial x} + \frac{1}{2} x \frac{\partial^2}{\partial x^2}, \ \frac{1}{2n} \frac{\partial}{\partial y} + \frac{1}{2} x \frac{\partial^2}{\partial x \partial y} \right) T(x,y) + O(\mu^7),$$

since $2\mu c V = \sin\phi$ and $U(x,y) = T(x,y) +$ constant. This establishes (1.12). The contributions from the main terms of (2.12) and (2.13) to these displacements are evidently

$$\sin^2\phi \frac{n-1}{2n} \left(\frac{\partial}{\partial x}, \ \frac{\partial}{\partial y} \right) T(x,y)$$

and

$$\sin^2\phi \,(n-1) \left(\frac{n+1}{2n} \frac{\partial}{\partial x} + \frac{1}{2} x \frac{\partial^2}{\partial x^2}, \ \frac{1}{2n} \frac{\partial}{\partial y} + \frac{1}{2} x \frac{\partial^2}{\partial x \partial y} \right) T(x,y)$$

respectively; this establishes (1.10) and (1.11).

In terms of the normalized variables u, v, and r, these displacement components become, by (2.17) and (2.18),

$$\tfrac{1}{2} c^2 \mu^5 V^2 \left(\frac{n+1}{n} \frac{\partial}{\partial u} + u \frac{\partial^2}{\partial u^2}, \ \frac{1}{n} \frac{\partial}{\partial v} + u \frac{\partial^2}{\partial u \partial v} \right) (r^4 - 2r_0^2 r^2) + O(\mu^7) \tag{2.20}$$

$$= 2c^2 \mu^5 V^2 \left\{ \left[\frac{n+1}{n} (r^2 - r_0^2) + r^2 \right] (u, v) + [(2u^2 - r_0^2)u, \ -(2v^2 - r_0^2)v] \right\} + O(\mu^7) \tag{2.21}$$

and the linear components are obtained on multiplying these by the focal length of the system. The first term inside the curly brackets represents a lateral spherical aberration; the second a species of higher astigmatism. When $n = \tfrac{3}{2}$ the angular displacements take the values

$$\tfrac{4}{3} c^2 \mu^5 V^2 (7u^3 + 4uv^2 - 4r_0^2 u, \ 4u^2 v + v^3 - r_0^2 v) + O(\mu^7). \tag{2.22}$$

In accordance with Chapter I, we call the leading term on the right of (2.17), namely

$$\tfrac{1}{2} \mu^6 c^2 V^2 \left(\frac{1}{n} + u \frac{\partial}{\partial u} \right) (r^4 - 2r_0^2 r^2), \tag{2.23}$$

---

† The error term is $O(\mu^7)$ here, not $O(\mu^8)$ because, owing to our scale-convention, a partial differentiation $\partial/\partial x$ or $\partial/\partial y$ increases numerical values by a factor $O(1/\mu)$.

the *sixth-order monochromatic aberration function* of the Schmidt camera, and denote it by $\mu^6\Phi^*(u, v, V)$. The quantities

$$\mu^5\frac{\partial\Phi^*}{\partial u}, \qquad \mu^5\frac{\partial\Phi^*}{\partial v}$$

$$= 2c^2\mu^5V^2\Big(\frac{n+1}{n}(r^2-r_0^2)u+(3u^2+v^2)u-r_0^2\,u,\ \frac{1}{n}(r^2-r_0^2)v+2u^2v\Big) \quad (2.24)$$

will be called the *fifth-order monochromatic aberration displacements* of the system. This differs from the usual terminology, according to which the terms in $r_0^2\,u$, $r_0^2\,v$ would be classed as third-order displacement contributions. Such a classification by means of total degree in u, v, V has practical value only in an optical system whose Seidel errors are not 'corrected', i.e. balanced against its higher errors. For only in such uncorrected systems do the total degrees of the terms give a true picture of their numerical sizes, on which the performance of the system depends.

When the focal ratio of the system is $1:3$ or longer, $\mu^2 < \frac{1}{100}$ and the fifth-order aberrations describe the size and shape of the geometrical image with an error of only 2 or 3 per cent. It will be seen that in an axially stigmatic system only the second- and fourth-power terms in the plate profile expansion contribute to these aberrations.

In the derivation of the expressions (2.20)–(2.24), it was assumed that the unit of length was equal to the radius of curvature of the mirror. When this assumption is dropped, (2.20)–(2.24) retain their form unchanged, since all the letters in these expressions represent dimensionless quantities.

The function $R\mu^6\Phi^*(u, v, V)$ describes the distortions of the near spherical wave-fronts converging towards the image-points in different parts of the field surface. Its value measures, with error $O(R\mu^8)$, the optical distance through which the point of parameter (u, v) on the wavefront is pushed backwards from the spherical wave-front centred at the image-point I'. Such approximate aberration functions not only allow the ray-theoretic properties of an optical system to be expressed in a compact form, but can also form a basis for the calculation of its diffraction properties by means of Huyghens's principle.

For example, in an f/2·5 Schmidt camera of 20-inch aperture, $\mu = \frac{1}{10}$ and $R = 100$ inches, so that $R\mu^8 = 10^{-6}$ inch $= \frac{1}{20}$ wavelength, approximately. Therefore the sixth-order aberration function can safely be used to compute the intensity distributions in the diffraction images of the system.

3. Corrector plate profile and colour-error in the classical Schmidt camera

To calculate, with accuracy sufficient for all practical purposes, the off-axis aberrations of a classical Schmidt telescope of focal ratio 1 : 3 or longer, it is enough to know the coefficients of the squared and fourth-power terms in the expansion of the aspheric plate profile. For, knowing these and knowing also that the axial image is stigmatic, we can, by the last section, write down the fifth-order aberration displacements (2.21) which describe the light distribution in the geometrical image.

Provided a suitable test is used during the final figuring, it is also possible to neglect sixth and higher powers in the aspheric grinding of the plate. For example, in an f/3 Schmidt telescope of 25-inch aperture the omission of these terms from the calculated profile creates a turn-down edge only 1 fringe deep, an error which can easily be corrected during the optical figuring of the system under an autocollimation test.

However, the same procedure applied to a 25-inch f/2 Schmidt would give 11 fringes of turn-down error on the plate as calculated, and applied to an 8-inch f/1 Schmidt would give 37 fringes. The removal of these errors by polishing would be a very laborious task.

Since the amount of turn-down caused by dropping sixth and higher powers in the plate profile varies rapidly with the focal ratio (namely as its sixth power) and much less rapidly with the aperture, it appears from the above that we may adopt the rough working rule that sixth powers should be taken into account whenever the focal ratio is shorter than f/3.

To calculate the plate profile as far as the sixth-power term, consider a ray QP entering the system, parallel to the axis, through the 'neutral zone' of the corrector plate, as shown in Fig. 73. After reflection at the point P of the mirror surface, this ray comes into the axial focal point F. Let C denote the centre of curvature of the mirror, A its pole and CQ a perpendicular through C to the axis of the system. If the plate is turned with its aspheric face towards the mirror, then this face passes through C, and Q is very close to it and just outside the glass. If the plate is turned with its plane face towards the mirror, then C and Q are inside the glass, at a distance from the plane surface equal to $1/n$ of the central thickness of the plate.

As in the last section, we suppose for the time being that $R = 1$, i.e. we choose as unit of length the radius of curvature of the mirror. Then the equations (2.3) and (2.5) become respectively

$$\mu = H \tag{3.1}$$

and
$$x = \mu u, \qquad y = \mu v, \qquad h = \mu r; \tag{3.2}$$

the edge of the aperture stop being still given by the equation $u^2+v^2 = 1$ or $r = 1$.

Fig. 73 can be taken to represent a section of the system by the plane $u = 0$. Set

$$CQ = \mu v_0, \qquad C\hat{P}Q = C\hat{P}F = P\hat{C}F = \theta_0;$$

the value $\frac{1}{2}\sqrt{3}$ for v_0 corresponds to the usual 'colour-minimized' plate profile with neutral zone of radius $\frac{1}{2}\sqrt{3}$ times that of the full aperture.

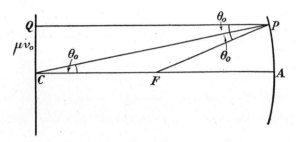

FIG. 73.

From the geometry of the figure

$$f = CF = \tfrac{1}{2}\sec\theta_0, \tag{3.3}$$

$$\sin\theta_0 = \mu v_0, \tag{3.4}$$

$$\cos\theta_0 = (1-\mu^2 v_0^2)^{\frac{1}{2}} = 1-\tfrac{1}{2}\mu^2 v_0^2-\tfrac{1}{8}\mu^4 v_0^4-...,$$

$$1-\cos\theta_0 = \tfrac{1}{2}\mu^2 v_0^2(1+\tfrac{1}{4}\mu^2 v_0^2+...). \tag{3.5}$$

By Gaussian optics, the paraxial focal length f_p of the plate is given by the equations

$$\frac{1}{f_p}+\frac{1}{\frac{1}{2}}-\frac{CA}{\frac{1}{2}f_p} = \frac{1}{f},$$

$$2-\frac{1}{f_p} = 2\cos\theta_0,$$

$$\frac{1}{f_p} = 2(1-\cos\theta_0). \tag{3.6}$$

Let the equation of the plate profile be

$$s = a_1\mu^2 v^2+a_2\mu^4 v^4+a_3\mu^6 v^6+..., \tag{3.7}$$

where $s = z/R$ is the z of § 2 measured in the new units. Then we find

(1) by considering coefficients of v^2

$$(n-1)a_1\mu^2 = -\mu^2/2f_P,$$

$$a_1 = -(1-\cos\theta_0)/(n-1); \tag{3.8}$$

(2)
$$FA+AC = 2-\tfrac{1}{2}\sec\theta_0,$$
$$FP+PQ = \tfrac{1}{2}\sec\theta_0+\cos\theta_0,$$
$$(FP+PQ)-(FA+AC) = \sec\theta_0+\cos\theta_0-2$$
$$= \sec\theta_0(1-\cos\theta_0)^2.$$

Since the wave-fronts issuing from a point source at F, and reflected at the mirror, emerge from the system as a set of planes perpendicular to the axis CA, it follows that the plate thickness at the central point Q must be less than its thickness at C by the amount

$$\sec\theta_0(1-\cos\theta_0)^2/(n-1).$$

That is to say

$$a_1\mu^2v_0^2+a_2\mu^4v_0^4+a_3\mu^6v_0^6 = -\sec\theta_0(1-\cos\theta_0)^2/(n-1)+O(\mu^8),$$
$$a_2\mu^4v_0^4+a_3\mu^6v_0^6 = -a_1\mu^2v_0^2-\sec\theta_0(1-\cos\theta_0)^2/(n-1)+O(\mu^8). \quad (3.9)$$

(3) Since the plate slope $ds/\mu\, dv$ vanishes for $v = v_0$, (3.7) gives

$$2a_1\mu^2v_0+4a_2\mu^4v_0^3+6a_3\mu^6v_0^5 = O(\mu^8)$$
$$2a_2\mu^4v_0^4+3a_3\mu^6v_0^6 = -a_1\mu^2v_0^2+O(\mu^8). \quad (3.10)$$

From (3.9), (3.10)

$$a_2\mu^4v_0^4 = -2\mu^2v_0^2a_1-3\sec\theta_0(1-\cos\theta_0)^2/(n-1)+O(\mu^8), \quad (3.11)$$
$$a_3\mu^6v_0^6 = a_1\mu^2v_0^2+2\sec\theta_0(1-\cos\theta_0)^2/(n-1)+O(\mu^8). \quad (3.12)$$

Equations (3.8), (3.11), (3.12) give the plate coefficients explicitly in terms of $uv_0 = \sin\theta_0$ and $(1-\mu^2v_0^2)^{\frac{1}{2}} = \cos\theta_0$, with an error $O(\mu^8)$. On substituting the power-series expansions of $\sec\theta_0$ and $1-\cos\theta_0$ in terms of uv_0, the expressions for the coefficients become

$$a_1 = \frac{-1}{n-1}\,(\tfrac{1}{2}\mu^2v_0^2+\tfrac{1}{8}\mu^4v_0^4+...),$$

$$a_2 = \frac{1}{n-1}\,(\tfrac{1}{4}-\tfrac{1}{2}\mu^2v_0^2+...), \quad (3.13)$$

$$a_3 = \frac{1}{n-1}\,(\tfrac{3}{8}+...)$$

and the plate profile is obtained in the form

$$(n-1)s = \tfrac{1}{4}\mu^4(v^4-2v^2v_0^2)+\mu^6(\tfrac{3}{8}v^6-\tfrac{1}{2}v^4v_0^2-\tfrac{1}{8}v^2v_0^4)+O(\mu^8), \quad (3.14)$$

or

$$(n-1)s = \tfrac{1}{4}\mu^4(v^2-v_0^2)^2(1+\tfrac{5}{2}v_0^2\mu^2)+\tfrac{3}{8}\mu^6(v^2-v_0^2)^3+\text{constant}+O(\mu^8). \quad (3.15)$$

(3.15) has been derived without specifying whether the aspheric surface of the plate is on the side towards or away from the mirror. It therefore holds with the plate either way round.

By (3.3), (3.4),

$$f/R = \tfrac{1}{2}(1-\mu^2 v_0^2)^{-\frac{1}{2}} = \tfrac{1}{2}(1+\tfrac{1}{2}\mu^2 v_0^2+\tfrac{3}{8}\mu^4 v_0^4+...). \qquad (3.16)$$

By (2.3), (3.4) the quantity

$$\lambda = \frac{H}{2f} = \frac{H}{R}\frac{R}{2f} = \mu\cos\theta_0 = \mu(1-\mu^2 v_0^2)^{\frac{1}{2}}; \qquad (3.17)$$

thus in an f/3 system with $v_0 = \tfrac{1}{2}\sqrt{3}$, μ differs from $1/4F$ by less than $\tfrac{1}{3}$ per cent.

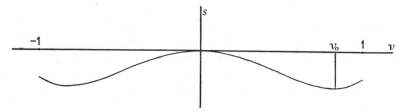

FIG. 74. Profile curve of Schmidt plate.

The Baker formulae. In a system with $\mu = \tfrac{1}{4}$ and $v_0 = \tfrac{1}{2}\sqrt{3}$, the difference between λ and μ amounts to about $2\tfrac{1}{2}$ per cent. of the value of each of them and the aperture of the system is very near to f/1. Thus, at the edge of the plate, the slope contribution from the sixth-power term is about $\tfrac{1}{6}$ of that from the fourth-power term or $\tfrac{2}{3}$ of that from the squared and fourth-power terms taken together. This suggests that the value $v_0 = \tfrac{1}{2}\sqrt{3}$ of the radius of the neutral zone, which minimizes the axial colour-spread of the system when sixth-power and higher terms in the plate profile are negligible, could be increased with advantage when the aperture ratio approaches f/1. Let

$$v_0 = \tfrac{1}{2}\sqrt{3}(1+b\mu^2+...) \qquad (3.18)$$

be the modified choice of the neutral zone radius. We wish to choose b so that the profile slope at the edge of the plate is equal to that at the steepest part of the central bulge. See Fig. 74.

By (3.15),

$$(n-1)\frac{ds}{dv} = \mu^4 v(v^2-v_0^2)(1+\tfrac{5}{2}v_0^2\mu^2)+\tfrac{9}{4}\mu^6 v(v^2-v_0^2)^2+..., \qquad (3.19)$$

$$(n-1)\frac{d^2s}{dv^2} = \mu^4(3v^2-v_0^2)(1+\tfrac{5}{2}v_0^2\mu^2)+\tfrac{9}{4}\mu^6(v^2-v_0^2)(5v^2-v_0^2)+.... \qquad (3.20)$$

Substituting from (3.18) into (3.20) and neglecting powers of μ higher than the sixth, we find that the slope is stationary where

$$(v^2-\tfrac{1}{4})(1+\tfrac{15}{8}\mu^2) = \tfrac{1}{2}b\mu^2-\tfrac{3}{4}\mu^2(v^2-\tfrac{3}{4})(5v^2-\tfrac{3}{4}),$$

i.e. where $\qquad\qquad v = \tfrac{1}{2}(1+b\mu^2+\tfrac{3}{8}\mu^2)+\dots.$

By (3.19), the value of the slope at this point is

$$-\tfrac{1}{4}\mu^4(1+3b\mu^2+\tfrac{3}{4}\mu^2)+\dots \qquad\qquad (3.21)$$

while its value at the edge of the plate, found by substituting from (3.18) into (3.19) and setting $v = 1$, is

$$\tfrac{1}{4}\mu^4(1-6b\mu^2+\tfrac{39}{16}\mu^2)+\dots. \qquad\qquad (3.22)$$

Since the leading term of (3.21) increases with b, while that of (3.22) decreases as b increases, it follows that the axial colour-spread is minimized when $\qquad \tfrac{1}{4}\mu^2(1+3b\mu^2+\tfrac{3}{4}\mu^2)+\dots = \tfrac{1}{4}\mu^2(1-6b\mu^2+\tfrac{39}{16}\mu^2)+\dots$

$$b = \tfrac{3}{16}, \qquad\qquad (3.23)$$

and that the value of the greatest slope is then

$$\tfrac{1}{4}\mu^4(1+\tfrac{21}{16}\mu^2)+\dots, \qquad\qquad (3.24)$$

while the neutral zone is at the radius

$$v_0 = \tfrac{1}{2}\sqrt{3}(1+\tfrac{3}{16}\mu^2)+\dots. \qquad\qquad (3.25)$$

On substituting this value for v_0 into (3.13), the values of the plate-profile coefficients a_1, a_2, a_3 become

$$a_1 = \frac{-1}{n-1}\,(\tfrac{3}{8}\mu^2+\tfrac{27}{128}\mu^4+\dots),$$

$$a_2 = \frac{1}{n-1}\,(\tfrac{1}{4}-\tfrac{3}{8}\mu^2+\dots), \qquad\qquad (3.26)$$

$$a_3 = \frac{1}{n-1}\,(\tfrac{3}{8}+\dots),$$

while the focal length

$$f = \tfrac{1}{2}\sec\theta_0 = \tfrac{1}{2}+\tfrac{3}{16}\mu^2+\tfrac{45}{256}\mu^4+\dots. \qquad\qquad (3.27)$$

These are the formulae first given by J. G. Baker (1940). They are especially useful at focal ratios shorter than f/1, for which indeed they were developed. At longer focal ratios, such as f/2, the choice of v_0 is not very critical. For example, colour-compensation by taking $v_0 = \tfrac{1}{2}\sqrt{3}$ gives maximum slope $-\tfrac{1}{4}\mu^4(1+\tfrac{15}{61}\mu^2)+\dots$ on the central bulge of the plate, and slope $\tfrac{1}{4}\mu^4(1+\tfrac{39}{16}\mu^2)+\dots$ at its edge. The worst slope is therefore at the edge, and in an f/1 system ($\mu = \tfrac{1}{4}$) this is about 16 per cent. greater than the worst slope when v_0 is chosen according to (3.25). In an f/2 system ($\mu = \frac{1}{8}$) the corresponding loss is only 2 per cent., so that in systems of focal ratio f/2 or longer the value $v_0 = \frac{1}{2}\sqrt{3}$ is sufficient for all practical purposes. On substituting this value into (3.14), the equation for the plate profile becomes

$$(n-1)s = \tfrac{1}{4}\mu^4(v^4-\tfrac{3}{2}v^2)+\mu^6(\tfrac{3}{8}v^6-\tfrac{3}{8}v^4-\tfrac{9}{128}v^2)+O(\mu^8). \qquad (3.28)$$

Proof of equation (2.2). If the focal ratio is f/3 or longer, terms in μ^6 can be neglected in practice and (3.15) becomes

$$(n-1)s = \tfrac{1}{4}\mu^4(v^2-v_0^2)^2+\text{constant}+O(\mu^6)$$
$$= \tfrac{1}{4}\mu^4(v^4-2v_0^2v^2)+O(\mu^6), \qquad (3.29)$$

since $s = 0$ when $v = 0$. We also have from (3.27)

$$f = \tfrac{1}{2}+\tfrac{3}{16}\mu^2+O(\mu^4). \qquad (3.30)$$

On reintroducing x, y, z, H by means of (2.3) and (2.5), dropping the assumption that $R = 1$ and writing z/R, f/R for s, f to allow for the change of unit, (3.29) and (3.30) take the form

$$(n-1)z = (y^4-2v_0^2H^2y^2)/4R^3+O(H^6/R^5), \qquad (3.31)$$

$$f = \tfrac{1}{2}R+\frac{3}{16}\frac{H^2}{R}+O(H^4/R^3). \qquad (3.32)$$

These equations give the equation of the plate profile and the focal length of the system in terms of R, H and v_0. On replacing $v_0 H$ by h_0 and y by $h = (x^2+y^2)^{\frac{1}{2}}$ and eliminating f between (3.31) and (3.32), we obtain

$$(n-1)z = \frac{1}{32f^3}(h^4-2h_0^2h^2)+O(H^6/R^5) \qquad (3.33)$$

as the Cartesian equation of the plate surface when terms of order H^6/R^5 can be neglected. This establishes (2.2); the parameter

$$a = 2v_0^2$$

takes the value $\frac{3}{2}$ when $v_0 = \frac{1}{2}\sqrt{3}$, i.e. when the neutral zone is given a diameter equal to 0·866 of the full aperture. When v_0 is given the Baker value (3.25) or, more generally, whenever $v_0 = \frac{1}{2}\sqrt{3}+O(\mu^2)$, the error committed by retaining the value $a = \frac{3}{2}$ in (2.2) is $O(H^6/R^5)$ and hence is absorbed in the error term. It follows that the sixth-order monochromatic aberration function of the colour-minimized Schmidt camera is obtained on setting $r_0 = \frac{1}{2}\sqrt{3}$ in (2.23), whether the axial colour compensation is done according to the simple recipe $v_0 = \frac{1}{2}\sqrt{3}$ or in a more refined way by giving v_0 the value (3.25).

The chromatic aberration function. The axial colour-spread of a Schmidt telescope is comparable with the monochromatic error-spread at the edge of the field when the obstruction ratio c is between $\frac{1}{4}$ and $\frac{1}{2}$. For example, in an f/3 system covering a 5-degree field the obstruction ratio is $\frac{1}{4}$, the monochromatic error-spread at the edge of the field is 0·36 seconds of arc, and the axial colour-spread, when the plate is figured in F-light, is 1 second of arc over the spectral range C–h. In such a system the angular colour deviations are of numerical size $O(\mu^5)$ and the error involved in treating them as constant over the field is of numerical size $O(\mu^7)$, that is to say negligible in the fifth-order theory.

To the same order of accuracy, the value of $a = 2v_0^2$ may be taken as $\frac{3}{2}$ in calculating the aberrations, even when it is actually given by (3.25). For, as already remarked, this approximation introduces an error of only $O(\mu^7)$ in the monochromatic aberrations and it introduces only an error factor $1 + O(\mu^2)$ into the axial colour-spreads.

It follows that, to the order of numerical accuracy involved in neglecting monochromatic aberrations beyond the fifth order, the aberration function $\mu^6\Phi(u, v, V; n')$, in light of index n', of a Schmidt camera designed to give axial stigmatism in light of index n is given by the equation

$$\mu^6\Phi(u, v, V; n') = \mu^6\Phi^*(u, v, V) + (n'-n)[T(x, y) - T(0, 0)] + O(\mu^8)$$

$$= \mu^6\Phi^*(u, v, V) + \frac{n'-n}{n-1}[\tfrac{1}{4}\mu^4(r^4 - 2r_0^2 r^2) + O(\mu^6)] + O(\mu^8),$$

by (2.6),

$$= \mu^6\left[\tfrac{1}{2}c^2V^2\left(\frac{1}{n} + u\frac{\partial}{\partial u}\right) + k_{nn'\mu}\right](r^4 - 2r_0^2 r^2) + O(\mu^8)$$

$$= \mu^6\Phi^*(u, v, V; n') + O(\mu^8), \tag{3.34}$$

where
$$\Phi^*(u, v, V; n') = \left[\tfrac{1}{2}c^2V^2\left(\frac{1}{n} + u\frac{\partial}{\partial u}\right) + k_{nn'\mu}\right](r^4 - 2r_0^2 r^2) \tag{3.35}$$

and
$$k_{nn'\mu} = \frac{n'-n}{4\mu^2(n-1)} = O(1) \tag{3.36}$$

in a practical case. We call the leading term $\mu^6\Phi^*(u, v, V; n')$ on the right of (3.34) the *sixth-order aberration function* of the Schmidt camera.

If the Schmidt plate, of a hard crown glass or of plate glass, is figured to give axial stigmatism in F-light, the value of the coefficient $k_{nn'\mu}$ is approximately

$$\frac{1}{240\mu^2} \simeq \frac{F^2}{15}$$

at either end of the spectral range C–h. In this last formula F stands for the focal ratio; in the large Schmidt cameras so far made, $F^2/15$ lies between 0·25 and 1.

From (2.6) the effect on the aberration function of moving the plate a small distance $GRc^2\mu^2$ along the axis can be calculated. First suppose that the plate consists simply of the figuring layer, so that it can be treated as a plane lamina in our approximations. On the wave-fronts of a pencil of rays of n-light parallel to the axis, the retardation imposed by the plate is then

$$\tfrac{1}{4}R\mu^4(r^2-r_0^2)^2+\tfrac{1}{8}R\mu^6 P(r^2)+O(R\mu^8),\tag{3.37}$$

where, as may be verified from (3.15), $P(r^2)$ stands for the polynomial $(3r^2+2r_0^2)(r^2-r_0^2)^2$.

If the plate is moved a distance $GRc^2\mu^2$ along the axis towards the mirror, the aperture stop remaining in its original position, then a ray of an off-axis pencil which passes through the point (u, v) of the aperture stop now meets the plate in the point

$$(u+GRc^2\mu\sin\phi, v) = (u+2Gc^3\mu^2 V, v).$$

The retardation imposed by the plate at this point is obtained on replacing r^2 by $r_V''^2$ in (3.37), where

$$\begin{aligned}
r_V''^2 &= (u+2Gc^3\mu^2 V)^2+v^2\\
&= r^2+4Gc^3\mu^2 Vu+O(\mu^6).
\end{aligned}\tag{3.38}$$

Hence the change in the aberration function is

$$\begin{aligned}
\tfrac{1}{4}R\mu^4\{(r_V''^2-r_0^2)^2&-(r^2-r_0^2)^2\}+\tfrac{1}{8}R\mu^6\{P(r_V''^2)-P(r^2)\}+O(R\mu^8)\\
&= 2RGc^3\mu^6 Vu(r^2-r_0^2)+O(R\mu^8).
\end{aligned}\tag{3.39}$$

The term $-2RGc^3\mu^6 Vur_0^2$ represents a simple tilt of the whole wave-front, causing a bodily displacement of the image through an angular distance $2Gc^3\mu^5 Vr_0^2$ towards the centre of the field, i.e. a change in the equivalent focal length of the system by a factor $1-Gc^2\mu^4 r_0^2$. The other main term, namely $2RGc^3\mu^6 Vur^2$, measures, with error $O(R\mu^8)$, the primary coma which the plate-shift contributes to the aberration function.

A change in the wavelength of the light, bringing with it a change $O(\mu^2)$ in the value of the refractive index, introduces a factor $1+O(\mu^2)$ into the expressions (3.37) and (3.39). Since the effect of this factor can be absorbed in the error term, it follows that the coma contribution is independent of wavelength to the present order of approximation.

If the aperture stop is moved with the plate, the expressions for the aberration function and for δX, δY remain unchanged in form. For if (u', v') are coordinates in the new aperture stop, measured parallel to (u, v), then evidently

$$u' = u+O(\mu^2), \qquad v' = v+O(\mu^2)\tag{3.40}$$

for all rays contributing to the image, and on substituting for u, v in (3.34) we obtain a new expression whose leading term has the same algebraical form as before, but with u', v' in place of u, v. Since the boundary of the new aperture stop is the circle $u'^2+v'^2 = 1$, it follows that moving the aperture stop through a distance $O(R\mu^2)$ has left the fifth-order aberrations unaffected. The assumption that the plate thickness is negligible can now be dropped in the case where the aspheric side of the plate is towards the mirror, since the addition of a plane parallel plate in front of the entry pupil does not affect the aberrations of the system.

When the plate is turned round with its aspheric side away from the mirror, all the above results continue to hold, by the arguments given earlier, provided that the plate thickness is $O(R\mu^2)$ and that in measuring the distance of the aspheric surface or the aperture stop from the pole A of the mirror, that part of the distance which lies in glass is taken with a factor $1/n$.

From (3.34) it is easy to calculate the fifth-order angular aberration components, measured in seconds of arc, of the ray entering the system through the point (u, v) of the aperture stop, at an angle $\phi = \arcsin 2c\mu V$ with the axis, in light from any part of the spectrum; they are

$$(\delta X', \delta Y') = K\mu^5\left(\frac{\partial}{\partial u}, \frac{\partial}{\partial v}\right)\Phi^*(u, v, V; n'), \qquad (3.41)$$

where $K = 648,000/\pi$. By plotting, for given V, n', the values of the aberration displacements corresponding to a lattice of points

$$u, v = 0, \pm 0 \cdot 1, \pm 0 \cdot 2, \dots$$

in the aperture stop $u^2+v^2 \leqslant 1$, we obtain a point-cluster or 'spot diagram' which represents fairly closely the light distribution in the geometrical image. Fig. 75 shows spot diagrams in F, G', and h-light at selected points of the field surface of an f/3·5 Schmidt camera in which the plate is designed to give axial stigmatism in G'-light; the effect of the central obstruction is ignored.† It will be seen that, over the spectral range $F–h$, which includes the brightest part of the mean astrographic spectrum, the geometrical images are comparable in size with the Airy disk corresponding to a 24-inch aperture. Even over the spectral range $C–h$, the geometric images only reach about three times the size of the

† Since the Airy disk corresponding to the central obstruction is several times larger than the geometrical images corresponding to the full aperture, the effect of the obstruction on the physical images cannot be approximately represented by deleting the corresponding points in the spot diagrams.

Airy disk. Thus the optical aberrations of a 24-inch f/3·5 Schmidt camera working over a field of 5 degrees diameter are negligible for practical purposes. The case is otherwise, however, with a 48-inch f/2·5 Schmidt camera; see Fig. 78.

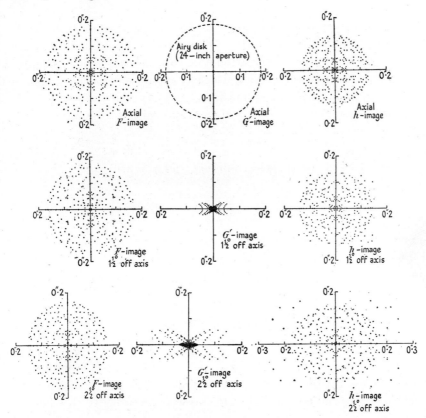

FIG. 75. Geometrical images by f/3·5 Schmidt camera (axially stigmatic in G'-light; $a = \frac{3}{2}$, $n_{G'} = 1·55$, $(n_F - n_{G'})/(n_{G'} - 1) = -0·0094$, $(n_h - n_{G'})/(n_{G'} - 1) = 0·0070$).

4. Aberration-balancing in Schmidt cameras†

Although its performance must be rated as high by ordinary standards, the Schmidt camera in its classical form possesses the disadvantage that its aberrations are not balanced over its field. The images are smallest in the centre of the field and increase in size towards the edge. In most of the existing astronomical Schmidt cameras this is probably of little practical consequence, since the confusion patches, even at the edge of

† A different type of aberration-balancing, which aims at minimizing the r.m.s. image-radii over the field by modifying the plate profile only, is discussed in Chap. I, § 1.76.

the field, are smaller than the diameter of the tremor disk of a star under conditions of moderate seeing. Nevertheless, it seems worth while to consider what improvements in optical performance can be made by modifying the design of the system so as to balance its monochromatic aberrations over a given field.

The methods of § 2 can be applied to discuss the problem of 'balancing' the fifth-order monochromatic aberrations of the Schmidt camera, namely lateral spherical aberration and a species of higher astigmatism, by the introduction of small, controlled amounts of primary spherical aberration and of Seidel astigmatism.

To introduce these balancing aberrations we put a figuring

$$\tfrac{1}{8}m_1\mu^6(r^4-2r_0^2\,r^2)\tag{4.1}$$

on the surface of the spherical mirror† and a figuring

$$\frac{1}{n-1}\frac{1}{4}(\mu^4+m_3\mu^6)(r^4-2r_0^2r^2)+\frac{1}{n-1}\mu^6(\tfrac{3}{8}r^6-\tfrac{1}{2}r^4r_0^2-\tfrac{1}{8}r^2r_0^4)\tag{4.2}$$

on the aspheric surface of the plate. (The coefficient of the term in μ^6r^6 is obtained from (3.14).) We also move the plate towards the mirror to a distance $m_4\mu^2$ behind the aperture stop. Lastly we change slightly the adopted field curvature, so as to add a term

$$\tfrac{1}{4}m_2\mu^4r^2\sin^2\phi+O(\mu^8) = m_2c^2\mu^6V^2r^2+O(\mu^8)\tag{4.3}$$

to the aberration function of the emerging wave-fronts. As in the first part of § 2, R has been given the value 1 and the system is supposed for the time being to be working backwards and with its aspheric plate surface facing the mirror. The off-axis contributions to the distortion of an emerging wave-front are now as follows:

(i) From the 'shearing' of mirror surface against stop and the change in adopted field curvature, a contribution

$$\tfrac{1}{4}m_1\mu^6[(r_V^4-2r_0^2\,r_V^2)-(r^4-2r_0^2\,r^2)]+m_2\mu^6c^2V^2r^2+O(\mu^8),\tag{4.4}$$

where

$$r_V^2 = (u+R\sin\phi/\mu)^2+v^2 = r^2+4cVu+4c^2V^2.\tag{4.5}$$

On substituting for r_V^2 from (4.5), we obtain (4.4) in the form

$$m_1\mu^6(cVu+c^2V^2)(2r^2+4cVu+4c^2V^2-2r_0^2)+m_2\mu^6c^2V^2r^2+O(\mu^8).\tag{4.6}$$

† It makes no difference to the final formulae whether the thickness of the figuring layer is measured normally to the mirror surface or parallel to the x-axis, since the discrepancy is $O(\mu^6)[1-\cos\{O(\mu)\}] = O(\mu^8)$.

(ii) From the 'foreshortening' of the aperture stop against the wave-fronts arriving from the sphere, a contribution

$$\tfrac{1}{2}\mu^6 c^2 V^2 u \frac{\partial}{\partial u}(r^4 - 2r_0^2 r^2) + O(\mu^8). \tag{4.7}$$

(iii) From the oblique passage of the wave-fronts through the plate, a contribution
$$\tfrac{1}{2}\mu^6 c^2 V^2(r^4 - 2r_0^2 r^2)/n + O(\mu^8), \tag{4.8}$$
in accordance with (2.12).

(iv) From the shearing of the plate against the aperture stop, a contribution

$$\tfrac{1}{4}(\mu^4 + m_3\mu^6)[(r_V'^4 - 2r_0^2 r_V'^2) - (r^4 - 2r_0^2 r^2)] + O(\mu^8),$$

where $\qquad r_V'^2 = (u + m_4\mu^2 \sin\phi)^2 + v^2 = (u + 2m_4\mu^2 cV)^2 + v^2,$

and the contribution can therefore be written

$$2m_4\mu^6 cVu(r^2 - r_0^2) + O(\mu^8). \tag{4.9}$$

It follows that the total distortion of the emerging wave-fronts is

$$\tfrac{1}{4}(m_1 + m_3)\mu^6(r^4 - 2r_0^2 r^2) + m_1\mu^6(cVu + c^2V^2)(2r^2 + 4cVu + 4c^2V^2 - 2r_0^2) +$$

$$+ m_2\mu^6 c^2 V^2 r^2 + \tfrac{1}{2}\mu^6 c^2 V^2\left(\frac{1}{n} + u\frac{\partial}{\partial u}\right)(r^4 - 2r_0^2 r^2) +$$

$$+ 2m_4\mu^6 cVu(r^2 - r_0^2) + O(\mu^8). \tag{4.10}$$

Terms independent of u and v in this expression may be dropped, since they have no effect on the aberrations. To get rid of primary coma in the image, we have to annul the terms in ur^2, namely

$$2(m_1 + m_4)\mu^6 cVur^2;$$

that is, we must set $m_4 = -m_1$. Then the aberration function can be written

$$\mu^6\Phi(u, v, V) = \mu^6\left[\tfrac{1}{4}(m_1 + m_3)(r^4 - 2r_0^2 r^2) + \tfrac{1}{2}c^2 V^2\left(\frac{1}{n} + u\frac{\partial}{\partial u}\right)(r^4 - 2r_0^2 r^2)\right] +$$

$$+ \mu^6 c^2 V^2[2m_1(2u^2 + r^2) + m_2 r^2] + 8\mu^6 c^3 V^3 m_1 u + O(\mu^8). \tag{4.11}$$

The term in u represents a bodily shift of the image sideways; it follows that the *distortion of the system*, in radians, is

$$8m_1\mu^5 c^3 V^3(1 + O(\mu^2)). \tag{4.12}$$

Dropping the term in u, we obtain

$$\mu^6\Psi(u, v, V) = \mu^6\left[\tfrac{1}{4}(m_1 + m_3)(r^4 - 2r_0^2 r^2) + \right.$$

$$\left. + \tfrac{1}{2}c^2 V^2\left(\frac{1}{n} + u\frac{\partial}{\partial u}\right)(r^4 - 2r_0^2 r^2) + 2c^2 V^2 m_1(2u^2 + r^2) + c^2 V^2 m_2 r^2\right] + O(\mu^8) \tag{4.13}$$

as the aberration function for the image errors, other than distortion, on the adopted field surface. The corresponding angular aberration displacements are

$$\mu^5\frac{\partial\Psi}{\partial u} = \mu^5\left[4c^2V^2u^3+\left(m_1+m_3+\frac{2n+1}{2n}4c^2V^2\right)(r^2-r_0^2)u+\right.$$

$$\left.+2c^2V^2(6m_1+m_2)u\right]+O(\mu^7),$$

$$\mu^5\frac{\partial\Psi}{\partial v} = \mu^5\left[4c^2V^2u^2v+\left(m_1+m_3+\frac{1}{2n}4c^2V^2\right)(r^2-r_0^2)v+\right.$$

$$\left.+2c^2V^2(2m_1+m_2)v\right]+O(\mu^7).\quad(4.14)$$

Consideration of the form of the off-axis errors suggests that something near to the best balancing of the performance over the whole field will be obtained by making the aberration displacements vanish for $V=1$, $(u,v)=(\pm1,0)$, and $(0,\pm1)$. This is equivalent to pulling in four selected margin-points of the image at the edge of the field, so that they meet in the centre of the image, which becomes folded over. The values of m_1, m_2, m_3 which achieve this are easily found to be

$$m_1 = -1+\tfrac{1}{2}r_0^2,\qquad m_2 = 4-\tfrac{3}{4}r_0^2,\qquad m_3 = 1-\tfrac{1}{2}r_0^2-\frac{2n+1}{2n}4c^2$$

$$(4.15)$$

and on inserting these values in (4.11) the aberration function becomes

$$\mu^6\Psi'(u,v,V) = \mu^6c^2\left[(u^4-v^4)-2(u^2-v^2)+\right.$$

$$\left.+(1-V^2)\left\{-2u^2r^2+2r_0^2r^2+2(u^2-v^2)-\frac{1}{2n}(r^4-2r_0^2r^2)\right\}\right]+O(\mu^8).$$

$$(4.16)$$

The scale restriction $R=1$, under which this formula has been established, may be dropped if a multiplying factor $2f$ is inserted on the right-hand side. By (4.2), the plate profile is

$$s = \frac{1}{n-1}\frac{1}{4}\left[\mu^4+\left(1-\tfrac{1}{2}r_0^2-4c^2\frac{2n+1}{2n}\right)\mu^6\right](r^4-2r_0^2r^2)+$$

$$+\frac{1}{n-1}\mu^6(\tfrac{3}{8}r^6-\tfrac{1}{4}r^4r_0^2-\tfrac{1}{8}r^2r_0^4),\quad(4.17)$$

so that the change in plate strength only amounts to a few per cent. of its original value. The figuring on the mirror, namely

$$-\tfrac{1}{8}\mu^6(1-\tfrac{1}{2}r_0^2)(r^4-2r_0^2r^2),\quad(4.18)$$

is of the same type as that on a paraboloid and when $r_0=\tfrac{1}{2}\sqrt3$ it amounts to only $\frac{3}{5}$ fringe in the case of an f/3·5 system working with a 24-inch plate and a 36-inch mirror; in the case of an f/2·5 system with a 48-inch plate and 72-inch mirror it amounts to 3 fringes. Fig. 76 shows the manner in which the geometrical images are folded over, in the system with aberration function (4.16) at selected points of the field.

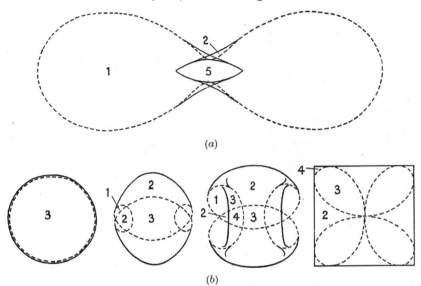

Fig. 76. Monochromatic images. (Folding and relative sizes of G'-images: (a) in the classical Schmidt camera of Fig. 78, 3° off axis; (b) in the modified system of Fig. 77. The numbers state the degree of many-sheetedness of the image. The dotted lines correspond to the edge of the aperture stop.)

Polychromatic aberrations. From (4.16) and (4.17) it follows, by the same arguments as those used to derive (3.34), that the sixth-order aberration function in light of index n' of the above system is

$$\mu^6 \Psi^*(u, v, V; n')$$

$$= \mu^6 c^2 \left[V^2 \{(u^4 - v^4) - 2(u^2 - v^2)\} - \frac{2n+1}{2n}(1 - V^2)(r^4 - 2r_0^2 r^2) \right] +$$

$$+ \mu^6 k_{nn'\mu}(r^4 - 2r_0^2 r^2) + O(\mu^8), \quad (4.19)$$

where $k_{nn'\mu}$ is again given by (3.36).

The fifth-order aberration displacements in n'-light, measured in radians, are then

$$\mu^5 \frac{\partial \Psi^*}{\partial u}, \; \mu^5 \frac{\partial \Psi^*}{\partial v} = 4\mu^5 c^2 V^2(-u + u^3, v - v^3) +$$

$$+ 4\mu^5 \left\{ k_{nn'\mu} - \frac{2n+1}{2n} c^2(1 - V^2) \right\}(r^2 - r_0^2)(u, v). \quad (4.20)$$

The distortion (4.12) is not included in the aberration function (4.19). To include it, we only need to add a term

$$8m_1\mu^6 c^3 V^3 u = -8\mu^6 c^3 V^3 (1-\tfrac{1}{2}r_0^2)u \qquad (4.21)$$

on the right of (4.19), since the variation of distortion with wavelength is $O(8m_1\mu^6 c^3 V^3(n'-n)) = O(\mu^8)$, which is negligible in the present approximation.

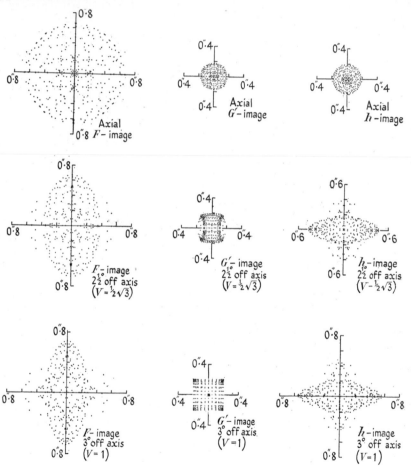

FIG. 77. Geometrical images by f/2·5 modified Schmidt camera, aberrations balanced in G'-light over a $6°$ field ($a = \tfrac{3}{2}$, $n_{G'} = 1·55$, $(n_F - n_{G'})/(n_{G'}-1) = -0·0094$, $(n_h - n_{G'})/(n_{G'}-1) = 0·0070$).

For the same reasons as in § 2, the leading terms of the aberration function remain unchanged when the plate, of paraxial thickness $d = O(\mu)$ is turned round and its distance from the mirror is readjusted in the manner there described (namely, by moving the plate mounting a distance d/n towards the mirror when the plate is turned round so as to bring its aspheric surface to the side away from the mirror).

Further, the leading terms in the expressions for the angular aberration displacements are the same whether the system works backwards or in the normal manner.

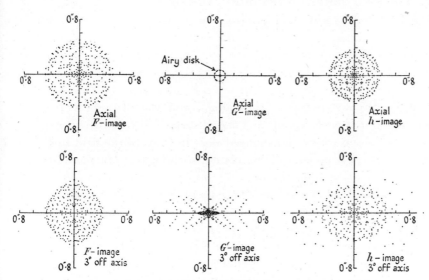

FIG. 78. Geometrical images by f/2·5 Schmidt camera, axially stigmatic in G'-light $(a = \frac{3}{2}, n_{G'} = 1·55, (n_F - n_{G'})/(n_{G'} - 1) = -0·0094 \; (n_h - n_{G'})/(n_{G'} - 1) = 0·0070)$.

Finally, a shift $O(\mu^2)$ of the aperture stop, since it alters the boundary of any entering pencil by at most $O(\mu^3)$, changes the value of the aberration displacements by at most $O(\mu^7)$; it therefore leaves the leading terms in the expressions for these displacements unaltered. The same formulae (4.19), (4.20) therefore describe the fifth-order aberrations of the system working forwards or backwards, with the plate either way round, and with the stop either on the plate or at the centre of curvature of the mirror.

In a 48–72-inch f/2·5 system with $r_0 = \frac{1}{2}\sqrt{3}$ and $c = \frac{1}{4}$, the distortion (4.21) amounts at the edge of the field to

$$8m_1 \mu^5 c^3 V^3 = -0·16 \text{ second of arc.}$$

(Zero distortion would mean that great circles on the sky are imaged into great circles on the spherical field surface.)

Fig. 77 shows the spot diagrams of this system, calculated from (4.20), for the images in F, G', and h-light, at selected points of the field. The effect of the central obstruction is ignored, as before; the Airy disk corresponding to the central obstruction is here comparable in size to the geometrical images given by the full aperture. Diagrams for the images at the edge of the field of a classical Schmidt camera of the same size, focal ratio, and field diameter are shown in Fig. 78 for comparison.

5. The field-flattened Schmidt camera

5.1. *Introductory.* As was remarked in § 1, the field surface of the ordinary Schmidt camera is not flat, but is convex towards the mirror, its radius of curvature being usually taken as equal to the focal length f. To the Seidel order of approximation, this agrees with the Petzval radius of the system and the image surface coincides with the Petzval surface. For the Petzval radius is $f[1+O(\mu^2)]$ and the distance between the adopted image surface and the Petzval surface is $O(f\mu^4)$ all over the field.

A thin plano-convex lens placed close in front of the field surface will change the Petzval sum of the system without introducing appreciable Seidel aberrations into the images; the system remains an anastigmat, that is to say the 'deviations' of the points where the rays meet its focal surface are still $O(f\mu^5)$. Its field surface therefore continues to coincide with its Petzval surface to the Seidel order of approximation.

If n_1 denote the refractive index of the plano-convex lens and f_1 its focal length, the Petzval contribution of the lens is $-1/n_1 f_1$ and the Petzval curvature of the whole system is $1/f - 1/n_1 f_1$. To the order of approximation here in question, the variation of n_1 from one part of the spectrum to another may be disregarded: more precisely, the effect of this variation is a contribution $O(f\mu^5)$ to the deviations in the adopted image surface. By choosing $f_1 = f/n_1$, we therefore obtain an anastigmat with a flat Petzval surface and consequently a flat image surface. This system is known as the field-flattened Schmidt camera.

Two different questions now present themselves for investigation. The first, and possibly the more important from the practical astronomer's point of view, is: given a Schmidt camera, how much is necessarily lost in image quality when a field flattener is added to the system and how can this loss be minimized?

In §§ 5.2, 5.3 below, general formulae are obtained which provide a means of answering this question, and in the first part of § 5.4 they are applied to discuss the case of an astronomical Schmidt camera with a central obstruction ratio $\frac{1}{4}$; for example, an f/3 camera working over a 5° diameter field. It appears that the ordinary Petzval equation

$$\frac{1}{f} - \frac{n_1 - 1}{n_1 r_1} = 0$$

provides a sufficiently accurate basis for the design of the field flattener (r_1 here denoting the radius of curvature of its convex surface) and that, as in the plain Schmidt of this focal ratio and field-size, colour-error dominates the aberrations. There is a considerable drop in performance, due to increased colour-error, when the field flattener is added. The off-axis coma, when suitably balanced by moving the corrector plate a small distance towards the mirror, is not so large as to affect visibly the symmetry of the photographic star-images formed by the system, but not so small that we can rule out of consideration the possibility of magnitude errors in their measured positions. An experimental investigation of this question seems desirable.

Field-flattened systems of the above type are convertible, in the sense that they can be used either with or without the field flattener, and nothing is sacrificed in the design of the plain Schmidt for the sake of improving performance when the field flattener is added. The further question therefore arises: what improvement in performance results when the field-flattened Schmidt is designed as a single unit? This point is taken up in the second part of § 5.4, where it is shown that, in systems of obstruction-ratio near to $\frac{1}{4}$, the performance of the field-flattened Schmidt is markedly improved by using a corrector plate with neutral zone close to the edge of the aperture. Such a corrector plate would be undesirable in an f/3 plain Schmidt, even though the monochromatic aberrations are reduced by using it, because of the chromatic difference of focus which it introduces. In the field-flattened Schmidt, this chromatic difference of focus can be used to balance the colour-error of the field flattener and the result is a system whose aberrations are not much larger than those of a plain Schmidt. They now include a small amount of coma, however, and this may prove a drawback in systems intended for positional measurements.

5.2. *Aberrations of the field-flattened Schmidt camera*

Fig. 79 shows the system with the field flattener inserted. The convex front face of the field flattener has the radius of curvature $[(n_1-1)/n_1]CI$, where n_1 is the index of refraction of the glass for light of a selected wavelength; its sharp edge coincides with the edge $\phi = \phi_0$ of the original field surface and its flat back forms the new field surface. In practice, we should use a lens which is not sharp at the edge, placed with its back face not quite in contact with the photographic plate; the effect of these changes on the aberrations will be considered later. It will appear later that performance is improved by moving the corrector plate a short

distance along the axis towards the mirror. For the present, we consider
the system without this refinement.

   PQ represents a ray, originating in the distant object point at an
angular distance ϕ below the axis of the system, which passes through
the point $P = (u, v)$ in the plane of the aperture stop. After reflection
by the mirror at the point Q and refraction by the field flattener at the
point T', this ray meets the focal plane in U'. To calculate the aberrations

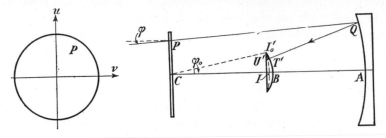

FIG. 79. Field-flattened Schmidt camera.

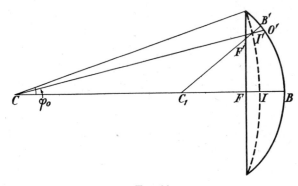

FIG. 80

of the system in n'-light, we first suppose the rays from the concave
mirror to converge exactly on to points of the virtual image surface II'
(see Fig. 80); that is to say, we disregard for the time being the aberrations
with which the converging pencils are loaded when they arrive at the
field flattener. Since the diameter of the field flattener is

$$2CI_0 \sin \phi_0 = O(R\mu),$$

its thickness is $O(R\mu^2)$ and the lateral aberrations introduced when the
virtual object point I' is imaged in the convex surface of the lens are
$O(R\mu^5)$. Moreover, the Gauss image of I' in the convex surface is at a
distance $O(R\mu^4)$ from the adopted focal plane FF', since the field

flattener has been given the Petzval curvature $1/CI$. Hence the image-spreads on the adopted field surface due to aberrations introduced by the field flattener are $O(R\mu^5)$; that is, they are of the same order of magnitude as the image-spreads in the ordinary Schmidt camera. The same is true, as will be shown below, of the chromatic aberrations introduced by the field flattener, provided that the refractive index of the field flattener varies by only $O(\mu^2)$ throughout the effective spectral range.

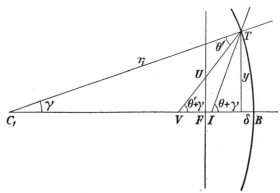

Fig. 81

It follows that, to obtain for the aberrations of the field-flattened system approximate formulae of the same order of accuracy as those derived in §§ 2, 3 above for the ordinary Schmidt camera, it is sufficient to calculate separately the aberrations introduced by the field flattener and by the rest of the system and to add the results, the cross-terms being of order $R\mu^7$.

In Fig. 81, TU shows the path of a ray, originally proceeding towards the axial image point I, after refraction at the first surface of the field flattener. U is the intersection of this ray with the back surface and V is the point in which TU produced meets the axis. Let n_1 be the refractive index of the lens for the light in which Petzval curvature is compensated, so that

$$r_1 = \frac{n_1-1}{n_1}CI = \frac{n_1-1}{n_1}\frac{R}{2}[1+O(\mu^2)], \tag{5.1}$$

where CI is the distance of I from the centre of curvature of the mirror. Let n_1' be the refractive index of the lens in the light under consideration and suppose, what is true in a practical case, that

$$n_1'-n_1 = O(\mu^2). \tag{5.2}$$

We write l for the distance IB and set

$$\theta = \mu\Theta, \qquad \theta' = \mu\Theta', \qquad l = \mu^2 L, \qquad y = \mu^3 Y, \qquad \gamma = \mu^3\Gamma; \tag{5.3}$$

then, by Fig. 81, the capital letters denote positive quantities which are $O(1)$ and whose ratios are all $O(1)$. Thus the power of μ in each term of our expressions will give an indication of its order of magnitude. Evidently

$$\delta = O(y^2) = O(\mu^6).$$

From Fig. 81

$$\tan(\theta+\gamma) = y/(l-\delta),$$

$$\theta+\gamma+\tfrac{1}{3}(\theta+\gamma)^3+O(\mu^5) = y/l+O(y\delta/l^2),$$

$$\mu\Theta+\mu^3\Gamma+\tfrac{1}{3}\mu^3\Theta^3 = \mu Y/L+O(\mu^5),$$

$$\Theta = \frac{Y}{L}-\mu^2\Big(\Gamma+\frac{1}{3}\frac{Y^3}{L^3}\Big)+O(\mu^4).$$

Now $\sin\gamma = y/r_1$; hence $\Gamma = Y/r_1+O(\mu^6)$ and we obtain

$$\Theta = \frac{Y}{L}-\Big(\frac{Y}{r_1}+\frac{1}{3}\frac{Y^3}{L^3}\Big)\mu^2+O(\mu^4). \tag{5.4}$$

By Snell's law

$$n_1'\sin\theta' = \sin\theta,$$

$$\theta' = \frac{1}{n_1'}\Big[\theta-\tfrac{1}{6}\theta^3\Big(1-\frac{1}{n_1'^2}\Big)\Big]+O(\theta^5),$$

$$\Theta' = \frac{1}{n_1'}\Theta\Big[1-\tfrac{1}{6}\mu^2\Theta^2\Big(1-\frac{1}{n_1'^2}\Big)\Big]+O(\mu^4). \tag{5.5}$$

Hence

$$\mu\cot\theta' = \frac{\mu}{\theta'}[1-\tfrac{1}{3}\theta'^2+O(\mu^4)] = \frac{1}{\Theta'}[1-\tfrac{1}{3}\mu^2\Theta'^2+O(\mu^4)]$$

$$= n_1'\frac{L}{Y}\Big[1+\Big(\frac{L}{r_1}+\frac{n_1'^2-1}{2n_1'^2}\frac{Y^2}{L^2}\Big)\mu^2+O(\mu^4)\Big]. \tag{5.6}$$

Now, from Fig. 81,

$$\frac{r_1}{C_1 V} = \frac{\sin(\theta'+\gamma)}{\sin\theta'} = \cos\gamma+\cot\theta'\sin\gamma$$

$$= 1+\frac{n_1' L\Gamma}{Y}\mu^2+\frac{n_1' L\Gamma}{Y}\Big(\frac{L}{r_1}+\frac{n_1'^2-1}{2n_1'^2}\frac{Y^2}{L^2}\Big)\mu^4+O(\mu^6);$$

$$C_1 V = r_1\Big[1-\frac{n_1' L}{r_1}\mu^2+\frac{n_1'(n_1'-1)}{r_1^2}L^2\mu^4-\frac{n_1'^2-1}{2n_1'}\frac{Y^2}{Lr_1}\mu^4+O(\mu^6)\Big] \tag{5.7}$$

$$= r_1\Big[1-\frac{n_1' l}{r_1}+\frac{n_1'(n_1'-1)}{r_1^2}l^2-\frac{n_1'^2-1}{2n_1'}\frac{y^2}{lr_1}+O(\mu^6)\Big],$$

$$BV = r_1-C_1 V = n_1' l-\frac{n_1'(n_1'-1)}{r_1}l^2+\frac{n_1'^2-1}{2n_1'}\frac{y^2}{l}+O(r_1\mu^6). \tag{5.8}$$

The first part of this expression, independent of y, is the expansion as far as terms of order μ^4 of the distance BF_0 of the Gaussian image F_0 from B. The remainder therefore gives an approximate expression for the longitudinal spherical aberration.

In the case of an off-axis pencil, shown in Fig. 82, we make use of an auxiliary optic axis $C_1 I'B'$, which no longer coincides with the principal

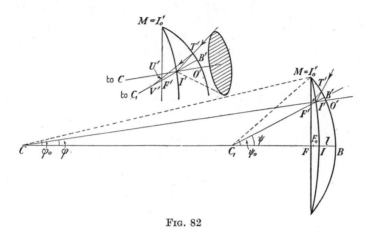

FIG. 82

ray $CI'O'$ of the incident pencil. An arbitrary ray of the pencil converging to the virtual object point I' meets the convex surface in T' and is refracted into the ray $T'U'V'$, which meets the back surface of the lens in U' and the auxiliary axis $C_1 B'$ in V'. (Fig. 81 illustrates the special case of a meridional ray.) y', l' are respectively the distance of T' from the auxiliary axis $C_1 I'B'$ and the distance $B'I'$ of the virtual object point inside B'.

We first need expressions for $l' = B'I'$ and for $B'F''$. From the figure,

$$B'I' = r_1 - C_1 I',$$

$$CI' = CI,$$

$$
\begin{aligned}
C_1 I'^2 &= CC_1^2 + CI'^2 - 2CC_1 . CI' \cos\phi \\
&= 2CI(CI - r_1 + l)(1 - \cos\phi) + (r_1 - l)^2.
\end{aligned}
\tag{5.9}
$$

Now $\quad l = BI = FB - FI = r_1(1 - \cos\psi_0) - CI(1 - \cos\phi_0),$ $\quad$ (5.10)

where ϕ_0 and ψ_0 are the values of ϕ, ψ at the edge of the field; also

$$\sin\psi_0 = \frac{CI_0'}{C_1 I_0'}\sin\phi_0 = \frac{n_1}{n_1 - 1}\sin\phi_0 \tag{5.11}$$

and, by (3.17),

$$\sin\phi_0 = 2c\lambda = 2c\mu(1 - \tfrac{1}{2}r_0^2\mu^2) + O(\mu^5). \tag{5.12}$$

On making use of (5.1), (5.11), (5.12) and the relation

$$CI = f = \tfrac{1}{2}R(1-\mu^2 r_0^2)^{-\frac{1}{2}},$$

equation (5.10) gives

$$l = r_1 \frac{2c^2\mu^2 n_1}{(n_1-1)^2}\left[1-r_0^2\mu^2+\frac{3n_1^2-3n_1+1}{(n_1-1)^2}c^2\mu^2+O(\mu^4)\right],$$

$$(r_1-l)^2 = r_1^2\left\{1-\frac{4n_1 c^2\mu^2}{(n_1-1)^2}\left[1-\left(r_0^2-\frac{3n_1-1}{n_1-1}c^2\right)\mu^2\right]+O(\mu^6)\right\}. \quad (5.13)$$

Also

$$1-\cos\phi = \tfrac{1}{2}\sin^2\phi[1+\tfrac{1}{4}\sin^2\phi]+O(\mu^6)$$
$$= 2c^2\mu^2 V^2(1-r_0^2\mu^2+c^2\mu^2 V^2)+O(\mu^6), \quad (5.14)$$

where V is defined by (2.9). Hence (5.9) gives

$$C_1 I'^2$$
$$= r_1^2\left\{1-\frac{4n_1}{(n_1-1)^2}c^2\mu^2(1-V^2)\left[1-r_0^2\mu^2+c^2\mu^2\left(\frac{3n_1-1}{n_1-1}+V^2\right)\right]+O(\mu^6)\right\},$$

$$C_1 I' = r_1\left\{1-\frac{2n_1}{(n_1-1)^2}c^2\mu^2(1-V^2)\left[1-r_0^2\mu^2+\right.\right.$$
$$\left.\left. +c^2\mu^2\left(\frac{3n_1^2-3n_1+1}{(n_1-1)^2}+\frac{n_1^2-3n_1+1}{(n_1-1)^2}V^2\right)\right]+O(\mu^6)\right\};$$

and we obtain finally

$$l' = B'I' = r_1-C_1 I' = r_1\left\{\frac{2n_1 c^2\mu^2}{(n_1-1)^2}(1-V^2)\left[1-r_0^2\mu^2+\right.\right.$$
$$\left.\left. +c^2\mu^2\left(\frac{3n_1^2-3n_1+1}{(n_1-1)^2}+\frac{n_1^2-3n_1+1}{(n_1-1)^2}V^2\right)\right]+O(\mu^6)\right\}, \quad (5.15)$$

as the desired expression for l'.

A similar calculation, starting from the equations

$$B'F' = r_1-C_1 F', \qquad C_1 F' = C_1 F \sec\psi, \qquad C_1 F = r_1-BF, \quad (5.16)$$

yields the equation

$$B'F' = r_1\frac{2n_1^2}{(n_1-1)^2}c^2\mu^2(1-V^2)\left\{1-r_0^2\mu^2+\frac{c^2\mu^2 n_1^2}{(n_1-1)^2}(1+3V^2)-\right.$$
$$\left. -\frac{4n_1}{(n_1-1)^2}c^2\mu^2 V^2\right\}+O(r_1\mu^6). \quad (5.17)$$

The next stage is to calculate $B'V'$. Let ϖ be a plane drawn through O' perpendicular to CO' and let x'', y'' be coordinates in this plane, $O'x''$ being in the plane BCO' and $O'y''$ at right angles to it. Let T'', B'' be the perpendicular projections of T', B' on the plane ϖ. See Fig. 83.

For a ray $T'I'$ (not necessarily a meridional ray) which entered the system through the point (u, v) of the aperture stop, T'' has the co-ordinates

$$(x'', y'') = (u, v)\frac{H}{\frac{1}{2}R}O'I'[1+O(\mu^2)]$$

$$= (u, v)2\mu B'I'[1+O(\mu^2)]$$

$$= (u, v)r_1\frac{4n_1 c^2 \mu^3}{(n_1-1)^2}(1-V^2)[1+O(\mu^2)], \qquad (5.18)$$

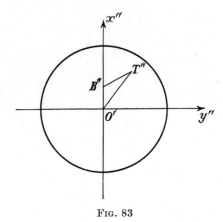

FIG. 83

by (5.15). Now

$$B''O' = B'O'[1+O(\mu^2)] = B'I'(\psi-\phi)[1+O(\mu^2)]$$

$$= r_1\frac{2n_1 c^2 \mu^2}{(n_1-1)^2}(1-V^2)(\sin\psi-\sin\phi)[1+O(\mu^2)]$$

$$= r_1\frac{4n_1 c^3 \mu^3}{(n_1-1)^3}V(1-V^2)[1+O(\mu^2)] \qquad (5.19)$$

and

$$y' = I'B'\sin T'I'B'[1+O(\mu^2)]$$

$$= T''B''[1+O(\mu^2)]$$

$$= r''[1+O(\mu^2)], \qquad (5.20)$$

where

$$r''^2 = T''B''^2 = \left(x''-r_1\frac{4n_1 c^3 \mu^3}{(n_1-1)^3}V(1-V^2)\right)^2 + y''^2$$

$$= r_1^2\left(\frac{4n_1 c^2 \mu^3}{(n_1-1)^2}\right)^2(1-V^2)^2\left[\left(u-\frac{cV}{n_1-1}\right)^2+v^2\right][1+O(\mu^2)], \quad (5.21)$$

and, by (5.15),

$$\frac{r''^2}{l'^2} = 4\mu^2\left\{\left(u - \frac{cV}{n_1-1}\right)^2 + v^2\right\}[1 + O(\mu^2)]. \tag{5.22}$$

Hence by (5.8), applied with the auxiliary axis $C_1 I'$ in place of $C_1 I$ and with l', y' in place of l, y,

$$B'V' = n_1' l' - \frac{n_1'(n_1'-1)}{r_1} l'^2 + \frac{n_1'^2-1}{2n_1'} \frac{y'^2}{l'} + O(r_1\mu^6)$$

$$= n_1 l' - \frac{n_1(n_1-1)}{r_1} l'^2 + \frac{n_1^2-1}{2n_1} \frac{y'^2}{l'} + (n_1'-n_1)l + O(r_1\mu^6), \tag{5.23}$$

in virtue of the hypothesis (5.2),

$$= r_1 \frac{2n_1^2 c^2\mu^2}{(n_1-1)^2}(1-V^2)\left\{1 - r_0^2\mu^2 + c^2\mu^2\left(\frac{3n_1^2-3n_1+1}{(n_1-1)^2} + \frac{n_1^2-3n_1+1}{(n_1-1)^2}V^2\right) - \right.$$

$$\left. - \frac{2n_1}{n_1-1}c^2\mu^2(1-V^2) + \frac{n_1^2-1}{2n_1^2}4\mu^2\left[\left(u - \frac{cV}{n_1-1}\right)^2 + v^2\right] + \frac{n_1'-n_1}{n_1}\right\} + O(r_1\mu^6), \tag{5.24}$$

by (5.20), (5.21), (5.22). This is the desired expression for $B'V'$.

From (5.17) and (5.24)

$$F'V' = B'V' - B'F'$$

$$= r_1 \frac{2n_1^2 c^2\mu^4}{(n_1-1)^2}(1-V^2)\left\{2\frac{n_1^2-1}{n_1^2}\left[\left(u - \frac{cV}{n_1-1}\right)^2 + v^2\right] - \right.$$

$$\left. - \frac{c^2}{n_1-1}(1+V^2) + \frac{4(n_1-1)}{n_1}k_{n_1 n_1'\mu}\right\} + O(r_1\mu^6), \tag{5.25}$$

where

$$k_{n_1 n_1'\mu} = \frac{n_1'-n_1}{4\mu^2(n_1-1)} = O(1) \tag{5.26}$$

in a practical case.

Now introduce deviation coordinates (ξ', η') in the adopted focal plane, i.e. the back face of the lens, taking as origin the intersection $F'\{cV/(n_1-1), 0\}$ of the ray $B'I'$ (for which $u = cV/(n_1-1), v = 0$) with this plane. Since the semi-angle in glass of the whole cone of rays is

$$\frac{H}{n_1 f}[1 + O(\mu^2)] = \frac{2\mu}{n_1}[1 + O(\mu^2)],$$

we obtain from (5.25)

$$\xi' + i\eta'$$

$$= \frac{2\mu}{n_1}\left(u - \frac{cV}{n_1-1} + iv\right)F'V'[1+O(\mu^2)]$$

$$= \frac{4n_1}{(n_1-1)^2}r_1 c^2\mu^5(1-V^2)\left(u - \frac{cV}{n_1-1} + iv\right) \times$$

$$\times \left\{\frac{2(n_1^2-1)}{n_1^2}\left[\left(u - \frac{cV}{n_1-1}\right)^2 + v^2\right] - \frac{c^2}{n_1-1}(1+V^2) + \frac{4(n_1-1)}{n_1}k_{n_1 n_1' \mu}\right\}$$

$$= 2R\mu^5 c^2(1-V^2)\left(re^{iE} - \frac{cV}{n_1-1}\right) \times$$

$$\times \left\{\frac{2(n_1+1)}{n_1^2}\left(r^2 - 2r\cos E\,\frac{cV}{n_1-1} + \frac{c^2V^2}{(n_1-1)^2}\right) - \frac{c^2}{(n_1-1)^2}(1+V^2) + \right.$$

$$\left. + \frac{4}{n_1}k_{n_1 n_1' \mu}\right\} + O(R\mu^7),$$

where $u+iv = re^{iE}$,

$$= 2R\mu^5 c^2(1-V^2)\left\{\frac{2(n_1+1)}{n_1^2}\left[r^3 e^{iE} - r^2\,\frac{cV}{n_1-1}(2+e^{2iE}) + \right.\right.$$

$$\left. + r\,\frac{c^2V^2}{(n_1-1)^2}(2e^{iE} + e^{-iE}) - \frac{c^3V^3}{(n_1-1)^3}\right] +$$

$$+ \left(re^{iE} - \frac{cV}{n_1-1}\right)\left(\frac{4}{n_1}k_{n_1 n_1' \mu} - \frac{c^2}{(n_1-1)^2}(1+V^2)\right)\right\} + O(R\mu^7). \quad (5.27)$$

The intersection $F'(0,0)$ of the principal ray $O'I'$ (for which $u = 0$, $v = 0$) with the focal place is obtained on setting $r = 0$ in (5.27). It follows that if we move the origin of the deviation coordinates to $F'(0,0)_{n_1'=n_1}$ and denote the new coordinates by (ξ'', η''), the deviations are given by the equation

$$\xi'' + i\eta'' = 2R\mu^5 c^2(1-V^2)\left\{\frac{2(n_1+1)}{n_1^2}\left[r^3 e^{iE} - r^2\,\frac{cV}{n_1-1}(2+e^{2iE}) + \right.\right.$$

$$\left. + r\,\frac{c^2V^2}{(n_1-1)^2}(2e^{iE} + e^{-iE})\right] - re^{iE}\frac{c^2(1+V^2)}{(n_1-1)^2} +$$

$$+ \frac{4}{n_1}\left(re^{iE} - \frac{cV}{n_1-1}\right)k_{n_1 n_1' \mu}\right\} + O(R\mu^7). \quad (5.28)$$

The corresponding angular deviation components $\delta X''$ and $\delta Y''$, measured in seconds of arc, are obtained on dividing by $\pi/648{,}000$ times the focal length of the system. They can be written in the form

$$(\delta X'', \delta Y'') = K\mu^5\left(\frac{\partial \Phi'}{\partial u}, \frac{\partial \Phi'}{\partial v}\right) + O(K\mu^7), \tag{5.29}$$

where $K = 648{,}000/\pi$, as before, and

$$\Phi' = \Phi(u, v, V; n_1')$$

$$= \frac{4c^2(1-V^2)}{n_1^2}\left\{\frac{n_1+1}{2}\left(1 - \frac{cV}{n_1-1}\frac{\partial}{\partial u}\right)r^4 + 2n_1 k_{n_1 n_1'\mu}\left(r^2 - \frac{2cVu}{n_1-1}\right) + \right.$$

$$\left. + \left[-\frac{n_1^2}{2(n_1-1)^2}c^2(1+V^2) + \frac{n_1+1}{(n_1-1)^2}c^2V^2\left(1+u\frac{\partial}{\partial u}\right)\right]r^2\right\}. \tag{5.30}$$

From (3.40), (5.29), (5.30), the angular deviation components $(\delta X, \delta Y)$ of the complete system, measured in seconds of arc, are given by the equation

$$(\delta X, \delta Y) = (\delta X', \delta Y') + (\delta X'', \delta Y'') + O(K\mu^7)$$

$$= K\mu^5\left(\frac{\partial}{\partial u}, \frac{\partial}{\partial v}\right)\Psi(u, v, V) + O(K\mu^7), \tag{5.31}$$

where

$$\Psi(u, v, V) = \Phi^*(u, v, V; n') + \Phi'(u, v, V; n_1')$$

$$= \left[\tfrac{1}{2}c^2V^2\left(\frac{1}{n} + u\frac{\partial}{\partial u}\right) + k_{nn'\mu}\right](r^4 - 2r_0^2 r^2) +$$

$$+ \frac{4c^2(1-V^2)}{n_1^2}\left\{\frac{n_1+1}{2}\left(1 - \frac{cV}{n_1-1}\frac{\partial}{\partial u}\right)r^4 + 2n_1 k_{n_1 n_1'\mu}\left(r^2 - \frac{2cVu}{n_1-1}\right) + \right.$$

$$\left. + \left[-\frac{n_1^2}{2(n_1-1)^2}c^2(1+V^2) + \frac{n_1+1}{(n_1-1)^2}c^2V^2\left(1+u\frac{\partial}{\partial u}\right)\right]r^2\right\}. \tag{5.32}$$

Here n, n_1 denote the refractive indices of corrector plate and field flattener at that point of the spectrum for which the corrector plate exactly compensates the primary spherical aberration of the mirror; n', n_1' denote their refractive indices in the light under consideration and it is assumed that

$$n' = n + O(\mu^2), \qquad n_1' = n_1 + O(\mu^2).$$

In a 24-inch f/3 system working over a 5° field, the diameter of the field flattener is 6 inches and its thickness decreases from about $\frac{3}{16}$ inch at the centre to zero at the edge. Such a lens would be too fragile for practical safety; it would be better to use a lens whose thickness decreases from about $\frac{5}{16}$ inch at the centre to about $\frac{1}{8}$ inch at the edge.

The above analysis can be applied to this more practical type of field flattener by treating it as the central portion of a sharp-edged lens originally designed to flatten a field of diameter $\sqrt{\tfrac{5}{3}}$ times that actually proposed. We need only replace c, V in (5.32) by $c\sqrt{\tfrac{5}{3}}$, $V\sqrt{\tfrac{5}{3}}$ respectively to obtain the sixth-order aberration function of the new system, namely $R\mu^6$ times the function

$$\Psi(u,v,V) = \left[\tfrac{1}{2}c^2V^2\left(\frac{1}{n}+u\frac{\partial}{\partial u}\right)+k_{nn'\mu}\right](r^4-2r_0^2\,r^2)+$$

$$+\frac{4c^2}{n_1^2}(\tfrac{5}{3}-V^2)\left\{\frac{n_1+1}{2}\left(1-\frac{cV}{n_1-1}\frac{\partial}{\partial u}\right)r^4+2n_1\,k_{n_1n_1'\mu}\left(r^2-\frac{2cVu}{n_1-1}\right)+\right.$$

$$\left.+\left[-\frac{n_1^2}{2(n_1-1)^2}c^2(\tfrac{5}{3}+V^2)+\frac{n_1+1}{(n_1-1)^2}c^2V^2\left(1+u\frac{\partial}{\partial u}\right)\right]r^2\right\}. \quad (5.33)$$

It is inconvenient in practice to have the photographic plate actually in contact with the back surface of the field flattener, since this is liable to result in the latter becoming scratched. The inconvenience can be avoided by moving forward the back surface of the field flattener towards its convex surface, so as to reduce its thickness by an amount $O(R\mu^4)$. This change introduces aberration displacements of only $O(R\mu^7)$ in the new focal plane, which is now in air and slightly in front of the old one. Its effects on the aberrations are therefore negligible in the present approximation.

In a 24-inch f/3 system, $R\mu^4 = \tfrac{1}{144}$ inch, and if the back face of the field flattener is cut away to a depth of $5R\mu^4 = \tfrac{1}{30}$ inch, the aberrations are altered by only a few per cent. There is then a clearance of about $\tfrac{1}{50}$ inch between the emulsion layer and the back surface of the lens.

5.3. Balancing the aberrations

From equation (5.33) we see that the only asymmetrical contribution to the fifth-order aberrations of the field-flattened Schmidt camera is that represented by the term

$$-2R\mu^6c^3V(\tfrac{5}{3}-V^2)\frac{n_1+1}{n_1^2(n_1-1)}\frac{\partial}{\partial u}r^4$$

$$= -8R\mu^6c^3V(\tfrac{5}{3}-V^2)\frac{n_1+1}{n_1^2(n_1-1)}ur^2. \quad (5.34)$$

This coma, being proportional to $V(\tfrac{5}{3}-V^2)$, vanishes at the centre of the field and is greatest at $V=\tfrac{1}{3}\sqrt{5}$. Its amount is very small in practice; in a 24-inch f/3 system working over a 5° field ($c=\tfrac{1}{4}$), the coma-spread is nowhere as large as 0·57 second of arc.

A still smaller coma-value can be obtained by moving the corrector-plate a distance

$$\frac{11}{3}\frac{n_1+1}{n_1^2(n_1-1)}Rc^2\mu^2 \quad (= 8Rc^2\mu^2, \text{ nearly}) \qquad (5.35)$$

along the axis towards the mirror. For, by (3.39), this adds a term

$$\tfrac{22}{3}R\frac{n_1+1}{n_1^2(n_1-1)}c^3\mu^6 Vu(r^2-r_0^2) \qquad (5.36)$$

to the aberration function, in which the coma-term (5.34) therefore becomes

$$-8R\mu^6c^3V(\tfrac{3}{4}-V^2)\frac{n_1+1}{n_1^2(n_1-1)}ur^2. \qquad (5.37)$$

Since the maximum value of $|V(\tfrac{3}{4}-V^2)|$ in the range $0\leqslant V\leqslant 1$ is $0\cdot25$, while that of $V(\tfrac{5}{3}-V^2)$ is $\tfrac{10}{27}\sqrt{5}=0\cdot83$, the plate-shift has reduced the maximum coma-spread to less than one-third of its previous value.

In a 24-inch f/3 system working over a 5° field, the plate must be shifted $0\cdot5$ inch towards the mirror to balance the coma, which then nowhere exceeds $0\cdot2$ second of arc.

In the coma-balanced systems, (5.33) is replaced by the equation†

$$\Psi(u,v,V) = \left[\tfrac{1}{2}c^2V^2\left(\frac{1}{n}+u\frac{\partial}{\partial u}\right)+k_{nn'\mu}\right](r^4-2r_0^2\,r^2)+$$

$$+\frac{4c^2}{n_1^2}(\tfrac{5}{3}-V^2)\left\{\frac{n_1+1}{2}r^4+2n_1\,k_{n_1n_1\mu}\left(r^2-\frac{2cVu}{n_1-1}\right)+\right.$$

$$\left.+\left[-\frac{n_1^2c^2}{2(n_1-1)^2}(\tfrac{5}{3}+V^2)+\frac{n_1+1}{(n_1-1)^2}c^2V^2\left(1+u\frac{\partial}{\partial u}\right)\right]r^2\right\}-$$

$$-8c^3V(\tfrac{3}{4}-V^2)\frac{n_1+1}{n_1^2(n_1-1)}ur^2. \qquad (5.38)$$

We have next to consider whether any appreciable improvement in performance can be obtained by small adjustments of the field curvature of the system and of the focal setting. (The field curvature adjustment could most conveniently be made by means of a small change in r_1, the radius of curvature of the convex surface of the field flattener.)

In the focal plane so far adopted, the fifth-order angular deviation components are, in seconds of arc,

$$(\delta X^*, \delta Y^*) = K\mu^5\left(\frac{\partial\Psi'}{\partial u},\frac{\partial\Psi'}{\partial v}\right),$$

where Ψ' is defined by (5.38). A moving forward of the focal plane by $\tfrac{1}{4}\epsilon f\mu^4$ (in air) adds $K\epsilon\mu^5(u,v)$ to these angular deviation components.

---

† Incorrectly given by Linfoot and Wayman (1949).

We define the effective image radius at a particular point of the field as the square root of the mean value

$$\frac{1}{\pi} \iint_{u^2+v^2 \leqslant 1} [(\delta X*)^2 + (\delta Y*)^2]\, du\, dv$$

and the 'best focus' as the focal setting which minimizes the effective image radius. Thus to obtain the best focus at any point of the field, we have to choose ϵ so as to minimize the expression

$$\iint_{u^2+v^2 \leqslant 1} \left\{ \left(\frac{\partial \Psi}{\partial u} + \epsilon u\right)^2 + \left(\frac{\partial \Psi}{\partial v} + \epsilon v\right)^2 \right\} du\, dv \qquad (5.39)$$

at this point. Let $\epsilon_0 = \epsilon_0(V)$ denote the minimizing value of ϵ; then ϵ_0 satisfies the equation

$$-\epsilon_0 \iint_{u^2+v^2 \leqslant 1} (u^2+v^2)\, du\, dv = \iint_{u^2+v^2 \leqslant 1} \left(u\frac{\partial \Psi}{\partial u} + v\frac{\partial \Psi}{\partial v}\right) du\, dv,$$

or

$$-\tfrac{1}{2}\pi\epsilon_0 = J(\Psi), \qquad (5.40)$$

where $J(f)$ stands for the expression

$$\iint_{u^2+v^2 \leqslant 1} \left(u\frac{\partial}{\partial u} + v\frac{\partial}{\partial v}\right) f\, du\, dv. \qquad (5.41)$$

We easily find

$$\left. \begin{array}{cc} J(r^4) = \tfrac{4}{3}\pi, & J\left(u\frac{\partial}{\partial u} r^2\right) = \pi \\[4pt] J(r^4 - 2r_0^2 r^2) = (\tfrac{4}{3} - 2r_0^2)\pi & \\[4pt] J\left[u\frac{\partial}{\partial u}(r^4 - 2r_0^2 r^2)\right] = (\tfrac{8}{3} - 2r_0^2)\pi & \end{array} \right\} \qquad (5.42)$$

and it follows from (5.38), (5.40), (5.41), (5.42) that

$$\epsilon_0(V) = 2(2r_0^2 - \tfrac{4}{3})\left(k_{nn'\mu} + \frac{2n+1}{2n}c^2 V^2\right) - 2r_0^2 c^2 V^2 -$$

$$- \frac{8c^2}{n_1^2}(\tfrac{5}{3} - V^2)\left[\frac{2}{3}(n_1+1) + 2n_1 k_{n_1 n_1' \mu} - \frac{5}{6}\frac{n_1^2 c^2}{(n_1-1)^2}\right] -$$

$$- \frac{4c^4}{n_1^2}V^2(\tfrac{5}{3} - V^2)\left(\frac{2n_1+5}{(n_1-1)^2} - 1\right). \qquad (5.43)$$

The value, in seconds of arc, of the effective image radius at this focal setting is $1 + O(\mu^2)$ times the square root of

$$K\mu^5\left[\iint \left\{\left(\frac{\partial \Psi}{\partial u}\right)^2 + \left(\frac{\partial \Psi}{\partial v}\right)^2\right\} du\, dv - \tfrac{1}{2}\pi\epsilon_0^2\right].$$

Equation (5.43) specifies the best field surface in each separate wavelength, measured from the originally chosen field surface as reference plane. On the right of (5.43), the terms independent of V represent, to the present order of approximation, a simple shift of the focal plane; those in V^2 represent a residual curvature of the best field and those in V^4 a deviation of the best-field surface from the spherical form. We next examine these residuals in a typical special case to see whether any appreciable improvement in the performance of the system can be obtained by adjusting the value of r_1.

We suppose that $c = \frac{1}{4}$, $n = \frac{3}{2}$ and that $a = 2r_0^2$ has the value which optimizes the axial colour-error of the original Schmidt camera in the sense of minimizing the effective radii of the axial colour confusion patches. This value is $\frac{3}{2}$, as may be shown by direct calculation or by setting $c = 0$ in (5.43); the corresponding value of r_0 is $\sqrt{\frac{2}{3}} = 0.816$. In most astronomical Schmidt cameras, a, c, and n are near to the above values.

Then (5.43) gives

$$\epsilon_0(V) = -\tfrac{1}{12}V^2 - \tfrac{2}{9}(\tfrac{5}{3} - V^2)(\tfrac{115}{96} + 3k_{n_1 n'_1 \mu}) - \tfrac{31}{144}V^2(\tfrac{5}{3} - V^2), \qquad (5.44)$$

and in particular, for $k_{n_1 n'_1 \mu} = 0$, i.e. for $n'_1 = n_1$,

$$\epsilon_0(V) = -0.444 - 0.176V^2 + 0.215V^4. \qquad (5.45)$$

Fig. 84 shows the values of $\epsilon_0(V)$, in the case (5.44), for C, F, and h-light, on the assumption that the field flattener is of hard crown glass (Chance HC 519604) with

$$(n_1)_C = 1.51637, \qquad n_1 = (n_1)_F = 1.52496, \qquad (n_1)_h = 1.53349. \qquad (5.46)$$

It appears from Fig. 84 that a constant focus shift $\epsilon = -0.45$ will improve the images in F-light and that there is no appreciable gain in performance to be obtained by changing the value of r_1. The choice $\epsilon = -0.45$ corresponds to a focus shift of $-\frac{1}{2} \times 0.45 f\mu^4$ in air, i.e. to an increase of $0.22 f\mu^4$ in the air-gap between the photographic plate and the back surface of the field flattener. (The difference between $\frac{1}{2}\epsilon f\mu^4$ and $\frac{1}{2}\epsilon f\mu^4 \sec\phi$, being $O(f\mu^6)$, is negligible in the present approximation.) In a 24-inch f/3 system this increase amounts to 0.0008 inch, which is within the practical focusing tolerance of an f/3 photographic telescope. However, because of the high theoretical performance of the system, it is necessary to take it into account in calculating the geometrical aberrations.

With the new choice of focal plane, the aberration function becomes

$$R\mu^6[\Psi'(u, v, V) + \tfrac{1}{2}\epsilon(u^2 + v^2)] = R\mu^6[\Psi'(u, v, V) - 0 \cdot 22(u^2 + v^2)],$$

$$(5.47)$$

where $\Psi'(u, v, V)$ is given by (5.38), and the angular aberration components, measured in seconds of arc, are

$$(\delta X, \delta Y) = K\mu^5\left(\frac{\partial\Psi'}{\partial u} - 0 \cdot 45u, \; \frac{\partial\Psi'}{\partial v} - 0 \cdot 45v\right) + O(K\mu^7). \qquad (5.48)$$

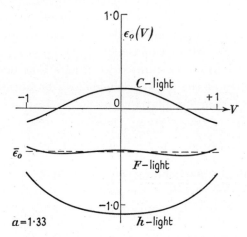

FIG. 84. Surfaces of best focus in the system with field flattener added.

5.4. *An application*

The general formulae (5.38) and (5.47) provide a convenient means of comparing the theoretical performance of the field-flattened Schmidt and the plain Schmidt at focal ratios such as are used in large astronomical cameras. As a typical example, we consider an f/3 system working over a 5° field.

We suppose that the corrector plate has its neutral zone radius $r_0 = 0 \cdot 816$ of the full aperture and that when used without the field flattener the system is axially stigmatic in F-light. The refractive indices in C, F, and h-light of the corrector plate, supposed made of white plate glass, are taken to be

$$n_C = 1 \cdot 5189, \qquad n_F = 1 \cdot 5278, \qquad n_h = 1 \cdot 5366. \qquad (5.49)$$

Since the system is assumed axially stigmatic in F-light, we have to set $n = n_F$ in the general formulae; we also have $\mu = \tfrac{1}{12}$, $c = \tfrac{1}{4}$. We suppose the field flattener to be of hard crown glass (Chance HC 519604) with the index values (5.46). Small variations in these constants, if allowed for in the design, would not appreciably alter the properties of the system.

Finally, we suppose the field flattener designed according to § 5.3 above, and the plate shifted a distance (5.35) towards the mirror when the field flattener is in use, so as to balance the coma. Then the sixth-order aberration function of the field-flattened system is given (apart from the factor μ^6) by (5.38) and (5.48); that of the system without the field flattener by (3.35).

As already remarked, it is possible in the great majority of cases to calculate the diffraction images of the two systems by means of these two sixth-order aberration functions. But the computation is very laborious, on account of the numerical integrations involved. A good idea of the quality of the off-axis images can be obtained, with comparatively little labour, by plotting in the (X, Y)-plane the deviations $(\delta X, \delta Y)$ of the set of rays through the corner points

$$u, v = 0, \pm 0\cdot 1, \pm 0\cdot 2, ...; \quad u^2 + v^2 \leqslant 1$$

of a lattice of small squares filling the entry-pupil. As in § 3 above, this gives a 'spot diagram' in which the spot-density distribution represents fairly well the intensity distribution in the geometrical images.

Fig. 85 shows the spot diagrams of the field-flattened system, in C, F, and h-light, at four selected positions in the field, namely $V = 0$, $V = \frac{1}{2}$, $V = \frac{1}{2}\sqrt{3}$, and $V = 1$. The second of these is one of the points of maximum coma and the third is the point at which the coma is in the act of changing its sign. Fig. 86 shows the corresponding spot diagrams for the system without the field flattener. To obtain the corresponding spot diagrams in cases where the focal ratio is no longer f/3, but c still has the value $\frac{1}{4}$, it is only necessary to multiply the coordinates of each point in Figs. 85 and 86 by $(12\mu)^5$.

From Figs. 84, 85, and 86 it appears that the addition of the field flattener results in a marked increase in the colour-error of the system, and since colour-error is the dominant aberration in a Schmidt camera of this focal ratio and field-size, the increase in colour-error carries with it a considerable loss in theoretical resolution.

An increase in the value of r_0, i.e. in the strength of the 'central bulge' on the corrector plate, would reduce this colour-error and could also be expected to improve the monochromatic aberrations. It therefore seems worth while to investigate quantitatively what improvement in performance can be obtained by designing the system *ab initio* as a field-

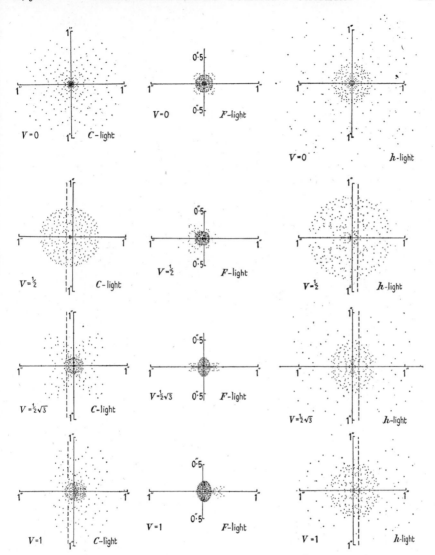

FIG. 85. Spot diagrams of f/3 Schmidt camera with field flattener added and corrector plate moved to balance coma, at selected points of a 5° field. Plate profile of type $r^4 - \frac{4}{3}r^2$. The origin of coordinates in each kind of light is the intersection with the receiving surface of the principal ray in that light. The vertical dotted lines in the C- and h-diagrams intersect the horizontal axes at the corresponding F-origins.

flattened Schmidt, instead of taking a plain Schmidt, adding a field flattener, and moving the corrector plate to balance the coma.

In order to improve the chromatism, we increase $a = 2r_0^2$ until the C and h curves in Fig. 84 have been brought as close together as possible.

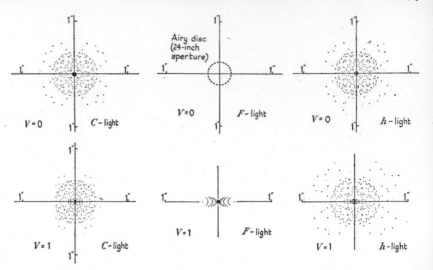

FIG. 86. Spot diagrams of f/3 Schmidt camera, axially stigmatic in F-light and with plate profile of type $r^4 - \frac{4}{3}r^2$, at the centre ($V = 0$) and edge ($V = 1$) of a 5° field.

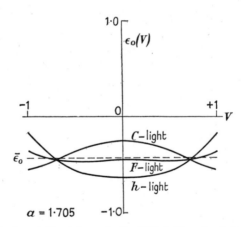

FIG. 87. Surfaces of best focus in the field-flattened sytem of Fig. 88. The dotted line represents the adopted focal surface.

(Owing to the dominance of colour-error over the monochromatic aberrations at focal ratios near f/3, the further refinement of dropping axial F-stigmatism in the original Schmidt would not here lead to any considerable improvement in the optical images.) To do this, we set

$$\epsilon_C(1) - \epsilon_h(1) = \epsilon_h(0) - \epsilon_C(0), \qquad (5.50)$$

where $\epsilon_C(V)$ and $\epsilon_h(V)$ are the values of $\epsilon_0(V)$ in C and h-light respectively,

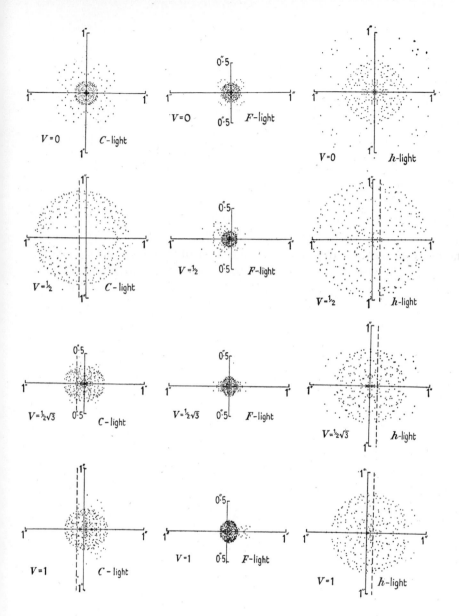

Fig. 88. Spot diagrams of f/3 field-flattened Schmidt camera, with plate profile of type $r^4 - 1 \cdot 705 r^2$, at selected points of a $5°$ field. The origin of coordinates in each kind of light is at the spot corresponding to the principal ray in that light. The vertical dotted lines have the same meaning as in Fig. 85.

and treat this as an equation for a. By (5.43) it can be written

$$4(a-\tfrac{4}{3})(k_{nn_h\mu}-k_{nn_C\mu}) = \frac{8c^2}{n_1^3}\frac{7}{3}2n_1(k_{n_1n_{1h}\mu}-k_{n_1n_{1C}\mu}),$$

i.e.
$$(a-\tfrac{4}{3})\frac{n_h-n_C}{n-1} = \frac{4c^2}{n_1}\frac{7}{3}\frac{(n_1)_h-(n_1)_C}{n_1-1}. \tag{5.51}$$

Here
$$c = \tfrac{1}{4}, \qquad n_h-n_C = 0\cdot0177, \qquad (n_1)_h-(n_1)_C = 0\cdot0171,$$
$$n-1 = 0\cdot52, \qquad n_1-1 = 0\cdot52.$$

Thus
$$a-\frac{4}{3} = \frac{1}{4n_1}\frac{7}{3}\frac{171}{177} = 0\cdot37,$$

$$a = 1\cdot705 \tag{5.52}$$

and the plate has its neutral zone close to the edge of the aperture. Fig. 87 shows the graphs of $\epsilon_0(V)$ in C, F, and h-light for a system with $a = 1\cdot705$. The chromatic variation of best focus is seen to be reduced to one-third of its previous size, shown in Fig. 84. A trace of residual field curvature in F-light can now be noticed, but it is too small in comparison with the colour-error to affect the images appreciably. It will be seen that the surfaces of best focus in C and h-light are approximately symmetrical about the focal plane $\epsilon = \bar{\epsilon}_0 = -0\cdot43$. Spot diagrams for the new system are shown in Fig. 88, from which it appears that its geometrical aberrations are not much larger than those of the classical Schmidt camera.

REFERENCES

J. G. BAKER, *Proc. Am. Phil. Soc.* **82**, 1940, 323.

C. CARATHÉODORY, *Hamb. Math. Einzelschrift* **28**, B. G. Teubner, 1940.

E. H. LINFOOT, *M.N.* **109**, 1949, 279.

—— and P. A. WAYMAN, ibid. 535.

F. E. ROSS, *Ap. J.* **92**, 1940, 400.

B. SCHMIDT, *Mitt. der Hamburger Sternwarte in Bergedorf* **7**, 1932, 15.

R. SCHORR, *Astr. Nachr.* **258**, 1936, 45.

K. SCHWARZSCHILD, *Mitt. der kgl. Sternwarte zu Göttingen*, Part II, 1905.

Y. VÄISÄLÄ, *Astr. Nachr.* **254**, 1935, 361.

PLATE-DIAGRAM ANALYSIS AND ITS APPLICATIONS

1. Plate-diagram analysis

1.1. *The plate diagram*

AN elegant and attractive method of discussing the Seidel errors of a centred optical system was described by C. R. Burch in 1942. It consists in representing a given system S as a sum of spherical surfaces (refracting or reflecting), each furnished with an anastigmatizing corrector plate, together with a 'plate system' which takes account (i) of the fact that the surfaces are not in general actually provided with such plates, (ii) of any asphericities which the surfaces may possess, (iii) of any aspheric plates which may be comprised in the system.

The physical difficulty that light could not, for example, reach the 'missing' anastigmatizing plate of a convex reflecting surface is removed when we Gauss-image such a plate through the part of the system which precedes it. (The Gauss image of a plate is here defined as follows: its position and lateral size are found by Gaussian optics, while the retardation which it imparts to the wave-fronts passing through it at each point is to be the same after transformation as before.) This procedure replaces the plate by one, situated in 'object space', which has the same effect on the Seidel errors of the system S. Figurings on the surfaces themselves, if present, are imaged through in the same way into the object space. The resulting set of plates, taken together with the entry pupil of the system,† will reproduce the first three Seidel errors (spherical aberration, coma, and astigmatism) of S. When the object is at infinity, which we suppose for the present to be the case, this set of plates, working in parallel light, is called the *plate system belonging to S*. If $\alpha_1, \alpha_2, ..., \alpha_n$ are the strengths of the asphericities of the respective plates and $x_1, x_2, ..., x_n$ their respective distances from the entry pupil (measured positively against the light), then we can describe the plate system completely by means of the diagram of Fig. 89, which we call the plate diagram of S. The strength of an aspheric plate is determined, in the manner explained in Chapter III, § 1, by the coefficient of the fourth-power term in its profile equation. We choose as unit of strength that of the paraxially

---

† The entry pupil of a system possessing an aperture stop is the Gaussian image of the stop through that part of the system which precedes it.

flat anastigmatizing plate of a concave reflecting sphere of unit focal length, and suppose for the present that all aspheric plates are paraxially flat and of negligible thickness. The effects of dropping this restriction will be considered in § 1.4.

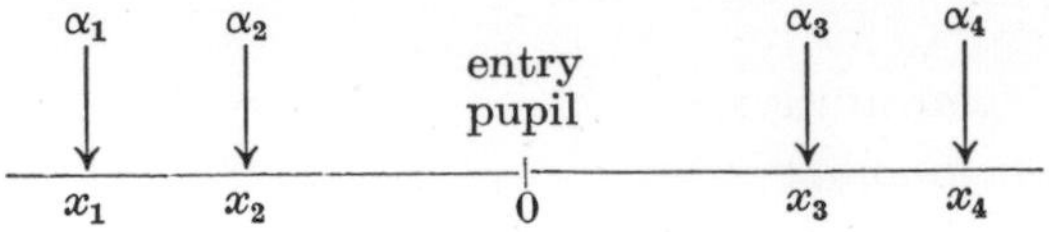

FIG. 89

1.2. The Seidel error coefficients (except distortion) in terms of the plate diagram

A paraxially flat aplanatizing plate for a sphere of radius 2 ($f = 1$) has surface equation $\xi = \beta h^4$, where $\beta = 1/[32(n-1)]$ and n is the refractive index. Its 'optical equation' is $\eta = (n-1)\beta h^4$, where η stands for optical path-length, normalized to zero on the axis. Thus $\eta = \frac{1}{32}h^4$ is the 'optical equation' of a plate of unit strength.

For a sphere of radius $2f_1$, the plate strength is $S_1 = 1/f_1^3$ and the optical equation $\eta = \frac{1}{32}S_1 h^4$. The lateral deviation imposed by such a plate on a meridional ray traversing it nearly normally at height h is thus $\frac{1}{8}S_1 h^3$ in circular measure.

Now consider a set of plates of strengths α_1, α_2,... $\gtrless 0$ at distances x_1, x_2,... $\gtrless 0$ from the entry pupil of a system S, as shown in Fig. 90. (It is evidently possible for plates to occupy positions in front of the entry pupil; for such plates $x > 0$.)

The angular deviation of a meridional ray, passing the entry pupil at a distance s from its centre and making an angle v with the axis, is (to the third order)

$$\tfrac{1}{8} \sum_i \alpha_i(s+vx_i)^3 = \tfrac{1}{8}s^3 \sum_i \alpha_i + \tfrac{3}{8}s^2 v \sum_i \alpha_i x_i + \tfrac{3}{8}sv^2 \sum_i \alpha_i x_i^2 + \tfrac{1}{8}v^3 \sum_i \alpha_i x_i^3. \quad (1.1)$$

Therefore the Seidel coefficients B, F, C of the optical system which possesses the above as its plate system are given by the equations:†

$$B = -\tfrac{1}{8} \sum_i \alpha_i \qquad \text{(spherical aberration)} \qquad (1.2)$$

$$F = +\tfrac{1}{8} \sum_i \alpha_i x_i \qquad \text{(coma)} \qquad (1.3)$$

$$C = -\tfrac{1}{8} \sum_i \alpha_i x_i^2 \qquad \text{(astigmatism)}. \qquad (1.4)$$

† Contrast the well-known expression

$$Bs^3 - 3Fs^2v + (2C+D)sv^2 - Ev^3$$

for the 'deviation' of the intersection of a meridional ray *with the Gauss image-plane*.

The fourth term $\frac{1}{8}v^3 \sum \alpha_i x_i^3$ is connected with the distortion but does not itself measure the distortion of the system, since additional distortion contributions originate in the field curvatures of the anastigmatized surfaces. To obtain the Seidel coefficient D, we use the equation

$$2(D-C) = \text{Petzval curvature of the system}$$
$$= \sum \pm 1/f_i \tag{1.5}$$

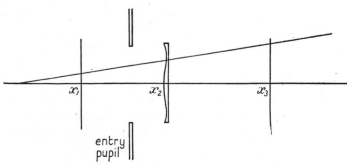

entry
pupil

FIG. 90

in the case of a system consisting of mirrors and aspheric plates, the summation being over the mirrors. The field curvature is then

$$C+D = 2C+(D-C) = -\frac{1}{4}\sum_i \alpha_i x_i^2 + \frac{1}{2}\sum \pm 1/f_i. \tag{1.6}$$

Conditions for aplanatism and for anastigmatism. The condition for Seidel aplanatism, that is to say freedom from primary spherical aberration and primary off-axis coma, is $B = F = 0$. By (1.2), (1.3) this can be written

$$\sum_i \alpha_i = 0 = \sum_i \alpha_i x_i. \tag{1.7}$$

Because a shift of the aperture stop alters the value of every x_i by the same amount, condition (1.7) is invariant under stop-shifting.

If the off-axis astigmatism vanishes ($C = 0$) as well as the spherical aberration and the off-axis coma, the system is called a Seidel anastigmat. By (1.2)–(1.4), the condition for this is

$$\sum_i \alpha_i = 0, \qquad \sum_i \alpha_i x_i = 0, \qquad \sum_i \alpha_i x_i^2 = 0. \tag{1.8}$$

Like the aplanatism condition, (1.8) is invariant under stop-shifting; the truth or falsehood of (1.8) remains unchanged when every x_i is replaced by x_i+c, because

$$\sum_i \alpha_i(x_i+c) = \sum_i \alpha_i x_i + c \sum_i \alpha_i,$$
$$\sum_i \alpha_i(x_i+c)^2 = \sum_i \alpha_i x_i^2 + 2c \sum_i \alpha_i x_i + c^2 \sum_i \alpha_i.$$

Seidel aplanatism and Seidel anastigmatism are not quite the same thing as the 'aplanatism' and 'anastigmatism' of the optical manufacturer. These latter terms are used in ordinary commercial practice to indicate a certain standard of performance.† However, a commercial aplanat must have only small primary spherical aberration and primary off-axis coma if it is to give reasonable performance, and its biggest remaining aberration is normally the off-axis astigmatism needed to flatten its field. Only if this astigmatism also is reduced to a very small amount (and field flattening achieved by improving the Petzval curvature of the system) can the normal standard of performance of a commercial anastigmat be attained.

Thus the commercial aplanats and anastigmats can be regarded respectively as modified Seidel aplanats and anastigmats, in which small controlled amounts of the Seidel aberrations are deliberately retained for the purpose of balancing, as well as may be, the higher aberrations of the system.

1.3. *Seidel distortion in terms of the plate diagram*

As we have seen in § 1.2, the plate diagram of an optical system S yields simple expressions for the first three Seidel errors of the system; used in conjunction with Conrady's 3:1 rule and the Petzval equation, it therefore enables the field curvature to be simply calculated. To deal with distortion, however, an extension of the analysis of § 1.2 is required, because an anastigmatized sphere does not give distortionless imaging between object and image *planes*, but only between object and image spheres concentric with itself. Thus the sphere-plus-anastigmatizing-plate elements into which we dissect S will make contributions to the distortion which must be added to those from the plate system to obtain the actual value of this error.

Fig. 91 shows one 'element of S', namely a spherical surface PAA' with anastigmatizing plate located at its centre of curvature C. We shall call this the 'element A' and PAA' the 'surface A'. The surface A refracts, or reflects, an arriving object-pencil from the (real or virtual) intermediate image O to form the intermediate image I; n and n' are the refractive indices of the two spaces. The case of reflection‡ is covered by setting $n' = -n$. The plate can be located either in n-space or (with

---

† Aplanatism is sometimes used in the older textbooks to mean axial stigmatism, but this custom has little to recommend it.

‡ This is the case which we shall require, but it is just as simple to discuss the more general case of arbitrary indices n, n'. When the surface A is a concave mirror, object and image are real in the figure; when A is a convex mirror both are virtual.

a suitable change of strength) in n'-space; one case can be obtained from the other by imaging the plate through the surface.

We define the 'positions' of the intermediate images by means of the principal rays of the corresponding pencils. These are the rays which originally entered S through the centre of its entry pupil. V in Fig. 91 therefore agrees (to Gaussian accuracy) with the axial point of the

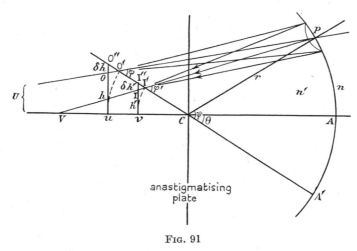

FIG. 91

Gauss image of the entry pupil in that part S' of S which forms the intermediate image I. Let U, V be the respective Gauss images of the axial point at infinity by the part S'' of S which forms the intermediate object O and by S'. Their distances from A (positive by convention in the figure) will be denoted by u, v. We call the planes through u, v perpendicular to the optic axis the 'object and image planes for A'; the spheres through u, v concentric with the surface A we call the 'object and image spheres for A'. The respective intersections of the principal rays PU, PV with the object and image planes define the *image positions O, I in these planes*; their respective intersections with the object and image spheres define the *image positions O', I' in these spheres*.

The line $O'C$ we call the *auxiliary optic axis* of the surface A for the incident pencil under consideration; its angle θ with the main axis CA is a first-order small quantity. Since a first-order tilt of an anastigmatizing plate about its centre leaves its Seidel properties unchanged, it follows that I' is on this auxiliary axis to third-order accuracy. We can express this by saying that *the anastigmatic imaging effected by the element A is distortionless between object and image spheres.*

The distortion between object and image *planes* we define as

$$\frac{\delta h'}{h'} - \frac{\delta h}{h}$$

(see Fig. 91); an alternative definition, equivalent to the first in Seidel approximation, is:

distortion = fractional increase in h' *minus* fractional increase in h.

Since $\delta h'/h'$ and $\delta h/h$ are second-order small quantities (negative in Fig. 91), we need only retain leading terms in calculating the condition that their difference shall vanish to the second order, i.e. that the Seidel distortion shall be zero. Therefore we can write

$$-\delta h = OO'\phi = \tfrac{1}{2}(u-r)\theta^2\phi,$$

where $r = CA$ is the radius of curvature of the surface A,

$$-\frac{\delta h}{h} = \tfrac{1}{2}\theta\phi; \qquad -\frac{\delta h'}{h'} = \tfrac{1}{2}\theta\phi'; \qquad \frac{\delta h'}{h'} - \frac{\delta h}{h} = -\tfrac{1}{2}\theta(\phi'-\phi).$$

Since $\phi'-\phi$ is a first-order small quantity we may, in calculating it, ignore the third-order bending of the principal ray in object or image by the anastigmatizing plate. Therefore we have, to the required accuracy,

$$n(\psi-\phi) = n'(\psi-\phi') \quad \text{and} \quad \phi'/r = \psi/v,$$

where ψ measures $\widehat{PCA'}$. Hence

$$\phi'-\phi = \frac{1}{n}(n'\phi'-n\phi) - \frac{n'-n}{n}\phi'$$

$$= \frac{n'-n}{n}\psi - \frac{n'-n}{n}\frac{r}{v}\psi$$

$$= \frac{n'-n}{n}\frac{v-r}{v}\psi,$$

and

$$\frac{\delta h'}{h'} - \frac{\delta h}{h} = -\frac{1}{2}\frac{n'-n}{n}\frac{v-r}{v}\theta\psi \qquad (1.9)$$

is the value of the fractional distortion.

To represent this in the plate diagram, we consider the effect of Gauss-imaging Fig. 89 in § 1.1 back through the part S' of the system whose last element is A.

Suppose that the focal length of S' is f' and that S' images the n'-space into an object space of index n_0; in this space the image of the V-plane is the original object plane of S and so lies at infinity. Of course n_0 will ordinarily be unity in applications. The right-hand side of (1.9) can be written

$$-\frac{n'-n}{nn'}\left(\frac{(v-r)n'}{f'n_0}\theta\right)^2\frac{rf'^2n_0}{n'v(v-r)}\frac{\psi}{\theta}\frac{n_0}{2r}. \tag{1.10}$$

Here $\frac{(v-r)n'}{f'n_0}\theta$ is the angle made by the principal ray in n_0-space (where

the rays are parallel) with the axis of the system, while $\frac{rf'^2n_0}{n'v(v-r)}$ is the

distance 'down light' in n_0-space of the image C_0 of the centre C from the image A_0 of the surface A.

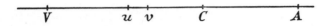

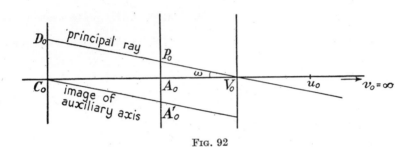

FIG. 92

We also have, to the required accuracy,

$$\frac{\psi}{\theta}=\frac{\text{height of } P \text{ above auxiliary axis } CA'}{\text{height of } A \text{ above auxiliary axis } CA'}=\frac{PA'}{A'A}.$$

Since (to Gauss accuracy) the auxiliary axis CA' and the principal ray PIV meet on the image plane, they are transferred by the collineation (Gauss-imaging back through S') into parallel lines through C_0 and V_0; V_0 is the image of V in n_0-space, and so is the centre of the entry pupil, as remarked earlier, while the image of PIV is the entering principal ray (see Fig. 92). V_0 is therefore the zero-point of the plate diagram of S. Expression (1.10) can now be written

$$-\frac{n'-n}{nn'}\omega^2(C_0V_0-A_0V_0)\frac{P_0A_0'}{A_0A_0'}\frac{n_0}{2r}=-\frac{n'-n}{nn'}\frac{n_0}{r}C_0V_0\frac{\omega^2}{2}.$$

Here $-C_0V_0$ is the x-coordinate, in the plate-diagram of S, of the image of the anastigmatizing A-plate, while $[(n'-n)/nn']/(n_0/r)$ is the contribution from the A-surface to the Petzval curvature of S; we denote this contribution by κ_A and obtain for the contribution of the A-element to the total fractional distortion the expression

$$\tfrac{1}{2}\kappa_A x_A \omega^2.$$

Summing over all the surfaces of S, we find

fractional distortion of S

$$= \tfrac{1}{2}\omega^2 \sum_A \kappa_A x_A + \text{contribution from the plate system.}$$

The plate contribution to the distortion may be deduced from the fact that a plate of strength α at a distance x from the entry pupil imposes an angular deviation $+\tfrac{1}{8}\omega^3\alpha x^3$ on the principal ray. This leads to a fractional distortion $-\tfrac{1}{8}\omega^2\alpha x^3$. Hence, finally,

$$\text{fractional distortion of } S = -\tfrac{1}{8}\omega^2\Big(\sum_P \alpha x^3 - 4\sum_A \kappa x\Big), \qquad (1.11)$$

where the first sum $\sum\limits_P$ is over *all* the plates of the plate system, the second $\sum\limits_A$ over the imaged and sign-reversed Schmidt plates of the power surfaces of the system. We write

$$\Delta = -\tfrac{1}{8}\Big(\sum_P \alpha x^3 - 4\sum_A \kappa x\Big) \qquad (1.12)$$

and call Δ the distortion coefficient. A positive value of Δ indicates pincushion distortion.

Evidently this Δ differs only by a change of sign from the Seidel distortion coefficient E:

$$\Delta = -E. \qquad (1.13)$$

1.4. *Extensions*

So far, it has been assumed that the object surface is at infinity, that the power-series expansions of all aspherical figurings begin with a fourth-power term (in particular, that all aspheric plates are paraxially flat), and that the plate thicknesses can be neglected.

In practice, the object surface is often at a large but finite distance, the aspherical figurings on the corrector plates usually begin with a squared term, comparable in numerical size with the fourth-power term, and the thicknesses of the corrector plates, though small in comparison with the focal length f of the system, cannot properly be left out of consideration.

Let $\lambda = 1/4F$, where F is the focal ratio of the system. (In the particular case of the Schmidt camera this agrees with the definition (3.17) of Chapter III.) Then the Seidel aberrations, expressed in radians, of a system which is not on an anastigmat are of numerical order of magnitude λ^3 and its (algebraically) fifth-order aberrations are of order λ^5. In an anastigmat, both the retained traces of Seidel aberration and the fifth-order aberrations which they balance are of order λ^5. In a 'Seidel anastigmat', the Seidel aberrations are strictly zero and the (algebraically) fifth-order aberrations, of numerical order of magnitude λ^5, are the leading aberrations.

We shall show that the plate-diagram analysis of the preceding sections remains valid, in the sense that it still predicts the aberrations correctly to the Seidel order of accuracy, provided the object distance is at least $O(f/\lambda^2)$ and provided that all glass aspheric plates comprised in the system are situated between the object and the first power surface.† The only change needed in the analysis is the introduction of a convention by which, in measuring the spacings of the components, each corrector-plate thickness is counted with a factor $1/n$ (not n), where n is the refractive index of the plate for the wavelength in question. In wide-aperture systems, where the fractional variation in n between different parts of the effective spectrum can be taken as $O(\lambda^2)$, n may be treated as independent of the wavelength so long as we remain in the Seidel theory, i.e. so long as terms of order λ^5 can be treated as negligible.

Object at a finite distance. We have already seen that the associated plate system S' of an optical system S is Seidel-equivalent to S itself in the sense that the total angular deviations imparted to any admissible ray on passing through S' agree, apart from an error $O(\lambda^5)$, with those which would be imposed on it by the aberrations of S. Admissible rays are those rays, meridional or skew, which pass through the entry pupil of S and make angles at most $O(\lambda)$ with the direction of the optic axis.

All the rays passing through the entry pupil from an object at a finite distance of order f/λ or greater are admissible provided that this object, viewed from the centre of the entry pupil, extends only to an angular distance $O(\lambda)$ from the axis. It follows that the imaging properties of the system for such an object can be deduced directly from its imaging properties for an infinite object; in principle we have only to reclassify rays whose trajectories are already sufficiently well known.

In particular, consider the rays $r_{u,v}$ issuing from one point P of an object at a distance of order f/λ^2 or greater and passing through the respective points (u, v) of the entry pupil. The principal ray $r_{0,0}$ specifies

† The last proviso can be dispensed with at the cost of some further complications; a tighter restriction is required on the thickness of plates working in convergent or divergent pencils. The proviso is satisfied in most cases of practical importance, but not in that shown in Fig. 99 below.

the direction of the object point P, and the pencil of rays $r'_{u,v}$ parallel to $r_{0,0}$ can be regarded as issuing from a point P' at infinity in the same direction as P.

Corresponding to the two object surfaces o and o' (one of them at infinity) are two Petzval surfaces p and p'; we obtain p and p' if we image the separate points of o and o' through the system by Conrady's method of thin radial pencils. To the object point P in o corresponds by this imaging process a point $P*$ in p; we call $P*$ the Petzval conjugate of P. Similarly P' has a Petzval conjugate $P'*$ in p'.

Corresponding to the two object surfaces are also two plate systems S' and S'' of S. The positions of the plates in these two systems coincide, but their strengths do not, because the strength of the anastigmatizing plate of a spherical reflecting or refracting surface depends on its working distances. In the present case, the fractional change in the reciprocals of the working distances for each surface of the system when the object point is moved from P on o to P' at infinity is only $O(\lambda^2)$; it follows that the difference between the strengths of corresponding plates in S' and S'' is only $O(\lambda^2)$ and the difference between the angular deviations which they impose on a ray meeting both in the same point is $O(\lambda^5)$.

For given (u, v) the rays $r_{u,v}$ and $r'_{u,v}$ make an angle $O(\lambda^3)$ with each other; hence they cut each plate of S' (or of S'') in a pair of points whose separation is $O(f\lambda^3)$. (It is supposed that the plates of S' are all within a distance $O(f)$ of the entry pupil.) Therefore the deviations imposed by S' on $r_{u,v}$ and on $r'_{u,v}$ differ by at most $O(f\lambda^3)O(\lambda^3/f\lambda) = O(\lambda^5)$. But the deviations imposed on $r'_{u,v}$ by S' and by S'' differ by at most $O(\lambda^5)$. Therefore the deviations imposed by S' on $r_{u,v}$ and by S'' on $r'_{u,v}$ differ by at most $O(\lambda^5)$.

But, as was shown earlier, these deviations, multiplied by the nearer focal length of the system in each case, agree to within $O(f\lambda^5)$ with the deviations $P*Q$, $P'*Q'$ from the respective Petzval conjugates $P*$, $P'*$ of the points Q, Q' in which $r_{u,v}$, $r'_{u,v}$ (after passing through S) meet the surfaces p, p'.

It follows that the third-order aberrations of the system† are unchanged by moving the object surface from infinity to a distance of order f/λ^2 or greater. In other words, if the reciprocal of the object distance is $O(\lambda^2/f)$, then it is a permissible approximation in the plate-diagram analysis of the system to suppose the object at infinity.

† Third-order in the sense that they can be written (when expressed in radians) in the form $\lambda^3 F(u, v; P') + O(\lambda^5)$. Thus a fractional change $O(\lambda^2)$ in the Seidel coefficients leaves the third-order aberrations unchanged. Compare the definition of fifth-order in Chap. III, § 2.

The same arguments apply, and lead to the same conclusion, if the object is a virtual one, at a distance f/λ^2 or more *behind* the entry pupil.

Corrector plates with a neutral zone; 'doughnut' figuring on mirrors. A corrector plate with a neutral zone of radius comparable with its semi-aperture is equivalent to a paraxially flat corrector plate of the same strength together with a thin lens of power (i.e. reciprocal focal length) $O(\lambda^2/f)$. For admissible rays, the angular aberrations of the thin lens are $O(\lambda^5)$, i.e. negligible in the third-order theory. Therefore its effect is equivalent to that of replacing the object by one at a finite distance $w \gtrless 0$ in front of the entry pupil, where $1/w = O(\lambda^2/f)$.

It follows from the previous discussion that the effect of modifying a paraxially flat corrector plate to give one with a neutral zone of radius comparable with its semi-aperture (for example, a colour-minimized plate) is to move the Petzval surface of the system through a distance $O(f\lambda^2)$ and to leave the third-order aberrations in the Petzval surface unchanged. (The fractional change $O(\lambda^2)$ in the Petzval curvature can be ignored in the third-order theory, since it corresponds to a negligible focus-shift $O(f\lambda^4)$ at the edge of the field.) A trivial extension of the argument shows that the result remains true when several plates are modified simultaneously.

In the case of figurings on power surfaces of 'finite' paraxial curvature (i.e. comparable with $1/f$) the effect of replacing a figuring of type $a_4\lambda^4 y^4 + a_6\lambda^6 y^6 + \ldots$ by one of type $a_4\lambda^4(y^4 - 2y_0^2 y^2) + a_6\lambda^6 y^6 + \ldots$ is to change the paraxial curvature of the surface by a fractional amount $O(\lambda^2)$. This changes by a fractional amount $O(\lambda^2)$ the strengths, and by an amount $O(f\lambda^2)$ the positions along the axis of all those elements of the plate system S' which have been obtained by imaging through this surface, and also of its own 'missing Schmidt plate'. The result is a change $O(\lambda^5)$ in the angular deviations of admissible rays passing through S', i.e. a change $O(\lambda^5)$ in the angular aberrations of the system on its new Petzval surface. This means that there is a shift of focus amounting to $O(f\lambda^2)$ but that the third-order aberrations are otherwise unaltered. As before, the extension of the argument to the case where several figurings are modified simultaneously is trivial.

Effect of plate thickness. It is enough to consider the effect of inserting into the nearly parallel beam between the object point and the first power surface, at a distance at most $O(f)$ from the entry pupil, a plane-parallel plate of thickness d with its faces perpendicular to the optic axis.

The leading term in the effect of refraction by such a plate is taken care of by introducing the convention that the plate-thickness d is to be counted with a factor $1/n$ in measuring axial distances through the plate. The remaining lateral effect, which is $O(d\lambda^3)$ for an off-axis pencil and $O(d\lambda^9)$ for an on-axis pencil, causes changes of at most

$$O(d\lambda^3)O(\lambda^3/f\lambda) = O(\lambda^5 d/f)$$

in the ray deviations, and these are negligible in the third-order theory even if the plate thickness is comparable with f. If $d = O(f\lambda^2)$, they are also negligible in the fifth-order theory.

To sum up: It is permissible, in discussing the third-order aberrations of plate-mirror systems by the plate-diagram method, to treat the thickness of the plates as negligible and the object as infinitely distant, provided that the plate thicknesses are in fact $O(f\lambda^2)$ and the object distance at least $O(f/\lambda^2)$, that the elements in the associated plate system all lie within a distance $O(f)$ of the entry pupil, and that a convention (given above) is used in measuring distances through corrector plates along the optic axis. The distinction between paraxially flat plates and those with a neutral zone can be ignored in calculating the third-order aberrations, though not in calculating the position of the Petzval surface in which these are measured; the true object distance must also be taken into account when calculating the position of this surface.

2. Seidel properties of the Schmidt–Cassegrain systems

To illustrate the plate-diagram method by a concrete example, and to obtain formulae which will be of use later, we now apply the method to a general analysis of the Seidel properties of Schmidt–Cassegrain systems.

By a Schmidt–Cassegrain system is meant one consisting of a large concave primary mirror M_1, usually pierced, a smaller convex secondary mirror M_2, and a thin aspheric corrector plate P (see Fig. 94), through which the light passes on its way to the primary. The subsequent path of the rays is similar to that in an ordinary Cassegrain telescope; that is to say, after reflection at the primary and secondary mirrors they come to a focus near the pole A of the primary.

Flat-fielded anastigmats of this pattern were proposed by J. G. Baker (1940) and by C. R. Burch (1942); in these systems at least one of the mirrors has to be aspherical, as well as the corrector plate, but the mirror-asphericities can be kept small by suitably choosing the parameters. Flat-fielded aplanats (near-anastigmats) with both mirrors spherical were proposed by H. Slevogt (1942) and by the writer (1943).

2.1. *Aplanatism and anastigmatism in Schmidt–Cassegrain systems*

First consider two spherical mirrors M_1, M_2, of radii $\rho_1 = 2f_1$ (concave) and $\rho_2 = 2f_2$ (convex) respectively, with the axial points of their surfaces spaced a distance d apart. See Fig. 93. Let C_1, C_2 be their centres of curvature. Rays parallel to the axis entering from the left will be focused on the axis at a distance $f_2(f_1-d)/(d+f_2-f_1)$ in front of the convex (i.e. to

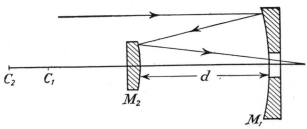

FIG. 93

its right). Thus $f_1-f_2 \leqslant d \leqslant f_1$ is the condition for a real image. This image will lie behind the concave mirror (i.e. to its right) if

$$d^2+d(2f_2-f_1)-f_1 f_2 < 0,$$

that is, if
$$0 \leqslant d \leqslant \sqrt{(\tfrac{1}{4}f_1^2+f_2^2)}+\tfrac{1}{2}f_1-f_2.$$

This is the condition for an 'accessible' image.

The convex mirror is working with paraxial distances

$$u = -(f_1-d), \qquad v = \frac{f_2(f_1-d)}{d+f_2-f_1},$$

where we agree to measure distances from a mirror positively in front of it, negatively behind it. Thus for this mirror the magnification $\Lambda = v/u = -f_2/(d+f_2-f_1)$. The surface deformation needed to remove its spherical aberration would be $(\Lambda-1)^2/(\Lambda+1)^2$ times parabolic correction. If this were done on a plate at the centre of curvature (ignoring for the moment the physical impossibility of this), the diameter of the plate would have to be $(\rho_2+u)/(-u) = (\Lambda-1)/(\Lambda+1)$ times that of the mirror. Then the plate would need strength $\{(\Lambda+1)/(\Lambda-1)\}^4$ times what it would have needed if it had been the same size as the mirror, viz. $\{(\Lambda+1)/(\Lambda-1)\}^4\{(\Lambda-1)/(\Lambda+1)\}^2$ times parabolic correction, or

$$-\left(\frac{\Lambda+1}{\Lambda-1}\right)^2 = -\left(\frac{f_1-d}{d+2f_2-f_1}\right)^2$$

times Schmidt plate strength S_2 for a (concave) sphere of radius ρ_2. The light could not actually reach such a plate; therefore we replace it by its image in the part of the system which precedes it, namely the concave mirror. It is imaged at a distance $f_1(2f_2+d)/(d+2f_2-f_1)$ in front of the concave and with magnification $f_1/(d+2f_2-f_1)$. Thus the image-plate has its strength increased in the ratio $\{(d+2f_2-f_1)/f_1\}^4$, to the value

$$-\frac{(f_1-d)^2(d+2f_2-f_1)^2}{f_1^4}S_2.$$

Since this plate is not in fact present, we conclude that the contributions of the convex mirror to the first four Seidel errors of the system agree (for an object at infinity) with those arising from a plate of strength $-\dfrac{(f_1-d)^2(d+2f_2-f_1)^2}{f_1^4}S_2$ situated at a distance $\dfrac{f_1(2f_2+d)}{d+2f_2-f_1}$ in front of the concave mirror.

In the same way, the contributions of the concave mirror to the first four Seidel errors of the system would be annulled by a Schmidt plate placed at its centre of curvature and of strength S_1 corresponding to its radius of curvature. Hence the contributions from the mirror itself agree with those from a plate of strength $-S_1$ situated $2f_1$ in front of it. Now the strength of a Schmidt plate for a sphere of radius ρ is proportional to $1/\rho^3$. Hence if we take as deformation unit the strength of the Schmidt plate for a sphere of radius 2 ($f=1$), we have

$$S_1 = \frac{1}{f_1^3}, \qquad S_2 = \frac{1}{f_2^3}.$$

We have thus determined the plate system corresponding to our system of two spherical mirrors. Now suppose that the mirrors are not spherical, but figured. In the domain of third-order optics such figurings can be represented as constant multiples of parabolic correction and imaged through the system to the object side, where they contribute additional members to the plate system. The figuring (of strength α, say) on the concave mirror images into itself. That on the convex mirror contributes a plate (of strength β, say) located $df_1/(f_1-d)$ behind the concave mirror. The strength of the actual figuring on the concave mirror is then $\{f_1/(f_1-d)\}^4\beta$.

Lastly, suppose that the system includes a thin glass aspheric plate P, of strength γ, located at a distance x in front of the concave mirror. See Fig. 94. (We can abolish this plate at will by setting $\gamma = 0$.) Then the plate system consists of five components:

(1) located $df_1/(f_1-d)$ behind the concave mirror, a plate of strength β (image of the figuring on the convex);

(2) located *on* the concave, its own figuring, of strength α;

(3) located $f_1(2f_2+d)/(d+2f_2-f_1)$ in front of the concave, a plate of strength $+(f_1-d)^2(d+2f_2-f_1)^2/f_1^4 f_2^3$ (image of the anastigmatizing plate which the convex lacks, with sign reversed);

(4) located $2f_1$ in front of the concave, a plate of strength $-1/f_1^3$ (Schmidt plate which the concave lacks, with sign reversed);

(5) located x in front of the concave, a thin glass aspheric plate of strength γ.

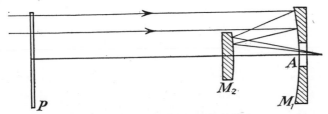

FIG. 94. Schmidt–Cassegrain system.

Suppose for the present that the aperture stop of the system is located on the concave mirror. Then its plate diagram is as shown in Fig. 95

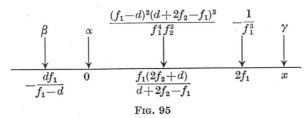

FIG. 95

and by § 1.2 the conditions for the vanishing of the first three Seidel errors of the system are respectively

(spherical aberration)

$$\alpha+\beta+\gamma+\frac{(f_1-d)^2(d+2f_2-f_1)^2}{f_1^4 f_2^3}-\frac{1}{f_1^3}=0, \tag{2.1}$$

(coma)

$$-\frac{df_1}{f_1-d}\beta+x\gamma+\frac{f_1(2f_2+d)}{d+2f_2-f_1}\frac{(f_1-d)^2(d+2f_2-f_1)^2}{f_1^4 f_2^3}-\frac{2}{f_1^2}=0, \tag{2.2}$$

(astigmatism)

$$\left(\frac{df_1}{f_1-d}\right)^2\beta+x^2\gamma+\frac{f_1^2(2f_2+d)^2}{(d+2f_2-f_1)^2}\frac{(f_1-d)^2(d+2f_2-f_1)^2}{f_1^4 f_2^3}-\frac{4}{f_1}=0. \tag{2.3}$$

In systems where the spherical aberration and coma both vanish (and only such systems will be considered in this chapter) these conditions are independent of the position of the aperture stop.

Change of notation. We can simplify the notation by writing

$$A = \alpha f_1^3, \quad B = \beta f_1^3, \quad \Gamma = \gamma f_1^3; \quad \sigma = \frac{x}{f_1}, \quad q = 1 - \frac{d}{f_1}, \quad \xi = \frac{f_2}{f_1}. \quad (2.4)$$

Then the plate diagram takes the form shown in Fig. 96, where now

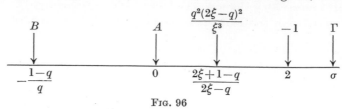

FIG. 96

plate strengths are measured in terms of the anastigmatizing plate of M_1 as unit and distances in terms of its paraxial focal length f_1 as unit. The conditions for the vanishing of the first three Seidel errors become respectively

(spherical aberration)

$$A + B + \Gamma + \frac{q^2(2\xi - q)^2}{\xi^3} = 1, \qquad (2.5)$$

(coma) $$-\frac{1-q}{q} B + \sigma\Gamma + \frac{q^2(2\xi - q)(2\xi + 1 - q)}{\xi^3} = 2, \qquad (2.6)$$

(astigmatism) $$\left(\frac{1-q}{q}\right)^2 B + \sigma^2\Gamma + \frac{q^2(2\xi + 1 - q)^2}{\xi^3} = 4. \qquad (2.7)$$

These three equations specify all the Schmidt–Cassegrain anastigmats, while (2.5), (2.6) taken alone specify all the Schmidt–Cassegrain aplanats, in terms of six parameters each of which has a simple physical meaning. In fact,

A, B, Γ are the figuring *depths* on primary, secondary, and plate expressed in terms of parabolic correction of the primary as unit;†

σ is the distance of the plate in front of the primary, expressed in terms of the paraxial focal length f_1 of the primary as unit;

ξ is the ratio f_2/f_1 of the paraxial focal length of the secondary to that of the primary;

q is the 'minimum obstruction ratio' for the on-axis pencil;‡ alternatively, $1-q$ is the separation between the mirrors, expressed in terms of f_1 as a unit.

† The *strength* of the figuring on the secondary is thus Γ/q^4 times the strength which would parabolize the primary.

‡ That is, the obstruction ratio when the secondary is just big enough to receive the on-axis pencil. It will need to be slightly larger than this in order to receive the off-axis pencils also.

In these systems, the image is formed at a distance

$$\left(\frac{2\xi-q}{\xi-q}q-1\right)f_1 \tag{2.8}$$

behind the pole of the primary and the focal length

$$f = \frac{\xi}{\xi-q}f_1. \tag{2.9}$$

2.2. *Astigmatism in Schmidt–Cassegrain aplanats*

The off-axis astigmatism of a thin lens centrally passed, or of the central elements of a spherical mirror,† is given by the equation

distance between centres of astigmatic focal lines $= \delta^2/f$, (2.10)

where f is the focal length and δ the linear displacement of the image off axis. It is sometimes convenient to express the astigmatism of a composite system as a fraction of that of a thin lens (or of a spherical mirror) of the same focal length. For a sphere of focal length f, imaging from infinity with entry-pupil at the mirror surface, the plate diagram is given by Fig. 97. For such a sphere, by § 1.2,

$$B = \frac{1}{8f^3}, \qquad F = -\frac{1}{4f^2}, \qquad C = \frac{1}{2f}, \tag{2.11}$$

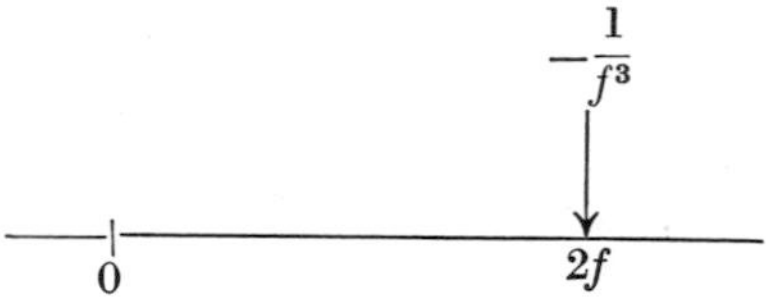

FIG. 97

and C has this same value for any centrally passed thin lens. Therefore the 'thin lens value' of C is $1/2f$ and the astigmatism of a system of focal length f is

$$2fC = -\tfrac{1}{4}f\sum_i \alpha_i x_i^2 \tag{2.12}$$

times the thin lens value. The distance between the centres of the astigmatic focal lines (or 'astigmatic interfocal distance') of the system at a distance δ off axis is therefore

$$-\frac{\delta^2}{f}\tfrac{1}{4}f\sum_i \alpha_i x_i^2 = -\tfrac{1}{4}\delta^2\sum_i \alpha_i x_i^2, \tag{2.13}$$

where α_i, x_i refer to its plate diagram.‡

† The restriction to central elements enables us to disregard spherical aberration and coma when evaluating the astigmatism.

‡ In the domain of third-order optics, the lengths of the astigmatic focal lines are third-order small quantities, while their distance apart is a second-order small quantity. Thus it is also legitimate to speak simply of the 'distance between the astigmatic focal lines' with the same meaning as above.

We can apply this formula to express the off-axis astigmatism of the general Schmidt–Cassegrain aplanat in terms of the thin-lens value or of the astigmatic interfocal distance. The focal length $f = \xi f_1/(\xi-q)$ by (2.9). The value of $\sum_i \alpha_i x_i^2 = -8C$ is independent of the position of the stop, as remarked in § 1.2. Taking the stop on the primary, we have by § 2.1

$$\sum_i \alpha_i x_i^2 = \left(\frac{df_1}{f_1-d}\right)^2 \beta + x^2\gamma + \frac{(2f_2+d)^2(f_1-d)^2}{f_1^2 f_2^3} - \frac{4}{f_1}$$

$$= \frac{1}{f_1}\left\{\left(\frac{1-q}{q}\right)^2 B + \sigma^2\Gamma + \frac{q^2(2\xi+1-q)^2}{\xi^3} - 4\right\}. \qquad (2.14)$$

The astigmatism coefficient C is $-\frac{1}{8}$ times this quantity, or

$$-\frac{\xi}{4(\xi-q)}\left[\left(\frac{1-q}{q}\right)^2 B + \sigma^2\Gamma + \frac{q^2(2\xi+1-q)^2}{\xi^3} - 4\right] \qquad (2.15)$$

times the thin-lens value and the astigmatic interfocal distance is accordingly

$$-\frac{1}{4}\frac{\delta^2}{f}\frac{\xi}{\xi-q}\left[\left(\frac{1-q}{q}\right)^2 B + \sigma^2\Gamma + \frac{q^2(2\xi+1-q)^2}{\xi^3} - 4\right]. \qquad (2.16)$$

2.3. Distortion in the Schmidt–Cassegrain systems

The contributions to the Petzval curvature from the two power surfaces of a Schmidt–Cassegrain system are $\kappa_1 = -1/f_1$ from the primary mirror M_1 and $\kappa_2 = +1/f_2$ from the secondary M_2. Applying equation (1.12) to the plate diagram of Fig. 95, we obtain for a Schmidt–Cassegrain with aperture stop on the primary

$$\Delta = -\frac{1}{8}\sum_P \alpha x^3 + \frac{1}{2}\sum_A \kappa x$$

$$= -\frac{1}{8}\left[-B\left(\frac{1-q}{q}\right)^3 + \frac{(2\xi-q)^2 q^2}{\xi^3}\left(\frac{2\xi+1-q}{2\xi-q}\right)^3 - 8 + \Gamma\sigma^3\right] +$$

$$+ \frac{1}{2}\left[(2f_1)\left(\frac{-1}{f_1}\right) + \frac{2\xi+1-q}{2\xi-q}f_1\frac{1}{f_2}\right]$$

$$= \frac{1}{8}B\left(\frac{1-q}{q}\right)^3 - \frac{(2\xi+1-q)^3 q^2}{8\xi^3(2\xi-q)} + 1 - \frac{1}{8}\Gamma\sigma^3 - 1 + \frac{2\xi+1-q}{2\xi(2\xi-q)}$$

$$= -\frac{1}{8}\left[\sigma^3\Gamma - \left(\frac{1-q}{q}\right)^3 B\right] - \frac{2\xi+1-q}{2\xi(2\xi-q)}\left[\frac{(2\xi+1-q)^2 q^2}{4\xi^2} - 1\right]. \qquad (2.17)$$

We next consider the effect on Δ of moving the aperture stop. Let ζf_1 be the change of position of the entry pupil caused by shift in stop-position; ζf_1 is measured positively against the light. Then the plate diagram is changed by having the origin shifted to the point formerly given by $x = \zeta f_1$. The new value of Δ is therefore

$$
\begin{aligned}
\Delta_\zeta &= -\tfrac{1}{8} \sum_P \alpha(x - \zeta f_1)^3 + \tfrac{1}{2} \sum_A \kappa(x - \zeta f_1) \\
&= \Delta + \tfrac{3}{8}\zeta f_1 \sum_P \alpha x^2 - \tfrac{3}{8}\zeta^2 f_1^2 \sum_P \alpha x + \tfrac{1}{8}\zeta^3 f_1^3 \sum_P \alpha - \tfrac{1}{2}\zeta f_1 \sum_A \kappa \\
&= \Delta + \zeta f_1 \left(\tfrac{3}{8} \sum_P \alpha x^2 - \tfrac{1}{2} \sum_A \kappa \right)
\end{aligned}
\tag{2.18}
$$

when the spherical aberration $\sum_P \alpha$ and the coma $\sum_P \alpha x$ both vanish. If we are dealing with an anastigmat, $\sum_P \alpha x^2$ also vanishes, and if this anastigmat is flat-fielded $\sum_A \kappa = 0$. Equation (2.18) then reduces to

$$
\Delta_\zeta = \Delta,
$$

which shows that *in a flat-fielded anastigmat, Δ is invariant under stop-shifting.* In the more general case of a flat-fielded aplanat, $\sum_P \alpha x^2$ and $\sum_A \kappa$ will not usually vanish and (2.18) expresses the way in which distortion in the image plane varies under shifts of the aperture stop. In an aplanat with flat best field, the field-curvature coefficient $C + D$ vanishes; it follows from (1.6) that in these systems

$$
-\tfrac{1}{4} \sum_P \alpha x^2 + \tfrac{1}{2} \sum_A \kappa = 0
\tag{2.19}
$$

and equation (2.18) takes the form

$$
\Delta_\zeta = \Delta + \tfrac{1}{4}\zeta f_1 \sum_A \kappa.
\tag{2.20}
$$

3. Plate-mirror systems and their application to astronomical photography

The striking success of the Schmidt camera as an astrographic telescope can be attributed to two causes. First, its high theoretical performance more than meets the needs of present-day astronomers, bounded as these are by the effects of atmospheric tremor and the finite grain-size of fast photographic plates. Second, an optical system consisting of a single mirror and a thin, nearly plane-parallel plate suffers far less from temperature troubles than do the large anastigmat lenses which alone could give images of comparable sharpness. (In the case of the larger Schmidt telescopes, of apertures of 24 inches and upward, the corresponding anastigmat lenses have never been made and are probably impracticable.) Moreover, good methods of alleviating the temperature and flexure troubles of large mirrors are already well known to astronomers from their experience with paraboloids, while the corrector plate is practically free from both.

Nevertheless, the Schmidt optical system presents some inconveniences when used in a photographic telescope. Because of the brightness of the sky background, the focal ratio of a Schmidt telescope of moderate size should not be shorter than f/3, and for most purposes f/3·5 is better. Because of the limitations imposed by plate grain on photographic resolution, the focal length should not fall below 100 inches if full advantage is to be taken of the high optical performance of the system at these focal ratios. Since the length of the telescope tube, without the dewcap, is twice the focal length, this means that to take full advantage of the design we need a telescope of 25 or 30 inches aperture, with a tube at least 17 feet long. So long a tube is inconvenient because it requires a relatively expensive mounting and dome.

Another inconvenience is the curved field of the Schmidt system. Photographic plates made with specially thin glass, held bent to the requisite curvature, give satisfactory results but need to be made up as a special order by the photographic manufacturer.

A third inconvenience is the position of the focal surface in the middle of the tube, half-way between the corrector plate and the mirror.

Evidently it is worth while to consider whether some of these drawbacks can be eliminated or reduced by a change in the optical design.

It is immediately clear that the addition of further corrector plates, or the aspherizing of the mirror surface, cannot yield the desired result of a flat-fielded anastigmat (or near-anastigmat).† For these changes leave the Petzval curvature unaltered, and unless the Petzval curvature is well compensated the astigmatism needed to flatten the field will spoil the definition. There remains the possibility of adding a second power surface to the system in the form of a convex secondary mirror, and of introducing aspherical figurings on either or both of the mirrors.

Since the additional figurings increase the amount of skilled labour involved in making the system, we try to keep them as light as possible. In particular, systems with one or both mirrors spherical have a claim to preference on that account.

The exploration of possible camera designs now proceeds as follows. We first try to do without aspheric figurings on the mirrors; accordingly we determine, in §§ 3.1 and 3.2, what anastigmats can be made up from two spherical mirrors and one corrector plate or (as a special case) from two spherical mirrors only. It appears that the only practicable designs

---

† The results of aspherizing the mirror surface are explored in § 3.8.

with large concave primary and small convex secondary are the mono-centric Schmidt–Cassegrain (§ 3.2) and a system equivalent to the field-flattened Schmidt camera discussed in Chapter IV, § 5. The designs with small convex primary and large convex secondary are examined in § 3.3; they are rather unsuitable for astronomical purposes because of their relatively small light-gathering power, but they seem to have possible applications as projector systems, especially in the case where the corrector plate is absent (two-sphere anastigmat).

To explore further, we must either allow aspherical mirrors or drop anastigmatism. We first examine the results of dropping anastigmatism, keeping the mirrors spherical. The two-sphere aplanats are *eo ipso* anastigmats (§ 3.4), so that nothing is gained here. But when we examine the Schmidt–Cassegrain aplanats with spherical mirrors (§ 3.5), we find that a range of flat-fielded systems exists in which the off-axis astig-matism is so small as to leave the definition unimpaired in some practical cases. These systems seem excellently suited to application as astro-graphic cameras.

In § 3.6 we consider the flat-fielded anastigmats with one or both mirrors aspherical and in particular those flat-fielded types singled out as especially promising by J. G. Baker.

3.1. *Anastigmats from two spheres and one plate*

We begin by supposing the primary mirror concave and the secondary convex. This is the case obtained on setting $A = B = 0$ in equations (2.5)–(2.7), which become

$$\Gamma = 1 - \frac{q^2(2\xi - q)^2}{\xi^3}, \tag{3.1}$$

$$\sigma\Gamma = 2 - \frac{q^2(2\xi - q)(2\xi + 1 - q)}{\xi^3}, \tag{3.2}$$

$$\sigma^2\Gamma = 4 - \frac{q^2(2\xi + 1 - q)^2}{\xi^3}. \tag{3.3}$$

These give, on eliminating σ and Γ,

$$\left(4 - \frac{q^2(2\xi + 1 - q)^2}{\xi^3}\right)\left(1 - \frac{q^2(2\xi - q)^2}{\xi^3}\right) = \left(2 - \frac{q^2(2\xi - q)(2\xi + 1 - q)}{\xi^3}\right)^2,$$

i.e.

$$q^2(2\xi - 1 - q)^2/\xi^3 = 0, \tag{3.4}$$

whence $q = 2\xi - 1$ or $q = 0$. That is to say (see (2.4)), $d = 2f_1 - 2f_2$ or $d = f_1$ are necessary conditions for anastigmatism. We conclude that *a Schmidt–Cassegrain system consisting of two spherical mirrors and one aspheric plate can only be anastigmatic in two cases:*

(1) *when the spheres are concentric*;

(2) *when the second sphere is at the paraxial focus of the first.*

Case 2: $q = 0$, i.e. $d = f_1$. Here the only (Seidel) effect of the second sphere is to change the field curvature. On setting $q = 0$ in equations (3.1)–(3.3), we obtain

$$\Gamma = 1, \qquad \sigma\Gamma = 2, \qquad \sigma^2\Gamma = 4,$$

i.e.

$$\gamma = 1/f_1^3, \qquad x\gamma = 2/f_1^2, \qquad x^2\gamma = 4/f_1;$$

thus

$$x = 2f_1, \qquad \gamma = S_1$$

and the system is simply a Schmidt with changed field curvature. Its new field curvature, being equal to its Petzval curvature, is $1/f_1-1/f_2$. Therefore flat-fieldedness is achieved when $f_2 = f_1$.

Case 1: $q = 2\xi-1$, i.e. $d = 2f_1-2f_2$ (concentric spheres). Equations (3.1)–(3.3) now become

$$\Gamma = 1-\frac{(2\xi-1)^2}{\xi^3}, \qquad \sigma\Gamma = 2-2\frac{(2\xi-1)^2}{\xi^3}, \qquad \sigma^2\Gamma = 4-4\frac{(2\xi-1)^2}{\xi^3}.$$

$$(3.5)$$

Thus $\sigma = 2$, i.e. $x = 2f_1$, and the glass aspheric plate goes at the centre of curvature of the concave. Its strength γ is no longer $S_1 = 1/f_1^3$, but is given by the equation

$$\gamma f_1^3 = \Gamma = 1-\frac{(2\xi-1)^2}{\xi^3}.$$

To get this strength down to zero, and so dispense with the aspheric plate, we should need

$$\xi^3 = (2\xi-1)^2, \qquad\qquad (3.6)$$

$$\xi = 1 \quad \text{or} \quad \xi = \frac{3\pm\sqrt{5}}{2},$$

i.e. $f_2 = f_1$ or $f_2 = \frac{1}{2}(3\pm\sqrt{5})f_1$. The first gives spheres in contact, while $f_2 = \frac{1}{2}(3+\sqrt{5})f_1$ gives $f_2 > f_1$, which is physically impossible. Thus the only two-sphere anastigmat with concave primary and convex secondary is that given by

$$f_2 = \frac{3-\sqrt{5}}{2}f_1 = 0{\cdot}3820f_1, \qquad d = (\sqrt{5}-1)f_1 = 1{\cdot}2361f_1 \qquad (3.7)$$

and shown in Fig. 98. Since $d > f_1$, the image is virtual; it is formed at a distance $\frac{1}{2}(5-\sqrt{5})f_1 = 1{\cdot}3819f_1$ in front of the concave mirror. The focal length

$$f = \frac{\sqrt{5}-1}{2} f_1 = \tfrac{1}{2}d = 0{\cdot}6181f_1.$$

The Petzval radius is f, since the system is monocentric. Because of the virtual image, it cannot be used as a camera. We therefore return to the case (3.5).

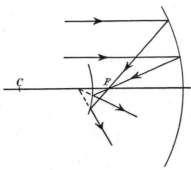

FIG. 98

3.2. The monocentric Schmidt–Cassegrain cameras

Since $\xi = \frac{1}{2}(1+q)$ in case (1), the first two of equations (3.5) are equivalent to

$$\Gamma = 1-\frac{8q^2}{(1+q)^3}, \qquad \sigma = 2; \tag{3.8}$$

the third is redundant (corresponding to the fact that a monocentric aplanat is *eo ipso* an anastigmat). Thus the monocentric Schmidt–Cassegrains are included in the general Schmidt–Cassegrain family as the case

$$A = 0, \qquad B = 0, \qquad \Gamma = 1-\frac{8q^2}{(1+q)^3}; \qquad \sigma = 2, \qquad \xi = \frac{1+q}{2}. \tag{3.9}$$

The auxiliary condition $q < 1$ ensures a real image; the distance of this image behind the primary is $[(3q-1)/(1-q)]f_1$, by (2.8). The Petzval curvature of the system is $1/f = [(1-q)/(1+q)](1/f_1)$. Since it is monocentric, the system gives distortionless imaging on its image *sphere*.

3.3. Anastigmats with convex primary and concave secondary mirror

To make the discussion more complete, we consider also the systems with convex primary and concave secondary mirror; the general plan of these systems is shown in Fig. 99. On repeating the analysis, we find that the only change needed in the equations of § 2.1 is the substitution of $-f_1$, $-f_2$ for f_1, f_2. The new plate diagram (taking the stop on the primary, now the convex, mirror) is shown in Fig. 99. In the case of two spheres ($\alpha = \beta = 0$) and one plate, anastigmatism is now only possible if $d = -2f_1 + 2f_2$, i.e. if the spheres are concentric. (The other solution of § 3.1 now becomes $d = -f_1$, which is physically impossible.) In this case $x = -2f_1$ and the plate, if in object space, has to go in a physically

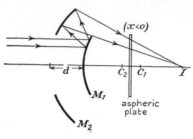

FIG. 99

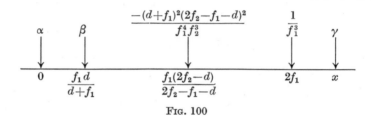

FIG. 100

impossible position *behind* M_1. When we try to get round this difficulty by imaging it in one or both mirrors, it always remains at their common centre C. Thus the plate must lie in a rather strongly converging beam, which much increases its contribution to the higher off-axis aberrations. Only in the case $\gamma = 0$ do we get an acceptable system.† This case, by § 3.1 with $-f_1$, $-f_2$ for f_1, f_2, is when $\xi = 1$ or $\frac{1}{2}(3 \pm \sqrt{5})$, i.e. $f_2 = f_1$ or $f_2 = \frac{1}{2}(3 \pm \sqrt{5})f_1$, just as in (3.6). $f_2 = f_1$ gives spheres in contact as before; $f_2 = \frac{1}{2}(3 - \sqrt{5})f_1$ gives $f_2 < f_1$, which is physically impossible. Thus the only two-sphere anastigmat with convex primary and concave secondary is that given by

$$f_2 = \frac{3 + \sqrt{5}}{2} f_1 = 2 \cdot 6181 f_1, \qquad d = (\sqrt{5} + 1)f_1 = 3 \cdot 2361 f_1.$$

† Small systems, for example microscope objectives, are practicable with $\gamma \neq 0$ if we are prepared to 'bend' the plate, so that the light passes through each part of it nearly normal to the surface. But such 'bent' plates are not well suited to large astronomical systems.

The image is real and is formed at a distance $6\cdot1771f_1$ from the concave. The focal length

$$f = \frac{f_1 f_2}{f_2 - f_1 - d} = \frac{\sqrt{5}+1}{2} f_1 = \tfrac{1}{2}d = 1\cdot6181f_1;$$

the Petzval radius is f.

We conclude from §§ 3.1, 3.3 that:

The only flat-fielded anastigmat with two spherical surfaces and one aspherical plate is the field-flattened Schmidt. (In practice, the convex secondary mirror M_2 will here be replaced by a field-flattening *lens*, in order that a photographic plate placed in the image surface may receive the light. See Chapter III, § 5.)

The only anastigmats obtainable with two spherical surfaces alone are the monocentric systems described above, of which only the second forms a real image.

3.4. *Two-sphere aplanats*

If in the conditions (3.1)–(3.3) of § 3.1 we retain only (3.1)–(3.2) and in them put $\Gamma = 0$, we obtain the conditions for a two-sphere aplanat, namely

$$q^2(2\xi-q)^2 = \xi^3, \qquad q^2(2\xi-q)(2\xi+1-q) = 2\xi^3, \qquad (3.10)$$

i.e. $(f_1-d)^2(2f_2-f_1+d)^2 = f_1 f_2^3,$

$$(f_1-d)^2(2f_2-f_1+d)(2f_2+d) = 2f_1 f_2^3. \quad (3.11)$$

By allowing f_1, f_2 to take positive and negative values, we cover the cases both of convex and concave mirrors under one head; $f_1 > 0$, $f_2 > 0$ means a concave primary and a convex secondary mirror.

Equations (3.10) give

$$2\xi+1-q = 2(2\xi-q),$$

$$q = 2\xi-1,$$

i.e. $d = 2f_1-2f_2$. Thus the spheres must be concentric and, by substituting for q in the first equations (3.10),

$$\xi^3 = (2\xi-1)^2$$

which, as we saw in § 3.1, is also the condition for anastigmatism. Therefore: *the only two-sphere aplanats are the two-sphere anastigmats.* It is easy to prove this directly from the plate diagram, by first proving the system monocentric.

3.5. *Schmidt–Cassegrain aplanats with spherical mirrors*

These are high-definition flat-fielded systems, whose off-axis astigmatism is so small as to cause no observable effect on their image-size in many practical cases. In such cases, as was remarked by Slevogt, they are for practical purposes anastigmatic.

Setting $A = 0$, $B = 0$, in the general equations (2.5), (2.6) we obtain

$$\Gamma = 1 - \frac{q^2(2\xi-q)^2}{\xi^3}, \tag{3.12}$$

$$\sigma\Gamma = 2 - \frac{q^2(2\xi+1-q)(2\xi-q)}{\xi^3}. \tag{3.13}$$

The Petzval curvature of the system

$$\frac{1}{\rho_P} = 2(D-C) = -\frac{1}{f_1} + \frac{1}{f_2} = \frac{1}{f_1}\frac{1-\xi}{\xi} \tag{3.14}$$

and by § 2.2 its astigmatism

$$\frac{1}{\rho_T} - \frac{1}{\rho_S} = 4C = -\tfrac{1}{2}\sum \alpha x^2 = \frac{1}{2f}\left[4 - \sigma^2\Gamma - \frac{(2\xi+1-q)^2 q^2}{\xi^3}\right]$$

$$= -\frac{1}{2f_1}\frac{q^2(2\xi-q-1)^2}{\xi^3-q^2(2\xi-q)^2} \tag{3.15}$$

$$= -\frac{q^2(2\xi-q-1)^2}{2f_1\,\xi^3\Gamma}. \tag{3.16}$$

Here ρ_P, ρ_S, ρ_T, are the radii of curvature of the Petzval surface, the sagittal focal surface and the tangential focal surface of the system, taken as positive when the surfaces are concave towards the incident light.

(3.16) can be written in the equivalent form

$$\text{astigmatism} = -\frac{\xi}{4(\xi-q)}\frac{q^2(2\xi-1-q)^2}{\xi^3\Gamma} \times \text{(thin lens value)} \tag{3.17}$$

from which, because ξ is nearly equal to 1 in all practical cases, we obtain the approximate formula

$$\text{astigmatism} \simeq -\frac{q^2(1-q)}{4\Gamma} \times \text{(thin lens value)}. \tag{3.18}$$

The various types of field flattening by controlled off-axis astigmatism are all covered by the equation

$$\frac{1}{\rho_T} - \frac{1}{\rho_S} = -\frac{\lambda}{\rho_P}, \tag{3.19}$$

where, in the Seidel approximation,

$\lambda = 1$ for a flat *best* field $\left(\dfrac{1}{\rho_T} + \dfrac{1}{\rho_S} = 0 \right)$,

$\lambda = \frac{2}{3}$ for a flat tangential field $(1/\rho_T = 0)$,

$\lambda = \frac{2}{5}$ for the type of field flattening, recommended by Conrady for high-definition systems, in which

$$\frac{1}{\rho_T} : \frac{1}{\rho_S} : \frac{1}{\rho_P} = 2{:}4{:}5. \tag{3.20}$$

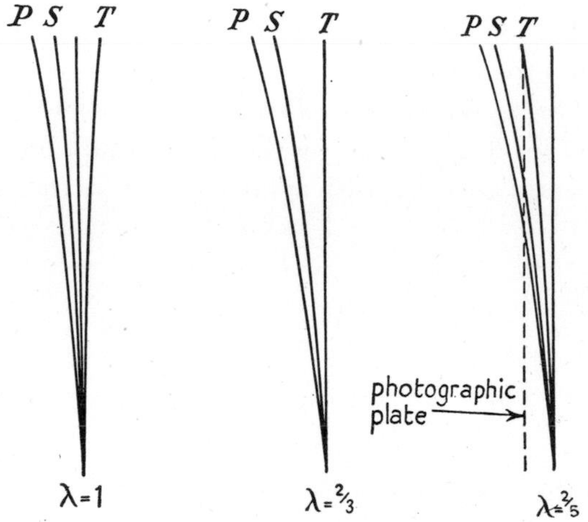

$$\lambda = 1 \qquad\qquad \lambda = \tfrac{2}{3} \qquad\qquad \lambda = \tfrac{2}{5}$$

Fig. 101

See Fig. 101. This 'field flattening equation' (3.19) becomes, on substituting for $1/\rho_P$ and $1/\rho_T - 1/\rho_S$,

$$\xi q^2 (2\xi - q - 1)^2 = 2\xi^3 \Gamma \lambda (1 - \xi),$$

or $\qquad\qquad \xi q^2 (2\xi - 1 - q)^2 = 2\lambda (1 - \xi)[\xi^3 - q^2(2\xi - q)^2]. \tag{3.21}$

Equation (3.21) gives the relation between ξ and q which will secure the desired type of field flattening. In practice, the value of ξ is generally between 0·95 and 1, and it is evident that unless ξ is rather close to 1, the Petzval curvature $1/\rho_P$ will not be small and the astigmatism needed to flatten the field will spoil the definition.

In considering these systems of very small Petzval curvature, there is little to be obtained from *a priori* comparisons between the above-mentioned three types of astigmatic field flattening. This is because the differences between them are comparable, at any rate in systems of fairly short focal ratio, with the small empirical changes which are required in each design, after the pilot model has been constructed and its field explored with a microscope, in order to balance the image errors as well as possible over the required field. By these small empirical changes account is taken, without any *a priori* analysis, of:

(1) the contributions to the field curvature and to the astigmatism from the slight convexity which is superposed on the plate figuring in order to minimize the colour-error;

(2) the higher aberrations;

(3) the effects of asymmetrical vignetting on the off-axis images.

Provided it is intended to make these empirical refinements at a later stage, we therefore do as well, when designing the pilot model, by simply setting $\xi = 1$ and then using (3.12), (3.13) as by first solving the equation (3.21) for ξ and so deriving the explicit Seidel solution.

Setting $\xi = 1$ in (3.12), (3.13) we therefore obtain for the flat-fielded Schmidt-Cassegrain aplanats with spherical mirrors the practical design equations

$$A = 0, \qquad B = 0, \qquad \Gamma = 1 - q^2(2-q)^2 = P;$$

$$\sigma = \frac{2 - q^2(2-q)(3-q)}{1 - q^2(2-q)^2} = \frac{Q}{P}, \qquad \xi = 1. \tag{3.22}$$

(The notation

$$P = 1 - q^2(2-q)^2, \qquad Q = 2 - q^2(2-q)(3-q) \tag{3.23}$$

is the same as that used in the next section.)

When $0\cdot4 \leqslant q \leqslant 0\cdot75$ these give

$$\sigma = 2 + \frac{q^2(1-q)(2-q)}{\Gamma} \simeq 2 + \frac{1}{6\Gamma}, \tag{3.24}$$

an approximate formula correcting plate strength with plate-primary separation which is sometimes useful.

Table I gives the numerical values of the constants of the system, calculated from equations (3.22), for a selected set of values of q.

TABLE I

q	A	B	Γ	σ	$f/f_1 = \dfrac{1}{1-q}$
0·30	0	0	0·7399	2·1447	1·4286
0·325	0	0	0·7037	2·1697	1·4815
0·35	0	0	0·6665	2·1971	1·5385
0·375	0	0	0·6287	2·2272	1·6000
0·40	0	0	0·5904	2·2602	1·6667
0·425	0	0	0·5519	2·2964	1·7391
0·45	0	0	0·5135	2·3362	1·8182
0·475	0	0	0·4753	2·3801	1·9048
0·50	0	0	0·4375	2·4286	2·0000

PLATE VI

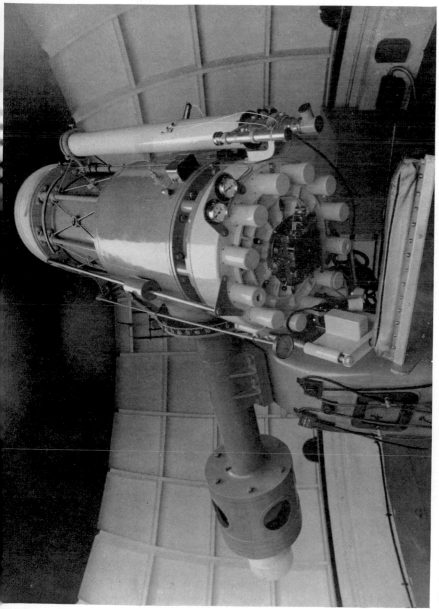

The St. Andrews Pilot telescope, an f/3 Schmidt–Cassegrain aplanat of 15 inches clear aperture. Both mirrors are spherical

Distortion in the spherical-mirror aplanats. By (2.17), (2.18) the distortion in a spherical-mirror aplanat with stop on the primary is given by the equation

$$\Delta = -\tfrac{1}{8}\sigma^3\Gamma - \frac{2\xi+1-q}{2\xi(2\xi-q)}\left[\frac{(2\xi+1-q)^2q^2}{4\xi^2}-1\right], \qquad (3.25)$$

while if the stop is situated at a distance ζf_1 in front of the primary the distortion coefficient becomes

$$\Delta_\zeta = \Delta + \zeta f_1\left(\tfrac{3}{8}\sum_P \alpha x^2 - \tfrac{1}{2}\sum_A \kappa\right) \qquad (3.26)$$

or, in the more special case of a flat-fielded system satisfying (3.19),

$$\Delta_\zeta = \Delta + \zeta\frac{1-\xi}{\xi}(\tfrac{3}{4}\lambda-\tfrac{1}{2}). \qquad (3.27)$$

(The image position is here defined by the intersection of the ray through the centre of the stop with the Gauss plane, that is to say by an ideal construction, since this ray is obstructed by the secondary in a Schmidt–Cassegrain system.) In most practical cases Δ is small; in the system†

$$\xi = 0\cdot9205, \qquad q = 0\cdot3979, \qquad \Gamma = 0\cdot5773, \qquad \sigma = 2\cdot2249 \qquad (3.28)$$

its value is $-0\cdot13$. This corresponds to a barrel distortion of $0\cdot03$ per cent. at $3°$ off axis. Since, further, the coefficient of ζ in (3.27) is small (its value is $0\cdot12$ in the above example) only a small change in the distortion will be produced by any practicable shift of the stop-position. The most satisfactory position of the stop is therefore governed mainly by considerations of vignetting. These more or less restrict the stop to lie between plate and primary, and point to a position approximately midway between them as desirable in those cases where plate and primary are of equal diameter and a uniformly illuminated field is aimed at. This position corresponds to a value slightly larger than 1 for ζ. It is of some interest that in most cases the 'distortion-free position' of the stop, given by the equation $\Delta_\zeta = 0$, is near this value; for example, in the system (3.28) the distortion-free position of the stop is given by $\zeta = 0\cdot9573$.

3.6. *Flat-fielded anastigmats*

These are the systems first described by J. G. Baker (1940). The Seidel condition for flat-fieldedness in an anastigmat is that the Petzval curvature shall be zero. Thus the Baker cameras satisfy, besides

---

† This system is a solution of (3.12), (3.13), and (3.21) with $\lambda = \tfrac{2}{5}$.

(2.5)–(2.7), the condition $1/f_2 - 1/f_1 = 0$, i.e. $\xi = 1$. Inserting this value, and writing

$$P = 1 - q^2(2-q)^2, \qquad Q = 2 - q^2(2-q)(3-q),$$

$$R = 4 - q^2(3-q)^2, \tag{3.29}$$

we obtain

$$A + B + \Gamma = P, \tag{3.30}$$

$$-\frac{1-q}{q} B + \sigma\Gamma = Q, \tag{3.31}$$

$$\left(\frac{1-q}{q}\right)^2 B + \sigma^2\Gamma = R, \tag{3.32}$$

together with $\xi = 1$, as the equations of the flat-fielded anastigmats.† Their fractional distortion, which is independent of the stop position, is

$$\theta^2\Delta = \tfrac{1}{8}\theta^2\left[\left(\frac{1-q}{q}\right)^3 B - \sigma^3\Gamma + \frac{3-q}{2-q}R\right]. \tag{3.33}$$

Equations (3.30)–(3.32) enable us to express all the parameters of the system in terms of q (obstruction ratio) and σ (plate–primary separation). We choose these as basic parameters because they describe the general proportions of the system and its vignetting properties, which demand first consideration in the practical design-problem. We find

$$A = \frac{(\sigma-2)(1+q) - 2q^2[\sigma(2-q)-(3-q)]}{\sigma(1-q)}, \tag{3.34}$$

$$B = -\frac{q^2}{1-q}\,\frac{2(\sigma-2)-q^2(3-q)[\sigma(2-q)-(3-q)]}{\sigma q + 1 - q}, \tag{3.35}$$

$$\Gamma = \frac{1}{\sigma}\left\{Q - q\,\frac{2(\sigma-2)-q^2(3-q)[\sigma(2-q)-(3-q)]}{\sigma q + 1 - q}\right\}. \tag{3.36}$$

† P, Q, and R can be seen to be the sign-reversed contributions of the two power-surfaces (excluding figurings) to the spherical aberration ΣA, the coma $\Sigma A\sigma$, and the astigmatism $\Sigma A\sigma^2$.

Table of values of P, Q, R

q	P	Q	R
0·30	0·73990	1·58690	3·34390
0·325	0·70366	1·52673	3·24419
0·35	0·66649	1·46437	3·13974
0·375	0·62866	1·40015	3·03101
0·40	0·59040	1·33440	2·91840
0·425	0·55194	1·26745	2·80234
0·45	0·51349	1·19962	2·68324
0·475	0·47528	1·13120	2·56150
0·50	0·43750	1·06250	2·43750

It is a practical convenience if the image lies behind the primary, or at any rate behind its front surface. By (2.8), the condition for this is

$$\frac{2-q}{1-q}q-1 > 0 \quad \text{or} \quad q > 0.387.$$

Since, however, the strengths of the figurings on the mirrors increase with increasing q (see Tables II–V below), it is sometimes better to choose q between 0·35 and 0·387. The image surface is then still near enough to the primary to enable the photographic plates to be conveniently inserted and removed through a central hole in the primary.

3.61. *The Baker camera types A, B, C, D.* The four one-parameter types singled out as especially valuable by Baker will now be derived as special cases of the general flat-fielded anastigmat.

Type A (*short tube*). This is characterized by having the corrector plate at the focus of the primary, i.e. $\sigma = 1$. Then equations (3.34)–(3.36) become

$$A = -1-2q, \qquad B = \frac{q^2}{1-q}[2-q^2(3-q)],$$

$$\Gamma = 2(1+q)-2q^2(3-q). \tag{3.37}$$

By (3.33), the distortion coefficient Δ satisfies the equation

$$8\Delta = \frac{2}{q}(1-q)(1-3q)+(1-q)^2(2-5q+q^2)+\frac{3-q}{2-q}R. \tag{3.38}$$

In a system with $q = 0.3$, this gives $\Delta = +0.7583$, corresponding to a pincushion distortion of $\frac{1}{5}$ per cent. at 3° off axis. Table II gives the numerical data of the system for selected values of q.

TABLE II

q	A	B	Γ	σ	Δ	$f/f_1 = \dfrac{1}{1-q}$
0·30	−1·6	0·2259	2·1140	1	+0·7583	1·4286
0·325	1·65	0·2687	2·0849	1	0·6880	1·4815
0·35	1·7	0·3157	2·0508	1	0·6278	1·5385
0·375	1·75	0·3669	2·0117	1	0·5729	1·6000
0·40	1·8	0·4224	1·9680	1	0·5250	1·6667
0·425	1·85	0·4822	1·9198	1	0·4820	1·7391
0·45	1·9	0·5462	1·8673	1	0·4431	1·8182
0·475	1·95	0·6147	1·8106	1	0·4076	1·9048
0·50	−2·0	0·6875	1·7500	1	+0·3750	2·0000

Type B (spherical secondary). Setting $B = 0$ in the defining equations (3.30)–(3.32), we obtain as the equations of the general Baker B system

$$A + \Gamma = P, \qquad \sigma\Gamma = Q, \qquad \sigma^2\Gamma = R. \qquad (3.39)$$

These have as solution

$$A = -\frac{q^2(1-q)^2}{R}, \qquad B = 0, \qquad \Gamma = \frac{Q^2}{R}; \qquad \sigma = \frac{R}{Q}. \qquad (3.40)$$

The distortion coefficient

$$\Delta = -\frac{1}{4}\frac{R}{Q}\frac{1-q}{2-q}. \qquad (3.41)$$

Thus all the Baker B systems suffer from barrel distortion. Its amount is small; in the system with $q = 0{\cdot}4$, $\Delta = -0{\cdot}2050$, corresponding to a distortion of $\frac{1}{20}$ per cent. at $3°$ off axis. Table III gives the numerical data of the system for selected values of q.

TABLE III

q	A	B	Γ	σ	Δ	$f/f_1 = \dfrac{1}{1-q}$
0·30	−0·0132	0	0·7531	2·1072	−0·2169	1·4286
0·325	0·0148	0	0·7185	2·1249	0·2141	1·4815
0·35	0·0165	0	0·6830	2·1441	0·2112	1·5385
0·375	0·0181	0	0·6468	2·1648	0·2082	1·6000
0·40	0·0197	0	0·6101	2·1871	0·2050	1·6667
0·425	0·0213	0	0·5732	2·2110	0·2018	1·7391
0·45	0·0228	0	0·5363	2·2368	0·1984	1·8182
0·475	0·0243	0	0·4996	2·2644	0·1949	1·9048
0·50	−0·0256	0	0·4631	2·2941	−0·1912	2·0000

Type C (spherical primary). This is the case $A = 0$. Equations (3.30)–(3.32) now become

$$B + \Gamma = P, \qquad -\frac{1-q}{q}B + \sigma\Gamma = Q, \qquad \left(\frac{1-q}{q}\right)^2 B + \sigma^2\Gamma = R, \qquad (3.42)$$

with solution

$$A = 0, \qquad B = -\frac{q^4(1-q)}{1+3q}, \qquad \Gamma = P + \frac{q^4(1-q)}{1+3q};$$

$$\sigma = 1 + \frac{1 + q(1-2q)}{(1-q)(1+2q-2q^2)}. \qquad (3.43)$$

The distortion coefficient

$$\Delta = \frac{1}{8}\left[-\frac{q(1-q)^4}{1+3q} - \sigma^3\Gamma + \frac{3-q}{2-q}R\right]. \tag{3.44}$$

Table IV gives the numerical data of the system for selected values of q.

TABLE IV

q	A	B	Γ	σ	Δ	$f/f_1 = \dfrac{1}{1-q}$
0·30	0	−0·0030	0·7429	2·1268	−0·2342	1·4286
0·325	0	0·0038	0·7075	2·1468	0·2317	1·4815
0·35	0	0·0048	0·6713	2·1684	0·2290	1·5385
0·375	0	0·0058	0·6345	2·1915	0·2264	1·6000
0·40	0	0·0070	0·5974	2·2162	0·2230	1·6667
0·425	0	0·0082	0·5602	2·2427	0·2197	1·7391
0·45	0	0·0096	0·5231	2·2709	0·2161	1·8182
0·475	0	0·0110	0·4863	2·3011	0·2124	1·9048
0·50	0	−0·0125	0·4500	2·3333	−0·2083	2·0000

Type D (*distortion-free*). By (3.33), the condition for zero distortion is

$$\left(\frac{1-q}{q}\right)^3 B - \sigma^3\Gamma + \frac{3-q}{2-q}R = 0.$$

Hence the equations of the distortion-free Baker systems are

$$A + B + \Gamma = P, \qquad -\frac{1-q}{q}B + \sigma\Gamma = Q,$$

$$\left(\frac{1-q}{q}\right)^2 B + \sigma^2\Gamma = R, \qquad -\left(\frac{1-q}{q}\right)^3 B + \sigma^3\Gamma = \frac{3-q}{2-q}R. \tag{3.45}$$

These give
$$\sigma = \frac{2R}{(2-q)[(1-q)Q + qR]}. \tag{3.46}$$

σ being determined, B, Γ, and A are successively given by the equations

$$B = \frac{q^2}{1-q}\frac{R-\sigma Q}{q\sigma + 1 - q}, \qquad \Gamma = \frac{1}{\sigma}\left(Q + \frac{1-q}{q}B\right),$$

$$A = P - B - \Gamma. \tag{3.47}$$

Their explicit expressions in terms of q are too heavy to be of much value. Table V gives the numerical data of the system for selected values of q.

Fig. 102 shows the general layout of the different types of system in selected special cases. The lateral dimensions are exaggerated, compared with those along the axis, by a factor of about 2 in each case.

TABLE V

q	A	B	Γ	σ	Δ	$f/f_1 = \dfrac{1}{1-q}$
0·30	−0·2028	0·0399	0·9028	1·8609	0	1·4286
0·325	0·2237	0·0499	0·8775	1·8580	0	1·4815
0·35	0·2451	0·0612	0·8504	1·8558	0	1·5385
0·375	0·2670	0·0741	0·8216	1·8544	0	1·6000
0·40	0·2895	0·0884	0·7914	1·8537	0	1·6667
0·425	0·3125	0·1044	0·7600	1·8536	0	1·7391
0·45	0·3360	0·1221	0·7274	1·8542	0	1·8182
0·475	0·3600	0·1414	0·6939	1·8554	0	1·9048
0·50	−0·3846	0·1625	0·6596	1·8571	0	2·0000

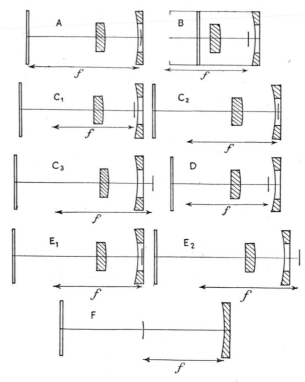

FIG. 102. (A) Monocentric Schmidt–Cassegrain, $q = 0·4$. (B) Baker A system, $q = 0·3$. (C_1), (C_2), (C_3) Baker B systems, $q = 0·35$, $0·4$, $0·45$. The Baker C systems are so close to these that the same diagrams can serve for both. (D) Baker D system, $q = 0·3$. (E_1), (E_2) two-sphere one-plate aplanats, $q = 0·4$, $0·45$. (F) Schmidt camera, for comparison.

3.7. *Achromatized Schmidt–Cassegrain systems; two-plate systems with spherical mirrors*

The colour error in a Schmidt–Cassegrain camera is small enough to be tolerated in systems of moderate size. For example, in an f/3·5 Baker *B* camera of 30 inches clear aperture, with stop on the corrector plate, the diameters of the red and blue confusion circles on axis are each about 0·00075 inch when the plate is figured in green mercury light.

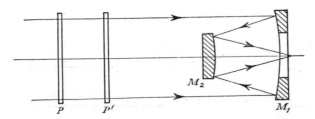

FIG. 103. Two-plate Schmidt–Cassegrain system.

In such a system the colour-error takes the form of chromatic variation of spherical aberration; in systems with the stop situated between plate and primary mirror, colour-coma and colour-astigmatism are also present. Their amount can be read off very easily from the plate diagram of the system.

In larger systems, the question of colour correction becomes important at apertures above f/3. Evidently two plates, of different glasses, are needed to achieve it; these plates must be of opposing asphericities and (if they are both to lie in the parallel incoming beam) of strengths inversely proportional to their dispersions. J. G. Baker (1940) proposed to use two such plates in contact, and A. Warmisham (1941, 1943) described systems in which each of two spherical mirrors is corrected by a plate placed at its (actual or imaged) centre of curvature. From the point of view of the plate-diagram theory of plate-mirror systems, the condition that the plates should be in contact, or that they should each anastigmatize one spherical mirror, appears as a somewhat arbitrary limitation and it is more natural to start from the general case, shown in Fig. 103, in which the system to be discussed consists of two corrector plates P, P', working in parallel light, and two spherical or figured mirrors, namely a large concave primary M_1 and a small convex secondary M_2. The procedure is the same as that of § 2.1. Let

A, B, Γ, Γ' be the figuring depths on M_1, M_2, P, P' respectively, expressed in terms of parabolic correction of M_1 as unit;

σ, σ' the distances of P, P' in front of M_1, expressed in terms of the paraxial focal length f_1 of M_1 as unit;

ξ the ratio f_2/f_1 of the paraxial focal length (taken positively) of M_2 to that of M_1;

$\delta = d/f_1$ the separation between the mirrors, expressed in terms of f_1 as unit;

$q = 1-\delta$ the 'minimum obstruction ratio' for the on-axis pencil.

Then, assuming for the present that the aperture stop is on the primary, the system possesses the plate diagram shown in Fig. 104. From this the aplanatism conditions can be read off in the form

(spherical aberration) $$A+B+\Gamma+\Gamma'+\frac{q^2(2\xi-q)^2}{\xi^3}-1 = 0, \qquad (3.48)$$

(coma) $$-\frac{1-q}{q}B+\sigma\Gamma+\sigma'\Gamma'+\frac{q^2(2\xi-q)(2\xi+1-q)}{\xi^3}-2 = 0, \qquad (3.49)$$

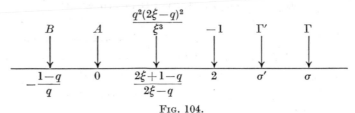

Fig. 104.

and the astigmatism of the system is measured by the quantity†

$$\chi = \frac{\text{astigmatism}}{\text{thin lens value}}$$

$$= \frac{-\xi}{4(\xi-q)}\left[\left(\frac{1-q}{q}\right)^2 B+\sigma^2\Gamma+\sigma'^2\Gamma'+\frac{(2\xi+1-q)^2q^2}{\xi^3}-4\right]. \qquad (3.50)$$

As before, the image is formed at a distance

$$\left(\frac{2\xi-q}{\xi-q}q-1\right)f_1 \qquad (3.51)$$

behind the pole of the primary, the focal length

$$f = \frac{\xi}{\xi-q}f_1. \qquad (3.52)$$

and the Petzval curvature of the system

$$\frac{1}{\rho_P} = 2(D-C) = -\frac{1}{f_1}+\frac{1}{f_2} = \frac{1-\xi}{\xi}f_1.$$

† The physical meaning of χ is as follows: at an angle θ off axis in a system of focal length f the 'astigmatic difference' is $\chi\theta^2 f$.

The distortion coefficient Δ is now given by the equation

$$-8\Delta = \sigma^3\Gamma + \sigma'^3\Gamma' - \left(\frac{1-q}{q}\right)^3 B + \frac{2\xi+1-q}{2\xi-q}\frac{(2\xi+1-q)^2q^2-4\xi^3}{\xi^3}; \quad (3.53)$$

when the astigmatism is zero, the value of Δ is not changed by moving the aperture stop.

  Two-sphere two-plate systems. Of special practical importance are the systems in which both mirrors are spherical and the colour-error is reduced to the amount corresponding to apochromatic correction in lens objectives. We call these the two-sphere two-plate systems. To obtain the aplanatism conditions for such a system, we set $A = B = 0$ in equations (3.48), (3.49). We agree to choose the notation so that P denotes the stronger plate and P' the weaker, and we define

$$k = -\Gamma'/\Gamma; \quad (3.54)$$

thus $0 < k \leqslant 1$ and k measures the ratios of the dispersions of the glasses required to give apochromatism. Equations (3.48)–(3.50) then take the form

$$(1-k)\Gamma = \bar{P}, \quad (3.55)$$

$$(\sigma - k\sigma')\Gamma = \bar{Q}, \quad (3.56)$$

$$\chi = \frac{\text{astigmatism}}{\text{thin lens value}} = \frac{-\xi}{4(\xi-q)}[(\sigma^2-k\sigma'^2)\Gamma - \bar{R}], \quad (3.57)$$

where

$$\left.\begin{array}{l}\bar{P} = 1 - \dfrac{q^2(2\xi-q)^2}{\xi^3} \\[2mm] \bar{Q} = 2 - \dfrac{q^2(2\xi-q)(2\xi+1-q)}{\xi^3} \\[2mm] \bar{R} = 4 - \dfrac{q^2(2\xi+1-q)^2}{\xi^3}\end{array}\right\}. \quad (3.58)$$

The aplanatism conditions (3.55), (3.56) are together equivalent to the equations

$$\Gamma = \frac{\bar{P}}{1-k}, \qquad \sigma' = \frac{1}{k}\left[\sigma - \frac{(1-k)\bar{Q}}{\bar{P}}\right] \quad (3.59)$$

and on substituting from (3.59) we obtain (3.57) in the form

$$\chi = \frac{-\xi}{4(\xi-q)\bar{P}}\left[\frac{q^2}{\xi^3}(2\xi-1-q)^2 - \frac{1}{k}(\bar{P}\sigma-\bar{Q})^2\right]. \quad (3.60)$$

Since this can only vanish if $k > 0$, it follows that the plate strengths must be of opposite sign in an anastigmat (or near-anastigmat). Equating the astigmatism to zero gives

$$\sigma = \frac{\bar{Q}}{\bar{P}} \pm \frac{1}{\bar{P}} \sqrt{\left(\frac{k}{\xi^3}\right) q(2\xi - 1 - q)}. \tag{3.61}$$

It follows that all the two-sphere two-plate aplanats are given by (3.59) and all the two-sphere two-plate anastigmats by (3.59) together with (3.61). From (3.59) we have

$$\sigma' - \sigma = \left(\frac{1}{k} - 1\right)\left(\sigma - \frac{\bar{Q}}{\bar{P}}\right) = \pm \left(\frac{1}{\sqrt{k}} - \sqrt{k}\right)\frac{q(2\xi - 1 - q)}{\bar{P}\xi^{\frac{3}{2}}}. \tag{3.62}$$

Thus to each choice of the three parameters q, k, ξ, subject to the inequalities

$$0 < q < 1, \qquad 0 < k \leqslant 1, \qquad 2\xi - 1 - q > 0, \tag{3.63}$$

correspond just two anastigmats, namely those given by

$$\left.\begin{array}{ll} \sigma = \dfrac{\bar{Q} \pm k^{\frac{1}{2}}q(2\xi - 1 - q)\xi^{-\frac{3}{2}}}{\bar{P}}, & \Gamma = \dfrac{\bar{P}}{1 - k} \\[3mm] \sigma' = \dfrac{\bar{Q} \pm k^{-\frac{1}{2}}q(2\xi - 1 - q)\xi^{-\frac{3}{2}}}{\bar{P}}, & \Gamma' = \dfrac{\bar{P}}{1 - 1/k} \end{array}\right\}, \tag{3.64}$$

where both the upper signs or both the lower signs are to be taken.

If $2\xi - 1 - q = 0$, i.e. if the mirrors are concentric, the two solutions (3.64) run together into the single solution

$$\sigma = \sigma' = \bar{Q}/\bar{P}, \qquad \Gamma = -\Gamma'/k = \bar{P}/(1 - k). \tag{3.65}$$

In all other cases the two solutions are distinct; they have the same plate strengths and the same plate separation, but the order of the plates is reversed on passing from one to the other. The overall length is less when the lower signs are taken, and this second system is therefore to be preferred.

Flat-fielded anastigmats. These are the solutions of (3.59), (3.61) with $\xi = 1$. In this case the inequalities (3.63) reduce to

$$0 < q < 1, \qquad 0 < k \leqslant 1,$$

$\bar{P}$, $\bar{Q}$, and $\bar{R}$ become the quantities P, Q, R of § 3.6, and the second solution (3.64) becomes

$$\left.\begin{array}{ll} \sigma = \dfrac{Q - k^{\frac{1}{2}}q(1 - q)}{P}, & \Gamma = \dfrac{P}{1 - k} \\[3mm] \sigma' = \dfrac{Q - k^{-\frac{1}{2}}q(1 - q)}{P}, & \Gamma' = \dfrac{P}{1 - 1/k} \end{array}\right\}. \tag{3.66}$$

Thus we obtain a two-parameter family of flat-fielded anastigmats, apochromatic and with both mirrors spherical, each of which, since it contains two separated aspheric surfaces, can be made to satisfy the exact sine condition. Setting $B = 0$, $\xi = 1$ in (3.53), we obtain for the distortion coefficient in these anastigmats the value

$$\Delta = -\frac{1}{8}\left[\sigma^3\Gamma + \sigma'^3\Gamma' - \frac{3-q}{2-q}R\right]$$

$$= -\frac{q^3(1-q)^3}{8P^2}\left(\sqrt{k} + \frac{1}{\sqrt{k}} - H\right), \tag{3.67}$$

where $$H = 3\frac{Q}{q(1-q)} - \left(\frac{Q}{q(1-q)}\right)^3 + \frac{3-q}{2-q}\left[\left(\frac{Q}{q(1-q)}\right)^2 - 1\right]. \tag{3.68}$$

Calculation shows that H is negative for $0\cdot3 \leqslant q \leqslant 0\cdot7$. Thus all the anastigmats in this q-range suffer from barrel distortion; its amount is given, to within 10 per cent. accuracy in the range $0\cdot4 \leqslant q \leqslant 0\cdot7$, by the approximate formula $$\Delta \simeq -0\cdot08q. \tag{3.69}$$

In a system with $q = 0\cdot4$ this corresponds to a fractional distortion of less than $\frac{1}{20}$ per cent. at $3°$ off axis.

The two-sphere two-plate aplanats. The conditions (i) spherical aberration $= 0$, (ii) coma $= 0$, (iii) astigmatism $= 0$, (iv) Petzval curvature $= 0$ of the Seidel approximation are to be replaced in practice by the conditions that these quantities should be small. This relaxation has only a small effect on the range of available systems so far as conditions (i), (ii), and (iv) are concerned and we can therefore obtain a satisfactory survey of the useful systems by keeping the spherical aberration, the coma and Petzval curvature strictly zero. With condition (iii) the case is different; the admission of a small amount of astigmatism widens the range of possible systems considerably. It follows that in making a survey of the useful two-sphere two-plate systems, it is necessary to consider not merely the Seidel anastigmats but the larger class of Seidel aplanats with zero Petzval curvature. When this is done, an interesting result appears. Fixing q and k, let us consider the changes in the system as σ varies. To each value of σ corresponds a unique aplanat; for two values of σ the astigmatism vanishes and we recover the two anastigmats (3.64). In between these two values of σ the astigmatism is negative and small. Thus we obtain not two, but a whole range of useful systems. At the σ-point where the negative astigmatism reaches its worst value the plates cross over, and when σ

is greater than this value the weaker σ'-plate is the farther from the primary. At the cross-over value of σ the system is equivalent to a two-sphere one-plate aplanat with achromatized plate.

To prove these statements, we set $\xi = 1$ in (3.59) and obtain the equations of the systems to be discussed in the form

$$\Gamma = \frac{P}{1-k}, \tag{3.70}$$

$$\sigma' = \frac{1}{k}\left[\sigma - \frac{(1-k)Q}{P}\right], \tag{3.71}$$

where P, Q are the quantities of § 3.6. Equation (3.60) now becomes

$$\chi = -\frac{1}{4(1-q)P}\left[q^2(1-q)^2 - \frac{1}{k}(P\sigma-Q)^2\right]. \tag{3.72}$$

From (3.71) we have

$$\sigma' - \sigma = \left(\frac{1}{k}-1\right)\left(\sigma - \frac{Q}{P}\right). \tag{3.73}$$

For given q, k the values of Γ and $\Gamma' = -k\Gamma$ are fixed by (3.70), while σ' is given in terms of q, k, and σ by (3.71). Thus the system is completely determined by choice of the parameter σ, which measures the distance of the stronger plate from the primary. Variation of σ is an operation which is very easily carried out experimentally; it consists merely in moving the plates P and P' along the axis of the system, the new position of P' being determined by (3.71). In this way the Seidel astigmatism of the system can be varied more or less at will. Of course the higher aberrations are also disturbed to some extent.

If, starting from the anastigmat (3.66), we increase σ by moving the plate P away from the primary, it follows from (3.73) that the plate P' moves out also and decreases its distance from P, overtaking and passing it when $\sigma = Q/P$. From (3.72) we see that the ratio

$$\chi = \text{astigmatism}/(\text{thin-lens value}),$$

which is negative when σ lies between the two anastigmat values $[Q \pm k^{\frac{1}{2}}q(1-q)]/P$, attains its numerically greatest negative value $-q^2(1-q)/4P$ when $\sigma = Q/P$, that is, when the plates are in the act of crossing over. Now for this value of σ the system is simply a two-sphere one-plate anastigmat with achromatized plate, and the astigmatism of such a system is so small when $q \leqslant 0.5$ that it is for all practical purposes anastigmatic, as will be seen from Table VI.

It follows that *throughout the σ-range between the two anastigmat values of σ, and for a short distance outside this range at either end, the two-sphere* *two-plate aplanats possess less astigmatism than a Schmidt–Cassegrain aplanat of zero Petzval curvature with the same value of q, and hence are for all practical purposes anastigmatic.* We have supposed $q \leqslant 0.5$; this covers the astrographically useful types.

TABLE VI

q	$\chi = -q^2(1-q)/4P$
0·3	−0·0213
0·35	0·0299
0·4	0·0407
0·45	0·0542
0·5	−0·0714

Distortion in the two-sphere two-plate aplanats. The value of the distortion now depends on the position of the aperture stop. Let Δ_ζ denote its value when the stop is at a distance ζf_1 in front of the primary mirror. When $\zeta = 0$, Δ_ζ reduces to the coefficient Δ of equation (3.53). In the general case, by (2.18),

$$\Delta_\zeta = \Delta + \zeta f_1 \left(\tfrac{3}{8} \sum_P \alpha x^2 - \tfrac{1}{2} \sum_A \kappa \right)$$
$$= \Delta + \zeta \left(\tfrac{3}{8} \sum_P A\sigma^2 - \tfrac{1}{2} f_1 \sum_A \kappa \right). \tag{3.74}$$

In a system with zero Petzval curvature, $\sum_A \kappa = 0$, while

$$\sum_P A\sigma^2 = -4\chi f_1/f,$$

by (3.50) and (3.52). Thus

$$\Delta_\zeta = \Delta - \tfrac{3}{2}\chi\zeta(1-q). \tag{3.75}$$

In a system with flat best field ($C+D = 0$),

$$\Delta_\zeta = \Delta + \tfrac{1}{4}\zeta f_1 \sum_A \kappa = \Delta - \tfrac{1}{2}\chi\zeta(\xi-q)/\xi, \tag{3.76}$$

by (2.20) and (1.6). In practice, the value of ζ will usually be near to 1 in order to minimize vignetting.

Two main types of system can now be selected as especially promising for astronomical application:

Type A. Systems in which σ is a little below the cross-over value Q/P. In these systems, the plates are near together but not in contact. Their separation makes it possible to satisfy the exact sine condition and so eliminate the most important error of a two-sphere one-plate aplanat with achromatized plate (namely higher coma varying linearly with the off-axis angle) at a negligible cost in off-axis colour arising from the shearing of the plates. Figs. 105 (*A*) and (*C*) show two systems of this type; their Seidel data are given in Table VII.

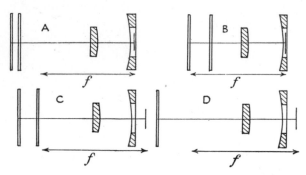

FIG. 105. (*A*) Type *A*, $q = 0\cdot4$, $k = 0\cdot6$, $\sigma = 2\cdot1$; (*B*) Type *B*, $q = 0\cdot4$, $k = 0\cdot6$, $\sigma = 1\cdot67$; (*C*) Type *A*, $q = 0\cdot45$, $k = 0\cdot5$, $\sigma = 2\cdot0$; (*D*) Baker *B* system, $q = 0\cdot45$, for comparison; in this system the primary mirror is aspherical.

Type B. Systems of short overall length. To obtain these we have to choose σ as small as possible. The practical lower limit to σ is determined by the astigmatism, which increases fairly rapidly when σ is decreased below its smaller anastigmat value. For a thin lens of 12 inches aperture the diameter of the astigmatic confusion circle 3° off axis is $0\cdot015$ inch at best focus. If we adopt one-tenth of this value as the upper limit to the admissible Seidel astigmatism, we are led to impose the condition

$$|\chi| \leqslant 0\cdot1, \qquad (3.77)$$

which then determines the least permissible value of σ. Fig. 105 (*B*) shows a system of this type; its Seidel data are given in Table VII.

TABLE VII

Seidel data of the systems shown in Fig. 105

Type	q	k	σ	σ'	Γ	Γ'	χ	Δ	f/f_1
(*A*) A	0·4	0·6	2·1	1·9932	1·4760	−0·8856	−0·0301	0·0430	1·6667
(*B*) B	0·4	0·6	1·6745	1·2840	1·4760	−0·8856	0·1000	0·2431	1·6667
(*C*) A	0·45	0·5	2·0	1·6638	1·0270	−0·5135	−0·0015	−0·1647	1·8182
(*D*) Baker B	0·45	—	2·2368	—	0·5363	—	0	−0·1984	1·8182

In case (*D*) the aspheric primary has $A = -0\cdot0228$.

3.8. *Schmidt cameras with aspherized mirror*

The overall length of the Schmidt camera can be reduced, though at the cost of giving up anastigmatism, if we are prepared to aspherize the mirror as well as the corrector plate. Fig. 106 shows a system consisting of an aspheric corrector plate situated in front of a 'figured' concave

PLATE VII

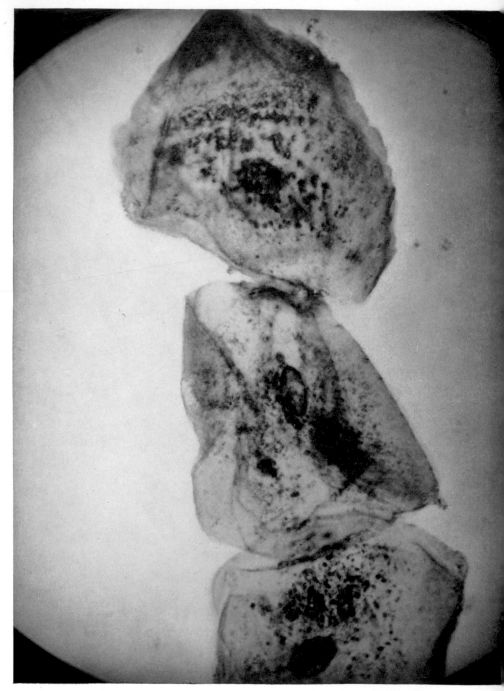

Unstained epithelial cells ($\times 1000$) seen under phase contrast in mercury green light. Phase ring $r = 0\cdot5 \times$ N.A, $\delta r = 0\cdot03 \times$ N.A., retardation $\frac{1}{4}\lambda$. *After* C. R. Burch

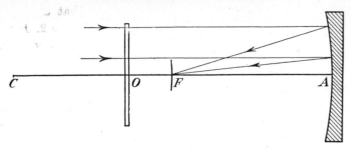

Fɪɢ. 106

mirror and nearer to the mirror than its centre C of paraxial curvature. Its properties can be investigated conveniently by the plate-diagram method. Using a notation similar to that of § 2.1, we define:

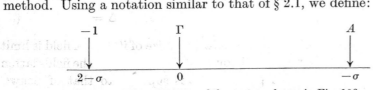

Fɪɢ. 107. Plate diagram of the system shown in Fig. 106.

A, Γ as the optical figuring depths on mirror and corrector plate respectively, expressed in terms of parabolic correction of the mirror as unit,

σ as the distance AO, taken as negative since the mirror is 'down light' from the aperture stop and expressed in terms of the paraxial focal length of the mirror as unit.

Then the point C is at a distance $2-\sigma$ 'up light' from the stop, and the plate diagram of the system is as shown in Fig. 107.

The conditions for aplanatism are therefore

(spherical aberration) $\qquad\qquad A+\Gamma-1 = 0,$ $\qquad\qquad$ (3.78)

(coma) $\qquad\qquad -A\sigma-(2-\sigma) = 0,$ $\qquad\qquad$ (3.79)

and the astigmatism is given by the equation

$$\chi = \frac{\text{astigmatism}}{\text{thin lens value}} = -\tfrac{1}{4}f\sum_i \alpha_i x_i^2 = -\tfrac{1}{4}\sum_i A_i \sigma_i^2$$

$$= -\tfrac{1}{4}[A\sigma^2-(2-\sigma)^2]. \qquad\qquad (3.80)$$

The first two equations are together equivalent to

$$A = 1-\frac{2}{\sigma}, \qquad \Gamma = \frac{2}{\sigma}, \qquad\qquad (3.81)$$

and the third can then be written

$$\chi = 1-\tfrac{1}{2}\sigma. \qquad\qquad (3.82)$$

(3.81) gives a one-parameter family of aplanats, with the overall length σ as free parameter; and (3.82) shows that there is only one anastigmat in the family, namely the system with $\sigma = 2$. By (3.81), this system has $A = 0$, $\Gamma = 1$; it is the ordinary Schmidt camera.

In the general case, the field curvature

$$C+D = -\tfrac{1}{4} \sum_i \alpha_i x_i^2 - \frac{1}{2f} = \frac{\chi}{f} - \frac{1}{2f},$$

by (1.6) and (3.80),

$$= \frac{1-\sigma}{2f}, \tag{3.83}$$

by (3.82). To get a flat best field, therefore, we must take $\sigma = 1$. This system, in which

$$A = -1, \qquad \Gamma = 2, \qquad \chi = \tfrac{1}{2}, \qquad \Delta = -\tfrac{1}{2}, \tag{3.84}$$

is usually called the Wright camera. The size of its useful field is limited by its off-axis astigmatism. Though inferior to that of the field-flattened Schmidt, its theoretical performance is superior to that of Schwarzschild's two-mirror aplanat, and its short overall length is a valuable practical advantage. In an f/4 Wright camera, the geometrical images at the edge of a 3° diameter field are nearly-circular patches 9 seconds of arc in diameter.

Because the dominating aberration in the system is the primary off-axis astigmatism which flattens its field, a discussion of the fifth-order aberrations would have little practical value. But there is a practical reason for eliminating coma of all orders as far as possible, since the presence of this aberration leads to systematic errors in the measured positions of star images on the photographic plate.

If the system is made to satisfy the exact sine condition (as it can be, since it contains two aspheric surfaces), it will be freed from all orders of coma varying linearly with the off-axis distance.

Once the paraxial focal length of the mirror and the position of the neutral zone on the corrector plate are chosen, the two aspheric profiles of the Wright camera satisfying the exact sine condition are completely determined. They can be obtained directly from those of the corresponding Schwarzschild two-mirror aplanat, a factor $-2/(n-1)$ being inserted into the profile-function of the pseudo-flat surface to take account of the fact that the light is refracted there instead of reflected.

F. B. Wright (1935), who first proposed this type of system, gave series expansions of the two profile functions as far as the sixth-power

terms in the form†

$$\Delta x' = -\frac{(f-m)}{2(n-1)e}\frac{y'^2}{f} + \frac{m}{16(n-1)e}\frac{y'^4}{f^3} + \frac{(4e+f)m}{192(n-1)e^2}\frac{y'^6}{f^5}, \quad (3.85)$$

$$\Delta x = \frac{e-(f-m)}{4e}\frac{y^2}{m} + \frac{m-(f-m)}{32e}\frac{y^4}{m^3} + \frac{(e+m)m}{384e^2}\frac{y^6}{m^5}, \quad (3.86)$$

where (see Fig. 108) $\Delta x'$ is the thickness of the corrector plate at a distance y' from its centre minus the thickness at the centre, Δx the depth of the

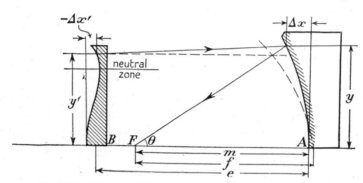

FIG. 108. Aplanat with aspheric mirror and corrector plate.

pole A of the mirror surface below the plane of a zone of radius y. m is the distance from A to the principal focus F of the system. If the figured side of the plate is towards the mirror, e denotes the distance of its central point from A. If the figured side is away from the mirror, e denotes the apparent distance of its central point B from A, as seen through the plate from A. This distance is less by $(n-1)d/n$ than the geometrical distance AB, where d is the central thickness of the plate.‡ By the same arguments as in Chapter III, § 2, the aberrations are unaltered as far as the fifth order of small quantities when the plate is turned round and its distance from the mirror readjusted to keep e unchanged.

f is the equivalent focal length of the system; it is shown in Fig. 108 as the radius of a dotted circle which may be thought of as representing a geometrical definition of the sine condition $y' = f\sin\theta$.

In (3.86), a part of the coefficient of y^4 involving $(f-m)^2$ and parts of the coefficient of y^6 involving $(f-m)$, $(f-m)^2$,... are omitted; in the present systems $f-m$ is a second-order small quantity and the contributions of the omitted parts to Δx are therefore eighth-order small quantities or less.

† The same equations are to be found in a paper of Y. Väisälä (1936). Equations (5) and (8) of Väisälä's paper appear to be incorrect.

‡ e is defined incorrectly on p. 302 of Wright's paper.

The value of $f-m$ is connected with the radius y'_0 of the neutral zone on the plate by the equation

$$f-m = e + \frac{e}{4f^2}y'^2_0 + \frac{(4e+m)m}{32ef^4}y'^4_0 + \ldots; \qquad (3.87)$$

the choice
$$f-m = \frac{3}{64}\frac{f}{F^2}\left[1 + \frac{0\cdot08}{F^2}\right], \qquad (3.88)$$

where F is the focal ratio, secures that the chromatic error-spread of the axial image is approximately minimized. In an f/4 Wright camera figured for D-light, the axial image-spread in G'-light is about 1 second of arc, twice as much as in the Schmidt camera.

Other manners of aspherizing the mirror of the Schmidt camera, which aim at improving the residual aberrations of the system without attempting to reduce its overall length or to flatten its field, have been investigated by the writer (1949, 1951) and by P. A. Wayman (1952).

4. Two-mirror systems

A concave primary is very desirable in an astrographic camera made with mirrors, or with mirrors and corrector plates, in order that its light-gathering power may reach the value corresponding to the aperture of its largest mirror. For the size of the largest mirror determines, more than any other single factor, the cost of the telescope and its mounting, just as the overall length of the telescope determines the cost of its dome or housing.

In projector systems (see Fig. 113) and in reflecting microscopes the situation is different. Here we wish the system to receive as wide a cone of light as possible from each point of the object, and it is an advantage if the beam proceeding from the objective to the screen or eyepiece has a small diameter. Therefore it appears that a larger concave mirror should receive the light from the object and a smaller convex one should send it out to the distant screen or eyepiece. For the reasons given in § 1.4, it is allowable, in exploring the useful design types, to treat the distance of screen or eyepiece as infinite; this simplifying approximation must, of course, be discarded when calculating out the final design of a particular system. When the working distance is taken as infinite, the projector system and the microscope can be treated as cases of the camera working backwards and can be covered by the same analysis. We shall adopt this procedure here; the small convex mirror sending light to the screen or eyepiece is treated in the analysis as a convex primary M_1, receiving light from infinity, and the larger concave mirror is treated as the secondary M_2.

Our analysis of two-mirror systems should therefore cover the cases:

(1) large concave primary M_1, small concave or convex secondary M_2 (astrographic cameras),

(2) small convex primary M_1, large concave secondary M_2 (projectors and reflecting microscopes).

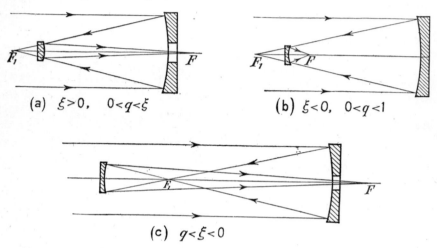

(a) $\xi > 0,$　$0 < q < \xi$　　　　　　(b) $\xi < 0,$　$0 < q < 1$

(c)　$q < \xi < 0$

Fig. 109. Two-mirror systems, giving a real image, with concave primary.

Case 1 (concave primary)

When the secondary M_2 is convex, we have only to set $\Gamma = 0$, $\Gamma' = 0$ in the analysis of §§ 2, 3. An examination of the analysis shows that it applies equally well when M_2 is concave provided we adopt the sign convention $f_2 < 0$ for concave M_2.† The parameter $q = 1 - d/f_1$ may now be positive or negative and the minimum central obstruction is $|q|$ in both cases. Only if $|q| < 1$ do we get a physically realizable system; the image may then be real or virtual. To find the condition for a real image, we consider separately the cases $\xi > 0$ (convex secondary) and $\xi < 0$ (concave secondary). When $\xi > 0$, the condition for a real image is $f_1 - f_2 < d < f_1$, i.e. $0 < q < \xi$. (See Fig. 109 a.) When $\xi < 0$, the condition is $q > 0$ or $q < \xi$. (See Figs. 109 b, c.) All the permissible alternatives are expressed by the single condition

$$\frac{1}{q} > \frac{1}{\xi}, \tag{4.1}$$

† Throughout the chapter, f_1 and f_2 are positive or negative according as the centre of curvature is on the same side of the mirror as the distant object or on the opposite side.

where ξ, q may take both positive and negative values; thus (4.1) is the condition for a real image. We suppose the aperture stop on the primary mirror. By (3.48), (3.49) with Γ, $\Gamma' = 0$ the aplanatism conditions are now:

(spherical aberration) $\qquad\qquad A + B = \bar{P}, \qquad\qquad\qquad$ (4.2)

(coma) $\qquad\qquad\qquad -\frac{1-q}{q} B = \bar{Q}. \qquad\qquad\qquad$ (4.3)

By (3.50) with Γ, $\Gamma' = 0$,

$$X = \frac{\text{astigmatism}}{\text{thin lens value}} = -\frac{\xi}{4(\xi-q)}\left[\left(\frac{1-q}{q}\right)^2 B - \bar{R}\right]. \qquad (4.4)$$

By (2.17), $\qquad\qquad 8\Delta = +\left(\frac{1-q}{q}\right)^3 B + \frac{2\xi+1-q}{\xi(2\xi-q)}\bar{R}. \qquad (4.5)$

Here $\bar{P}$, $\bar{Q}$, $\bar{R}$ are the quantities (3.58); $\Delta\theta^2$ measures the fractional distortion at an angle θ off axis when the system is used with a flat receiving surface.

The coma condition gives

$$B = -\frac{q}{1-q}\bar{Q}, \qquad\qquad\qquad (4.6)$$

and the other equations then become

$$A = \bar{P} + \frac{q}{1-q}\bar{Q}, \qquad\qquad\qquad (4.7)$$

$$X = \frac{\xi}{4(\xi-q)}\left(\frac{1-q}{q}\bar{Q} + \bar{R}\right), \qquad\qquad (4.8)$$

$$8\Delta = -\left(\frac{1-q}{q}\right)^2\bar{Q} + \frac{2\xi+1-q}{\xi(2\xi-q)}\bar{R}. \qquad (4.9)$$

Equations (4.6)–(4.9) give the figuring strengths, the off-axis astigmatism, and the distortion coefficient of the general two-mirror aplanat with concave primary, in terms of the two design-parameters q and ξ.

Two-mirror anastigmats with concave primary. By (4.8), the condition for anastigmatism is

$$(1-q)\bar{Q} + q\bar{R} = 0$$

i.e.

$$(1-q)\left[2-\frac{q^2(2\xi-q)(2\xi+1-q)}{\xi^3}\right]+q\left[4-\frac{q^2(2\xi+1-q)^2}{\xi^3}\right]=0,$$

$$(1+q)-\frac{2q^2}{\xi}-\frac{q^2(1-q)}{\xi^2}=0,$$

$$\frac{1}{\xi}=\frac{1}{q}\quad\text{or}\quad\frac{1}{\xi}=-\frac{1+q}{q(1-q)}.\qquad(4.10)$$

The first solution does not satisfy (4.1); it gives an image at infinity, since $f_1/f=\xi/q-1=0$ when $1/\xi=1/q$. In this case

$$\bar{P}=1-q,\qquad\bar{Q}=1-q,\qquad\bar{R}=-(1-q)^2/q,$$

giving $\qquad\qquad\qquad A=1,\qquad B=-q.\qquad\qquad(4.11)$

The mirrors are confocal paraboloids, both concave if $q<0$, one concave and one convex if $q>0$.

In the second solution (4.10), the distance between the mirrors

$$d=(1-q)f_1=\frac{2\xi}{\xi-q}f_1=2f;\qquad(4.12)$$

and, conversely, if (4.12) is satisfied, then

$$\frac{1}{\xi}=-\frac{1+q}{q(1-q)}$$

and $\chi=0$. We conclude that: *the only two-mirror anastigmats with concave primary and with object at infinity are* (1) *the systems consisting of two confocal paraboloids and forming an image at infinity,* (2) *those aplanats in which the distance between the mirrors is twice the focal length.*

In the second type

$$\bar{P}=\frac{(1+4q-q^2)(1+2q-q^2)}{(1-q)^3},\qquad\bar{Q}=\frac{-1-4q+q^2}{1-q},$$

$$\bar{R}=\frac{1+4q-q^2}{q};\qquad\qquad(4.13)$$

giving

$$A=\bar{P}-B=\frac{(1+4q-q^2)(1+q)}{(1-q)^3}=1+\frac{8q}{(1-q)^3},$$

$$B=-\frac{q}{1-q}\bar{Q}=\frac{q}{(1-q)^2}(1+4q-q^2).\qquad(4.14)$$

The condition for a real image in these anastigmats is, by (4.12) and the second of equations (4.10),

$$\frac{1}{q} > -\frac{1+q}{q(1-q)}, \quad \frac{1}{q}\left[1+\frac{1+q}{1-q}\right] > 0, \quad \frac{2}{q(1-q)} > 0,$$

$$0 < q < 1. \tag{4.15}$$

That is, the secondary must be inside the focus of the primary; and since (4.10), (4.15) give $\xi < 0$, the only possible type of system is that shown in Fig. 109 b. This is the curved-field anastigmat proposed by A. Couder (1926).

Flat-fielded aplanats with concave primary. Here the equations to be satisfied are the aplanatism conditions (4.2), (4.3) and the field-curvature condition $C+D = 0$. Since, by (1.6),

$$C+D = -\tfrac{1}{4}\sum_i \alpha_i x_i^2 - \frac{1}{2}\left(\frac{1}{f_2}-\frac{1}{f_1}\right)$$

$$= \frac{\chi}{f} - \frac{1}{2}\left(\frac{1}{f_2}-\frac{1}{f_1}\right), \tag{4.16}$$

the condition for a flat field is

$$\chi = \tfrac{1}{2}f\left(\frac{1}{f_2}-\frac{1}{f_1}\right), \tag{4.17}$$

which, by (4.8), can be written

$$\frac{1-q}{q}\bar{Q}+\bar{R} = \frac{2(1-\xi)}{\xi}.$$

On replacing $\bar{Q}$, $\bar{R}$ by their explicit expressions (3.58) and reducing, the condition for a flat field takes the form

$$\xi^2-\xi q-\frac{q^2(1-q)}{1+2q} = 0, \tag{4.18}$$

or

$$\frac{1}{q}-\frac{1}{\xi} = \frac{q(1-q)}{\xi^2(1+2q)}. \tag{4.19}$$

Taken together with the condition (4.1) for a real image, (4.19) gives $0 < q < 1$ or $q < -\tfrac{1}{2}$. The latter alternative is excluded because then (4.18) has no real root in ξ. Therefore $0 < q < 1$ in all these aplanats. To each value of q correspond two values of ξ whose signs are opposite, by (4.18). The negative value yields a Schwarzschild aplanat, the positive a flat-fielded aplanat with convex secondary. By (2.8), the distance of its image behind the pole of the primary is

$$\left(\frac{2\xi-q}{\xi-q}q-1\right)f_1 = \left(\frac{\xi q}{\xi-q}-1+q\right)f_1$$

$$= \left(\frac{\xi^2(1+2q)}{q(1-q)}-1+q\right)f_1,$$

by (4.19),

$$= \left(\xi\frac{1+2q}{1-q}-1+2q\right)f_1 \tag{4.20}$$

by (4.18). It is a practical convenience if the image is formed just behind the cell which supports the primary mirror. To see whether the one-parameter family of flat-fielded aplanats with convex secondary contains any members with this property, we first set the right-hand side of (4.20) equal to zero, obtaining

$$\xi = \frac{(1-2q)(1-q)}{1+2q}, \tag{4.21}$$

and then solve for ξ, q between (4.21), (4.18). Substitution from (4.21) into (4.18) gives, after a little calculation,

$$(1-q)(1-5q+2q^2) = 0$$

$$q = 1, \qquad \tfrac{5}{4}\pm\tfrac{1}{4}\sqrt{17}.$$

Only the third root satisfies the necessary condition $0 < q < 1$; thus

$$q = \tfrac{1}{4}(5-\sqrt{17}) = 0{\cdot}2192$$

is the only member of the family for which (4.21) vanishes. Since ξ increases with q (by (4.18) together with the relations $\xi > q$, $0 < q < 1$), the expression (4.20) likewise increases with q; thus a member of the family for which q is slightly larger than $0{\cdot}22$ will form its image a short distance behind the pole of the primary. For example, the system of central obstruction-ratio $\tfrac{1}{4}$, in which $q = 0{\cdot}25$, $\xi = 0{\cdot}3416$, forms its image at a distance $0{\cdot}1831f_1$ behind the primary mirror. The figuring strengths are given by the values

$$A = 1{\cdot}0479, \qquad B = -0{\cdot}3421,$$

from which we see that the primary is very close to a paraboloid.

In this system, the astigmatism

$$\chi = \tfrac{1}{2}f\left(\frac{1}{f_2}-\frac{1}{f_1}\right) = \frac{1-\xi}{2(\xi-q)} = 3{\cdot}5984 \tag{4.22}$$

times the thin-lens value, and the focal length is approximately five times the distance between the mirrors. With a 30-inch f/4 primary and a mirror separation of 90 inches, the focal length is 448 inches, and the nominal focal ratio f/15. The largest field over which the astigmatic confusion circles remain below 0·002 inch is 0° 45′, or about 5 inches in diameter. At the edge of this field, their angular size is only 1·33 seconds of arc. The general appearance of the system is shown in Fig. 110.

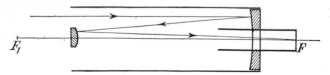

FIG. 110. Flat-fielded aplanat.

Chrétien's aplanat with curved field. A Cassegrain-type aplanat with curved field, having a conveniently situated image and working at a focal ratio near f/8, was proposed by H. Chrétien (1922). In the example of this system constructed in 1926 at the Paris Observatory by A. Couder, $q = 0·4500$, $\xi = 1·8863$ and the figuring strengths have the values

$$A = 1·9487, \qquad B = -1·2818, \tag{4.23}$$

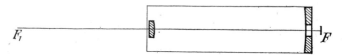

FIG. 111. Chrétien aplanat.

in accordance with (4.6), (4.7). The off-axis astigmatism

$$\chi = 1·8992 \tag{4.24}$$

and the distance of the focal plane behind the pole of the primary mirror is $0·0410f_1 = 0·0312f$ (see Fig. 111). Since the mirror separation is only $0·4188f$, the overall length of the system can be less than $\frac{1}{2}f$. The aperture is 80 cm. = 31·5 inch and the nominal focal ratio f/8. At 0° 30′ off axis, the images in the surface of best focus are 1″·73 in diameter, or 0·002 inch. This surface is concave towards the incident light, with radius of curvature $f/2·90$.

Case 2 (*convex primary*)

If the system is to form a real image of an infinite object, the secondary M_2 must be concave and larger than the primary, as shown in Fig. 112. The analysis of Case 1 will suffice to cover the present case also provided we now take the paraxial focal lengths f_1, f_2 as negative. When M_2 is on the front side of M_1, the distance d between the mirrors is still taken as positive.

In all the sections of this chapter, the sign conventions are in accordance with the statement that the focal length f_i of either reflecting surface M_i is positive or negative according as its centre of curvature is on the side towards the distant object or away from it, while d is positive provided M_2 is 'in front of' M_1.

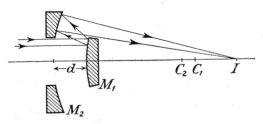

FIG. 112. Two-mirror system with convex primary.

The parameter $\xi = f_2/f_1$ is now positive, while $q = 1-d/f_1$ is always greater than 1 and no longer possesses the physical interpretation of a minimum obstruction ratio.

The condition for a real image is now

$$|f_1|+d > |f_2|,$$

i.e.

$$d+f_2-f_1 > 0,$$

or

$$0 < \frac{1}{q} < \frac{1}{\xi}; \qquad (4.25)$$

this therefore replaces (4.1).

Equations (4.6), (4.7) give the figuring strengths on the two mirrors in the Seidel aplanats of this type, in terms of the two free parameters q and ξ. (As before, the figuring strength on M_2 is not B itself but B/q^4.)

If we also impose the anastigmatism condition $\chi = 0$, which by (4.8) can be written

$$(1-q)\bar{Q}+q\bar{R} = 0,$$

we again obtain

$$\xi = q \quad \text{or} \quad \xi = \frac{q(q-1)}{1+q}. \qquad (4.26)$$

The value $\xi = q$ does not satisfy the condition (4.25) for a real image; it gives an image at infinity. Therefore we reject it and, taking

$$\xi = \frac{q(q-1)}{1+q},$$

obtain once more the values (4.14) for A and B, where now $q > 1$. As before, the equation $\xi = q(q-1)/(1+q)$ implies that the distance

$d = 2\xi|f_1|/(q-\xi)$ between the mirrors is equal to twice the focal length of the system.

From (4.14) we see that in the anastigmats

$$A = \frac{1+q}{q(1-q)} B, \qquad (4.27)$$

so that in general both mirrors need to be aspherized and if one is spherical then so, to Seidel accuracy, is the other. This case can occur,

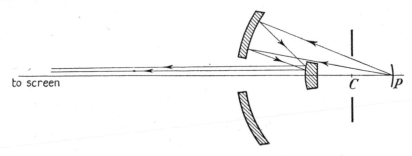

FIG. 113. Bispherical projector system.

since $A = B = 0$ when $1+4q-q^2 = 0$, i.e. when $q = 2\pm\sqrt{5}$. Only $q = 2+\sqrt{5}$ gives a real image; in this case the mirrors are concentric and the obstruction ratio has a value (approximately $1/\sqrt{5}$) which is inconveniently high in a reflecting microscope.† It is, however, acceptable in a projector system, working with a suitably curved object surface or with a Piazzi–Smyth field flattener added (see Fig. 113).

Reflecting microscopes. In a two-mirror micro-objective, the required field is much smaller than in a projector system and the effects of field curvature are usually harmless (though field curvature must be kept low in an objective intended for metallurgical work). Obstruction ratio must be small and numerical aperture large. Coma varying linearly with the off-axis angle is the most objectionable of the aberrations; the design should therefore come very close to satisfying the exact sine condition. An account of the way in which these requirements have been met in practice may be found in an interesting paper by C. R. Burch (1947). Plate VII shows the appearance of unstained epithelial cells seen under phase-contrast in one of the reflecting microscopes described in this paper. Plate VIII shows a stained preparation (spirochaetes) seen without phase-contrast in the same microscope.

† Because it accentuates the diffraction effects which limit the interpretation of fine structure in a good microscope.

PLATE VIII

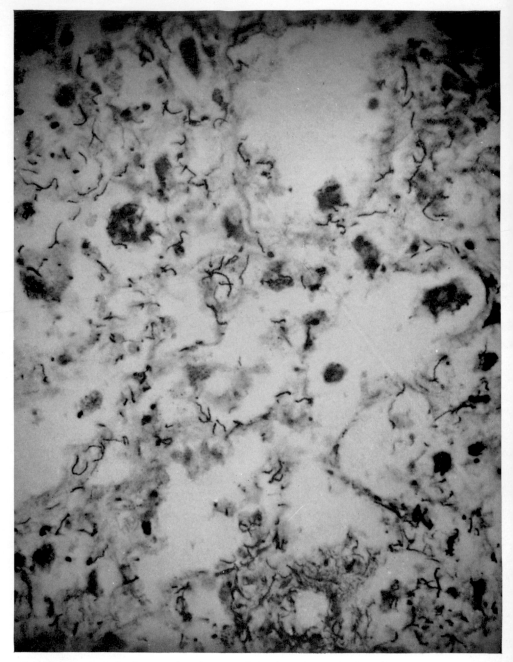

Spirochaetes ($\times 850$) photographed in green light through a reflecting microscope of N.A. 0·65.
After C. R. Burch

REFERENCES

J. G. BAKER, *J. Amer. Phil. Soc.* **82**, 1940, 339.

C. R. BURCH, *M.N.* **102**, 1942, 159.

—— *Proc. Phys. Soc.* **55**, 1943, 433; **59**, 1947, 41.

A. COUDER, *C.R. Paris*, **183**, 1926 II, 1276.

E. H. LINFOOT, *M.N.* **103**, 1943, 216.

—— ibid. **104**, 1944, 48.

—— *Proc. Phys. Soc.* **57**, 1945, 199.

—— *M.N.* **109**, 1949, 279.

—— ibid. **111**, 1951, 75.

K. SCHWARZSCHILD, *Astron. Mitt. Göttingen* **10**, 1905, 3.

H. SLEVOGT, *Z. für Instrumentenkunde*, October 1942.

Y. VÄISÄLÄ, *Astr. Nachr.* **259**, 1936, 198.

A. WARMISHAM, B.P. 541,650 (1941), B.P. 551,082 (1943).

P. A. WAYMAN, Thesis, Cambridge 1952.

F. B. WRIGHT, *P.A.S.P.* **47**, 1935, 300.

INDEX

PRINTED IN
GREAT BRITAIN
AT THE
UNIVERSITY PRESS
OXFORD
BY
CHARLES BATEY
PRINTER
TO THE
UNIVERSITY